YESHUA

Also by Dave Anthony:

Working to End Violence against Women
Love and Struggle Beyond the Rubber Estate
Kaatu Perumal, folk hero of Sungai Siput
The Red Bicycle

YESHUA
ECCE HOMO

JESUS
BEHOLD THE MAN

A Religio-Historical Fiction

DAVE ANTHONY

Published in 2022 by
   Dave Anthony
   No. 77, Jalan SS 2/75
   47300 Petaling Jaya
   Selangor Darul Ehsan, Malaysia

Perpustakaan Negara Malaysia /Cataloguing-in-Publication Data
Anthony, Dave
   YESHUA ECCE HOMO : JESUS BE HOLD THE MAN :
   A Religio-Historical Fiction / DAVE ANTHONY.
   ISBN 978-967-26525-0-2
   1. Historical fiction.
   2. English fiction.
   3. Malaysian fiction (English).
   I. Title.
   823

Proofreading by Wan Kum Keong

Editing by tan beng hui

Cover art by Daniel Anthony

Printed by Vinlin Press Sdn Bhd
2, Jalan Meranti Permai 1,
Meranti Permai Industrial Park,
Batu 15, Jalan Puchong
47100 Puchong, Selangor, Malaysia

To those seeking healing
from blindness in belief

Contents

Introduction

From the beginning, everything was handed down by 'word of mouth', which in Greek means mythos, stories describing the origins of the world with gods and heroes and all the creatures in it. When stories about the universe, humanity and natural events are explained and interpreted in terms of the supernatural, a religion is born.

Faith is something not necessarily based on evidence. It is a conviction of things not seen. Is the portrayal of Jesus in the Gospels a factual narrative? Did Jesus do all the things that he was said to have done and say all the things that were attributed to him? From the messages in the Gospels, we can sum up what kind of a person he could have been, and what doings and sayings are consistent with his personality.

In this book the readers are invited to immerse themselves in this fictional oral tradition, a parallel gospel story and to transport themselves to walk among the followers in the footsteps of Yeshua, re-creating images of different scenarios. The narrative is developed seamlessly in a series of 100 scenarios of Yeshua's movements. To enter the context of this narrative I have incorporated the spoken language of the time by referring to proper names and places and significant terms of reference in Aramaic and Greek and some others. When first introduced they are italicized and explained in footnotes and for subsequent references a glossary is provided at the back.

Yeshua was a man who had an extraordinary understanding of

the social realities of his time. He walked among people living between poverty and destitution, besieged by malnutrition, physical impairment, disease and illness for which they knew no remedy. They were also overburdened by taxation and debt. Yeshua addressed these issues with very practical solutions.

This story about Yeshua is in the genre of religio-historical fiction. It portrays the life of Yeshua from a different approach, a story yet to be told. It is narrated by Yeshua himself in the present tense.

Main Characters

- Yeshua bar Yôsēp̄, a short form of Yehoshua - main character - Jesus
- Yôsēp̄ – Yeshua's father - Joseph
- Maryam – Yeshua's mother - Mary
- Ya'aqov – Yeshua's first brother - James
- Yehudah – Yeshua's second brother - Judas
- Bethanna – Yeshua's first sister
- Yôsēp̄ – Yeshua's third brother - Joseph
- Shemayon – Yeshua's fourth brother - Simon
- Tabby – Yeshua's second sister
- Mariam of Magdala – Yeshua's friend and follower - Mary Magdalene
- Hordos Antipas – also known as Hordos Antipater, Hordos the Tetrarch and Malka Hordos, ruler of HaGalil and Perea – King Herod Antipas, son of Herod the Great.
- Y'hochanan ha-mmatbil – Son of Zachariah and Elizabeth, Jesus' cousin - John the Baptist
- Marta – a young woman in Beth anya - Martha
- Yehudah – an activist, zealot from Kerioth - Judas
- Shimon Qan'anaya – another activist, zealot – Simon
- Andreia, – a fisherman from Kafr Nahum - Andrew
- Pilip – a fisherman from Beth-tsaida - Philip
- Miriamne – the younger sister of Pilip

- Arsinoe – from Japha, adopted into the family of Yeshua
- Mattithyahu bar Halfay – a Levite, a tax collector employed by the Romans - Matthew son of Alphaeus.
- Ya'aqov – James, son of Zebedee
- Y'hochanan – John, son of Zebedee
- Shemayon – a fisherman from Kfar Nahum - brother of Andreia - Simon Peter
- Natan'el bar Tôlmay – Nathaniel or Bartholomew
- Shoshana – Susana
- Joa'ana – wife of Chusa
- Tauma – Didimus -from Tarichea - Thomas
- Shául – Shául of Tarsus - Paul

For other names of people, things, and places, please refer to the Glossary.

Part One

Baptism of Fire

Map 1

Scenario 1 - Massacre

Magdala

Looking up at the back of an attractive young woman leading the way, I climb the steps of a high tower. Once on top, cool easterly breeze blows in our faces from *Yam Chinneroth*[1]. The plains below are rich with olive, walnut, and fig trees.

Mariam, who I know only a short time ago, points to the land, "That is *Har Arbel*[2] with high rugged cliffs. The shoreline running south leads to Tiberias."

Oh! what a beautiful day! The sun shimmering on the lake with white sails of boats plying to and from this port city of Magdala.

"Yeshua, Magdala means 'Tower of Fish.' Magdala is a centre of trade and commerce, exporting salted fish, figs and nuts to markets far and wide reaching the lands of the East and the cities of Europe. Merchants and princes come from the northern cities of Tyre and *Dimashqu*[3] bringing merchandise of jewels and perfumes, silks and embroideries, tapping the silk and incense routes," says Mariam.

---

[1]   The sea of Galilee

[2]   Mount Arbel

[3]   Damascus

4

The ground below is filled with an array of colourful mats with fish drying in the sun. Mariam's family owns the dried fish processing business. She is wearing an ankle-length tunic and sandals and a headscarf around her neck. She seldom covers her head and is wearing a hairnet.

I am wearing a short knee-length tunic without sleeves with a cincture, a strip of leather. My sandals have wooden soles fastened with straps of leather. I normally wear a long ankle-length tunic and a head covering, but I am dressed like this because I have taken a break from work.

I have come to Magdala with my father Yôsēp̄ and my brother Ya'aqov as contract labourers to mend broken boats. We are engaged to do the work by Mariam's family. The boats are used for exporting the dried fish.

Mariam was supervising the loading of fish onto boats. That's when we met and became friends.

Mariam begins, "There is trouble brewing below. Malka Hordos Antipas, rules *HaGalil*[4] with an iron fist. He is envious of Magdala's prosperity. The people here have shown their dislike for him by rebelling. His tax collectors harass the fisherfolk, the toll collectors, impose the harbour tax on fish and goods. Antipas has also given contracts to his official tax farmers who threaten the people to pay up.

"The fisherfolk, have to apply for fishing rights and we have become indebted to the middlemen. If we don't pay, they send the fishing police after us. This collection makes up most of the annual revenue of Antipas. He loves to live in luxury. Do you know that he collects 200 talents or 1.2 million denarii in taxes every year?

"On top of that, we must pay other taxes like the salt tax, crown tax,

---

[4]   Galilee

5

grain tax, tax on fruit and nut trees, poll tax, tithes, rents, tribute. If not, our goods will be confiscated. The people are so heavily burdened that they are pushed to the level of resistance."

"That must be hard on the people. I have heard of such talk in the boat shed and even about a rebellion." say I.

Mariam goes on, "Everybody in Magdala has been talking about a rebellion. Magdala has always been a gathering place for rebels who defy the *Kittim*.[5] The rebels are not all citizens but people who come from the surrounding regions. They come to Magdala to trade and are equally affected by the taxes. They are encouraging the locals to support the rebellion."

Mariam is leaning against the parapet facing me. I move towards her, and we both turn and lean on the parapet facing the sea. We are almost touching each other. I feel drawn to her by some magnetic emotional force. She must feel the same by the blush on her face. The memory of this momentary flash of attraction is to play in our hearts and minds in the years to come.

"It has been wonderful meeting and talking to you. I have to go down to the boat shed and help my father and brother with the work."

"I too have to help my family and workers to fortify the factory because we are expecting violence," says Mariam.

Together we walk down the street paved with stone along water canals leading to a thermal bath displaying ceramic crockery, perfume jars, hairbrushes and combs cut out of horns. The walls of villas are decorated in mosaic art works. Before we part at the marketplace, Mariam says, "Why don't you ask your father and brother to join us in the evening meal. We cook a lot for the workers."

"That would be great," I say walking away when Mariam shouts after me, "Be careful."

---

5   Romans

Aba and Ya'aqov are already back at work patching up a hole in one of the boats when I say, "The rumours about the rebellion are more serious than we thought. The anti-Kittim faction is joining forces with the fishermen to protest the taxes. People are expecting trouble."

"Yes, we know," says Aba. "When people refuse to pay taxes, Antipas will send his troops and the Kittim soldiers will also be standing by to trap the people."

I become apprehensive, "Don't you think we should pack up and go home? We should not get involved in this. It is not our problem."

"Yeshua, we are workers and high taxes impact us too. We should stand with those who are fighting and not run away. Besides, we've got to complete the contract work, or we will not get paid," explains my father particularly.

Having lived a quiet and sheltered life in Naṣrath I dislike violence.

Ya'aqov interjects, "Whether we like it or not, we are caught up in this struggle."

As we are finishing the day's work, I tell them of Mariam's invitation. We wash up and go over to her house which is next to the pickling shed. Over a simple meal of fish and pickles and *taboon*[6] bread we discuss what can happen the next day and what precautions we should take.

Protest and Devastation

The next day, as we are about to begin work, a crowd has gathered on the streets rallying to protest. From bitter experience they know that a protest like this could end up in a blood bath. The people were armed with sticks and forks, knives and axes to defend themselves.

---

[6] Flat bread baked in a taboon oven (a clay oven with an opening at the bottom)

My Aba knows more about this, "Antipas has rebuilt and fortified *Zippori*[7] after it was attacked and destroyed previously. Now he is developing Tiberias with impressive constructions to make it the capital of HaGalil. Progressive and rebellious Magdala is a rival to his plans. He aims to cripple its trade and divert it to Tiberias. His army consists of *Yehudim*[8] as well as *goyim*[9] mercenaries who he always sends to the front line."

Antipas has amassed his troops at the city gates. He has conferred with the Kittim centurion saying that the protesters are also against Roma and manages to get the Kittim soldiers deployed. The mounted Kittim soldiers are men with light body armour carrying small shields and swords, wearing greaves on their legs.

I huddle between Aba and Ya'aqov as the people march towards the *beit k'nesset*,[10] Antipas' mercenaries move in formation. These mercenaries are carrying heavy shields and long spears. The peasants quickly move to the sides and converge on them laterally. Long spears were useless in close combat, and they only use their heavy shield to protect themselves while the peasants attack them with knives and axes.

Seeing the fight, the mounted Kittim soldiers bear down on the crowd. They don't distinguish between Antipas' forces or the peasants. They charge in and cut everyone in their path. Antipas' forces move out of their way and rioters are ploughed to the ground by the horses. The fishermen are no match against trained and well-armed soldiers. Many of those cut down are trampled by the horses. Seeing this, the remaining peasants run to seek shelter. We too run

---

[7]   Sepphoris

[8]   Jews

[9]   Gentiles (singular goy)

[10]   synagogue

into the boat shed. The soldiers pursue and set fire to the boat shed. They also set fire to the dried fish storehouse. Mariam and her family have locked themselves up in the house. We run out the back and I am the first to reach the olive grove with the others. Women and children are killed ruthlessly. Many men are caught and taken away. It is indeed a bloodbath, typical of Antipas. He wants to teach the people a lesson that he would tolerate no rebellion.

A commander of Antipas' army goes up to the beit k'nesset and nails a notice on the door. "All taxes and dues must be paid by sundown the next day. Failure to pay will be met with severe punishment or death," words are written in big bold letters.

After the armies have retreated beyond the city the people slowly emerge from hiding. There is wailing and moaning as the dead and wounded are carried away. We find Mariam and her family surveying the damage to their workers and property.

Mariam approaches us, "It is good they didn't harm you. I was worried."

"It will take you a very long time to recover your loss," says Aba.

"You know we cannot pay you for your work now, but I will speak to my Aba and see if we can make some compensation," says Mariam close to tears.

"We can help to rebuild the boat shed and the storehouse," Aba adds.

I am devastated looking at the dead and wounded. The dead are buried outside the city, and I visit the wounded and try to be of help with remedies I have learnt from my Ama. This dreadful scenario makes me ashamed of my cowardice in trying to run away from the soldiers.

As the dust settles, we move into the workers' quarters. Aba, seeing how distraught I am, says, "Son, we ran because we were overpowered. We live to resist again. Simply to run away from oppression is to be on the side of the oppressors." I take note of these words. We join the other survivors to rebuild the place.

"Yehudah, why have you come?" asks Aba. Yehudah's my second brother.

"Ama and the family are so worried. We heard what happened here and feared the worst. I am sent to find out if you are safe."

Aba assures him, "Yes, we are very lucky to be able to escape into the olive grove. We are staying back for a few more days to help restore the place. You go back and tell them we are alright."

Mariam says, "Yehudah, stay and have something to eat before you go back."

The next day me and Mariam meet again on the tower.

I am disturbed and tell her, "I am shocked. This is my first such experience. I did not expect such a ferocious attack."

"This is not the first time. Antipas has been steadily increasing the toll rates on the boats and taxes on the harbour and fishing licenses. He is constructing a big harbour in Tiberias and wants to make Tiberias the new capital of HaGalil. He sees Magdala as a rival. We will survive, we will carry on," declares Mariam.

"I am lost. I am traumatized, I do not know how people should respond to a situation like this. I need to reflect and think this out."

"We need a good, strong leader who will wake the people up and show us a way out of this servitude, a way to seek justice for all the oppressed," declares Mariam.

"You are right. Perhaps you can lead the way."

"A woman leader? No; the people will not accept that."

"Mariam, soon we will have to get back to Naṣrath. Hopefully Magdala will recover, and your salted fish business will pick up again. It has been nice knowing you," say I, feeling sad to leave her.

Once again, I feel drawn to her. Hopefully she feels the same.

After working for another week, we are paid but only half of what was agreed on. The three of us make our way home to Naṣrath. I am silent all the way home, deeply disturbed by what has happened, pondering on my own reaction and my feelings for Mariam.

Scenario 2 - I take leave

Nasrath

Carrying our tools and bundles of spare clothes, we turn off the main road, walk along a dirt track cutting through green grass with tiny white and yellow flowers of Narcissus between outcrops of rock on a hill slope.

"*Shalama aleikhem*[11]", we are greeted by some young boys watching over their sheep and goats. There are hardly any strangers, for Naṣrath is a small village of not more than 400 people. As farmers they are physically strong, practical and respectful of tradition. They grudgingly pay their taxes and try to live peacefully.

We draw spring water from the only well. Home is a small house with stone and mud walls. The framework of the doors and windows are of carved wood. On seeing us, Maryam, my Ama, and sisters, Bethanna and Tabby, come running out. Bethanna means the house of God's grace and Tabby, a gazelle.

"Oh, praised be *Elahh!*[12] exclaims Ama. We were so relieved when Yehudah told us that you three are alive and well. We heard what

---

[11]   Peace be with you

[12]   God in Aramaic; El is the ancient word for God

happened in Magdala." My other brothers, Yehudah, Yôsēp̄ and Shemayon who are busy in the workshop also come out.

All of us who are *naggarim*[13], soon settle back into our normal work. Aba has trained us in the skills of woodwork and stonework. We build furniture and household wooden structures, and stone cisterns for holding water.

Although I throw himself into the work, my mind and heart are not in it. I am very disturbed by the violence I have witnessed in Magdala and ashamed of my own reaction to it. The other perplexing thing is my feelings for Mariam. Her image keeps lingering in my mind. I am somewhat lost in the search for meaning in my life.

My thoughts fly back to the time when my parents took me to *Yerushalayim*[14] for the *Paskha*[15]. I was 12 years old.

* * *

Yerushalayim

The *Beit HaMikdash*[16] is crowded and noisy with people haggling with money changers and squealing animals being slaughtered for sacrifice. The place is bloody and messy with flies buzzing around attracted by the stench. The *Perushim*[17] stand by watching to ensure that the laws and traditional ordinances are strictly observed,

---

[13] Carpenters/craftsmen (singular- naggara)

[14] Jerusalem

[15] Passover

[16] Jewish Holy Temple

[17] Pharisees

although they are not the *kohanim*[18]. The Ṣĕdûqîm[19] kohanim are also there all dressed up in their rich robes and supervising the prayers and offerings. I can't wait to get out of the place.

I find out that there is a group of *Hasidim*[20] that broke away from the Beit HaMikdash and set up their own community in the desert, in the caves near the *Yām HamMáwet*.[21] I want to visit them.

"There is an *orechah*[22] moving east. Can I go with them to visit the desert community? It is boring here. I will come back before we leave for home." I ask my parents.

"Son, you are only twelve and you have never gone away on your own before. We are worried that it may not be safe," says Ama. "Many young men and boys often disappear and are sold off as slaves," adds Aba.

"My cousin *Elisheva*[23] and Zachariah are also here for the feast. Let's consult them," says Ama.

My cousin Y'hochanan is also with them.

Elisheva immediately says, "Why don't Y'hochanan and Yeshua go together? You can come and stay with us until they come back."

Zachariah and Elisheva live close by in Ain Karim, east of Yerushalayim. My parents reluctantly accept the idea and let us go on our own. They give us some money for meals.

"Don't stay too long, come back within a week," instructs Aba gently.

---

[18] Priests (singular -kohana)

[19] Sadducees

[20] Hasidians (holy ones) members of a Jewish sect that observes a form of strict Orthodox Judaism

[21] The Dead Sea

[22] caravan

[23] Elizabeth

We join an orechah heading towards the Yām HamMǻweṭ. We want to taste the water of the lake which is extremely salty. We get off the orechah at a place called Qumran, a short distance before the Yām HamMǻweṭ and climb the desert cliffs of mudstone to the settlement. The Hassidim live amid nature, away from the cities. They are very hospitable, even invite us to join them for the evening meal.

They live a simple, austere and pious life under a community rule. We immediately take a liking to them.

After staying five days, we thank them for their hospitality and catch another orechah to Yerushalayim. There are always orechahs on the move.

* * *

Now at this moment of time I feel a calling to revisit Qumran. As we are finishing the evening meal, I ask, "Aba, Ama," I want to go away for a while and think of what I want to do with my life."

"Aren't you happy here working with me and your brothers?" replies Aba.

"I am, Aba, but..."

"Yôsēp̄, can't you see that Yeshua has been very disturbed by what happened in Magdala? Son, what do you plan to do?" asks Ama.

"Do you remember the time, many years ago when we visited Yerushalayim? Y'hochanan and I went to visit the community in Qumran. I'd like to go and stay with them for some time and do some soul searching."

"Will they accept you?" asks Ya'aqov.

"Yes, they told Y'hochanan and me that we are always welcome back."

"If you are so attracted, then you should go," chimed in Ya'aqov.

Maryam and Yôsēp̄ look at each other.

15

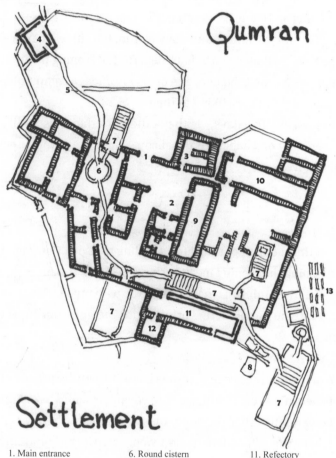

Qumran

Settlement

1. Main entrance
2. Central courtyard
3. Tower
4. Reservoir
5. Aqueduct
6. Round cistern
7. Cistern/bath
8. Potter's workshop
9. Scriptorium
10. Kitchen
11. Refectory
12. Larder
13. Cemetery

Map 2

16

Scenario 3 - Qumran

Yehuda

I travel to Yerushalayim and from there to Qumran. I scale the mud cliff, enter a cave, climb out onto a plateau on which lay the Qumran community. Seeing some men collecting rocks I introduce myself saying I want to meet the elder.

One of them points toward to a tower, "You go there and ask them."

There again I repeat myself. A young man offers me an earthen jar of water and a mug and asks me to wash my feet, have a drink and wait.

An older man appears, "Welcome to Qumran. Who are you and what is it you seek?'

"My name is Yeshua. About twelve years ago I visited this place, and I was impressed with your way of life. I wish to join your community."

The elder introduces himself as Tadeo, and enquires about my family background, then he says, "Are you willing to live by a strict community rule?" I nod. Tadeo takes me inside the settlement to a courtyard to meet some others. While talking to them I hear my name being called. I turn towards the voice and see my cousin Y'hochanan.

"Y'hochanan!" I exclaim in surprise. Y'hochanan comes over and

YESHUA

slaps me on the back.

"Ah, you both know each other," comments Tadeo.

"Y'hochanan is my cousin. We came together to visit. I had no idea he was here," I explain excitedly.

"In that case, Y'hochanan, why don't you take Yeshua and show him around the place," instructs Tadeo and leaves us.

Y'hochanan says, "Come with me." He leads me along the paths between stone buildings then through a long hall. "This is the place where we gather for our meals."

They climb some steps and come out on a ledge. I shield my eyes because of the sunlight reflected from the sand hills. At an open-air workplace beside a pool some women are working a potters' wheel while others were tending to kilns for firing the clay pots. Y'hochanan points to a pool, "The sediment in that pool produces very fine clay. We make all kinds of clay vessels for our use as well as for trade. In the tall pots like those we store our manuscripts."

While walking along the ledge, Y'hochanan points to the cemetery where the graves were in north-south oriented rows. I ask, "When did you join the group?"

"Five years ago. I started as a postulant, then became a novice, now I am a full member."

We walk past some cisterns and skirt the kitchen. I was wondering, "I see a pool and cisterns of water. Where do you get your water from?"

"Let me show you," says Y'hochanan, leading me up the steps inside a tower with thick stone walls. "This tower was built as a lookout post to warn the settlers of raids by desert tribes."

At the top we have a bird's eye view of the complex.

"When the settlers first came here, they had to live in the wilderness. They built their settlement on the desert plateau by the cliffs of mudstone, but they didn't have water. The

Yām HamMáwet was so salty they had to harvest rainwater, which they tapped from the slopes of the rock." Pointing to an aqueduct he continues, "They also built that complex system to bring water from Wadi[24] Qumran down to the settlement into a reservoir. The water then winds its way to eight internal cisterns in different locations. These cisterns provide water for all purposes including two baths. They even serve as miqva'ot[25] just like those near the Yerushalayim Har ha-Báyith[26]. With this vast water system, we are self-sufficient."

"I am interested in that aqueduct."

"Right on top of those cliffs is the source of Wadi Qumran. When there is water, it comes cascading down the cliffs to the wadi floor."

"But it is dry!" exclaim I.

"Yes, it is only filled by the winter floodwaters. At the foot of the cliff there is a dam that collects flood water and rainwater. The aqueduct begins there. It is a narrow channel built with stone."

Although Qumran is built on a plateau the whole place is mudstone. This mud is marl or marlstone[27] with variable amounts of sand, clay and silt used to build the aqueduct.

"Water is vital to us because the summer is dry and very hot. That large round cistern is deep and contains plenty of water. The other small cisterns have steps used for ritual baths," explains Y'hochanan.

"Some very skillful naggarim must have built this massive aque-duct," I comment.

"We have people of various skills here."

---

[24] A dry riverbed that fills with rainwater in winter

[25] Jewish ritual bath

[26] Temple Mount

[27] Marlstone contains calcium carbonate. When the calcium-containing inorganic material, which is lime, is mixed with silicate materials a hydraulic plaster is obtained. This thick grey hydraulic plaster is spread on the floor of the aqueduct, sealing it, making it waterproof.

Then we enter a large room with benches built along its walls. "Here we assemble to study the *Torah*[28]. The community has always lived by a strict community rule which is the correct interpretation of the Torah."

We climb to an upper level. "Come, I'll show you where the main work is done."

We enter a long room with benches and low tables of plastered mud with small clay inkwells. "We spend long hours here copying and rewriting from very old scripture manuscripts in papyrus. We use leather parchments."

"Very interesting," is my reaction.

"Are you sure you want to dedicate your life to a strict and austere rule?"

"That's why I am here. I went to Magdala to repair boats with Aba Yôsēp̄ and my brother Ya'aqov. It was there that I experienced the brutal attack of Antipas' forces with the Kittim soldiers on horseback and witnessed how they massacred the people who were protesting the heavy taxation. I was a coward and I wanted to run away from that conflict. Aba told me that running away was like being on the side of the oppressor. I was confused and wanted time to think. This is the best place I could think of to gather my thoughts."

We pass another cistern on the way to the refectory where the elder asks me what I thought of the place.

I say, "This is an ideal place for me."

"Before you make up your mind," says Tadeo, "you should meet our *Moreh ha-Tsedek*[29]. He is the one who will decide if you can join the community. Come, I will take you to him."

Leaving Y'hochanan to his chores, Tadeo leads me past a pantry

---

[28] Pentateuch, the first five books of the Bible

[29] Teacher of Righteousness

stocked with hundreds of tall pottery jars about two feet high, an oven, and a flour mill. Entering another section, we come to some rooms and approach a large room. Tadeo tells me to wait outside while he goes in. After a while he comes out and ushers me into the room with a fireplace, a sleeping platform and a table made with mud bricks. Seated on a wooden chair behind the table was the Moreh ha-Tsedek whose name was Jethro.

"Welcome to Qumran, Yeshua." I bow. Indicating a couple of chairs by the fireplace, he says, "Come, sit." Tadeo takes his leave.

"Why have you chosen to come to Qumran?"

"I remember this place I visited when I was twelve years old. I like it. It's a good place to reflect on my life."

"What you have to reflect on is the life we live here and see if you can adapt to the austerity of our lifestyle."

"I am willing to learn."

"Good. We live by a Community Rule which is the correct interpretation of the Torah."

"Do you mean to say that there are incorrect interpretations of the Torah?" ask I.

"Indeed. Let me tell you how it all began.[30]

"In *Mamlekhet Yisra'el*[31] there is an upper-class elite group known as the Ṣĕdûqîm claiming priestly privileges. Within the group of the Hasidim there is also a lay group distinct from the priestly group. They are the Perushim. They believe themselves to be the custodians

---

[30] When Alexander the Great, the Seleucid Emperor died the Greek Empire was divided yet controlled Israel. Judas the Maccabaean led a revolt and took control of Judea reinstating the Jewish religion by removing the Greek statues from the Temple. The Hasmonian dynasty under the Maccabees ruled Judea as priests and kings for over a hundred years.

[31] Kingdom of Isreal

of the Scriptures and the Law, claiming the authority of *Aba Moshe*[32] for their interpretation of the Yehudi Laws, adding more rules and regulations to the Law, calling it the oral Torah claiming their ideas are implied in the Law. The Şĕdûqîm refuse to accept the oral Torah and follow the strict letter of the Law claiming priestly privileges and prerogatives as the authority derived from *Malka Sh'lomoh*[33]. This is nothing new. Their struggle involved the *malke*[34] and became very political.

"Both the groups were aligning themselves as tools of the kings and foreign power and the Yehudim became very confused and divided.

"During the confusion there was a teacher who served as a priest. He became dissatisfied with the politics of the religious sects in Yerushalayim. He wanted the true interpretation of the Law. The rulers set up a wicked priest to challenge him and usurped the priesthood making it exclusive. This teacher had the following of several Hasidim who disagreed with the different interpretations of the Perushim and Şĕdûqîm who had profaned the Yerushalayim Beit HaMikdash.

"The Perushim had strong influence over the common people, the Şĕdûqîm were the elite. They were all part of the power structure of Yerushalayim and the Hasidim felt that they will never achieve the proper ordering of society."

"Following the leadership of this religious teacher, a group of Hasidim who the *Yavan*[35] call *Essenoi*[36], quietly withdrew to the outskirts to create a new society that would achieve the proper

---

[32] Moses

[33] King Solsomon

[34] kings

[35] Greeks

[36] Essenes, Essaioi (Greek)

ordering of society. We are this breakaway community in the wilderness."

I interrupt him, "Why didn't they stay and fight the misinterpretations and bring about a change instead of withdrawing, and what is the proper ordering of society?"

"We believe in the proper ordering of society where Yerushalayim is established as the religious capital of the world according to *Nebi*[37] *Yeshayahu*[38]. Yisra'el would be free of foreign oppressors, having just ownership of land in society, and finally, practicing the Beit HaMikdash worship correctly. The way the Perushim, the Ṣĕdûqîm and the high priests of the Beit HaMikdash are carrying on, compromising with the Yavan culture and civilisation, and playing politics with the Kittim imperial powers, would not bring about this vision.

"Scripture, Tradition and Revelation are the fundamentals of faith for the Hasidim. We believe that the true Law, containing the true *Berith*[39] was revealed to our founder, the Moreh ha-Tsedek, the true interpreter of the Law. For us, the true Elahh is not necessarily in the Beit HaMikdash. Our strict observance appeals to the tsedek of Elahh. In his infinite compassion he will not let the ignorant be lost. Hence there is salvation for those who surrender themselves to the tsedek of Elahh. All this began over 170 years ago. We today remain faithful to this teaching.

"About 70 years ago, there was war that caused a big fire. The Qumran settlement was destroyed. Before the settlers could recover from it, an earthquake brought ruin to the place. This left the community devastated for about 20 years. Many of the community

---

[37] Prophet, *nebim* (plural)

[38] Isaiah

[39] Covenant

members went to other places and started their own communities with the same purpose. The members here rebuilt this place and elected another Moreh ha-Tsedek who was not a priest. This tradition has been continued and now I am the Moreh ha-Tsedek. Formerly this place was only for men, but now we have opened it up to women and have a separate place for married couples and their families.

"We live a simple, austere and pious life. We live by a Community Rule which we consider to be the correct interpretation of the Torah. We devote our time to study the Scriptures, worship, and prayer and do manual labour to maintain the place. The members have their meals in common in the community dining hall. The upper level contains a large room with benches and inkwells. That is where we spend long hours writing and rewriting from very old scripture manuscripts in papyrus. This is our main task. Are you prepared to accept our belief and lifestyle?"

"I am prepared to give it a try and learn more."

"Do your parents and family depend on you for their living and do they have any objections to your joining our community?

"I have discussed this with them, and I am free to make up my mind."

"Alright, we will accept you as a postulant for one year, at the end of which you may leave or decide to continue. If you stay on you will become a novice for a further two years. If we find you acceptable you may continue with us as a permanent member. You will also be allowed to get married."

"Thank you, Moreh ha-Tsedek."

"Elder Tadeo will brief you on other details. You may go."

I begin my life in Qumran.

Tadeo briefs me on the routine followed in the community after showing me a cubicle which has a bunk bed and table made of mud bricks and a wooden chair and an oil lamp.

I fall in line with the routine of prayer, meditation, study of the *Mikra*[40], copying and writing of manuscripts and time for manual labour and maintenance all carried out by the sound of the bell even for mealtime and bedtime. The common prayers contain minimal rituals and there is no animal sacrifice. We are forbidden from swearing and must control our tempers. All chores and maintenance, cooking, cleaning, gardening, are done in rotation. We are to serve each other. We do not believe in having slaves. Ownership is communal.

I enthusiastically throw myself into this peaceful and sheltered life, especially in the study of the Scriptures. I become so absorbed in it that I forget about Magdala and Mariam.

We work on manuscripts that are 400 years old, torn and disfigured. They were found in 11 caves around Qumran. We faithfully copy the manuscripts on new parchments and bind them with leather made from the skin of sheep, goats and ibex. The parchments are meticulously prepared in the tannery, smoothed and cut into even pieces. We often take the liberty to replace the illegible parts with our own writings as we see fit.

One day while working on the manuscripts, I stretch himself. "Oh, this is no good," I say, "we've been standing and leaning over the desk to for hours. I will construct a long wide table with chairs. We can spread the manuscripts and look at them together." I get the approval from the authority to do it. Wood is scarce and we source it

---

[40] The Hebrew Bible – used in preference to the Tanakh in Jesus' time

from the orechah merchants. I am also assigned to repair furniture and broken cisterns. Many are engaged in pottery and tannery work.

Every hour of the day is so fully occupied that a whole year has passed quickly. I remain to become a novice. I am committed to practise piety towards Elahh and tsedek towards humanity, to maintain a pure lifestyle, to abstain from criminal and immoral activities, to preserve our books and to transmit the rules uncorrupted.

Often when we have time for recreation, Y'hochanan and I would take a walk into the desert to an oasis, sit under a date palm and talk.

"Yeshua, you seem to be enjoying your stay in Qumran," says Y'hochanan.

"I like Qumran because it is quiet and peaceful, and I am so absorbed in the literature of the manuscripts. We are kept so busy that I did not even notice one year has gone by," I respond.

"How do you find our Moreh ha-Tsedek?"

"He is a very learned man and strict on the observances."

"He is quite different from the previous morehs."

"How so?"

"The first Moreh ha-Tsedek was a priest. He was a High priest in the Beit HaMikdash and a descendent from Zadok, a royal priest. The Zadokites were a priestly family. Their descendants are the Ṣĕdûqîm. The subsequent morehs were not priests and neither is the current moreh but he believes he belongs to the lineage of the Zadokites. He is sympathetic to the Ṣĕdûqîm even though we differ in our ideology. He has also cultivated good relations with Hordos Antipas."

"How could he do that with such a cruel and evil person!"

"I also do not approve of that, and because of that loyalty Hordos leaves us alone. The *Kana'im*[41] often clash with the Beit authorities and the royalty. In the past the Kana'im would seek refuge in Qumran

---

[41] Zealots

when they were pursued. Our present moreh refuses to accept them."

"He is quite old and looks poorly."

"Quite so. How is your family?"

"They're alright. My brothers were not happy when I left. They wanted me to help with the family. How's your family?"

"Aba is still very much involved with the Beit HaMikdash and disapproves my association with this cult, as he calls us."

The hot dry wind is slowing down. It gets very hot here during the day and very chilly soon after sunset, so we walk back to the community.

After two more years, I must go through a baptism of water for which repentance is a prerequisite according to the Community Rules. The theology includes belief in the immortality of the soul which we will receive back after death. I accept all this teaching without question, believing it to be the right way.

As the years go by, the reading of the scriptures make me wonder about how they were being interpreted. The Yerushalayim authorities are interpreting the scriptures in one way and we in another way. Is there only one way of interpreting? The scriptures themselves contain a lot of contradictions.

On my fifth year in Qumran the Moreh ha -Tsedek gets sick and dies. I am elected as the new Moreh ha-Tsedek. I accepted it reluctantly. It becomes my responsibility to give the proper interpretation of the Law and enforce the observance of the Community Rule. I am in a bit of a dilemma.

With this new responsibility on my shoulders, I begin to search the scriptures again on the true interpretation of tsedek. It makes me more confused. I also discover that there are more than 800 manuscripts and not all of them are scripture. Apart from the parchments on the Mikra and commentaries, and the Community Rule, there are non-religious material from the time of *Tre-Qarnayia*[42] which are in the Yavan language. I polish up my Yavan and read Yavan philosophy and mythology. It is so different from *Yahadut*[43] which happens to have a rather narrow vision of reality.

Every year during the Paskah festival in Yerushalayim there would be trouble usually agitated by the Kana'im. When harassed by the Beith authorities or attacked by the Kittim soldiers, the Kana'im would flee under hot pursuit and seek refuge in Qumran. The previous Moreh had put an end to this refuge and forbade them from entering Qumran. I come to know of their struggle and entertain them because most of the time they take a legitimate stance against the abuses of the Beith. I come to know them, especially Yehûdâh Ish-Kerayot and Shimon Qan'anaya.

---

[42] Alexander the Great

[43] Judaism

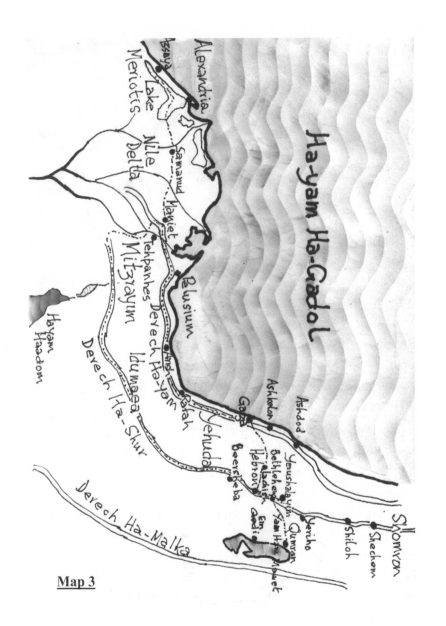

Map 3

Scenario 4 - Assayya

Mitzrayim

My function as the Moreh ha-Tsedek is also to oversee other Hasidim communities.

In finding these communities, I discover the existence of another such independent community called the Assayya[44]. The main centre for them is in Mitzrayim[45], near the port city of Alexandria along the shores of Lake Mareotis. They are Yahudi who settled in Mitzrayim and live in communities like the Qumran community. They have invited me to visit them. But first I want to visit an active Hasidim community in Ein Gedi. It is on the west bank of the Yām HamMáwet̩.

With the help of a local guide, I negotiate the difficult terrain reaching a ravine 18 *milin*[46] south called Nahal Darga with the Wadi Murabba'at that runs from the Judean desert into the Yām HamMáwet̩. Here the guide points out several small caves where manuscripts were found.

We approached Ein Gedi, 34 milin from Qumran, an oasis named

---

[44] Healers, Therapeutae

[45] Egypt

[46] One mil is a distance of 1,050 yards, milin (plural)

"Spring of the kid" referring to a young goat. The houses of the small village are built close together on terraces; each consists of two rooms and a courtyard. In them are large clay vats for the storage of precious drinking water. There are some wealthy people buying goods at the bazaar where I also notice beggars, the disabled and some with *tsara'ath*[47] and other diseases.

The Yehudi community is well established with a fortified citadel called Tel Goren to protect the village and its agricultural products against raiding nomads. Northwest of Tel Goren into the wilderness of Ein Gedi, clustered around a small spring, are thirty small build-ings made of stone. This is the Hasidim community, very much like that of Qumran.

They welcome me as the Moreh ha-Tsedek with great reverence. I hold sessions with them speaking about tsedek and encourage them in their endeavours.

After I returned to Qumran, I begin to probe more deeply on the true interpretation of tsedek searching the scriptures where tsedek is used and abused.

On my sixth year I begin to consider seriously the invitation of the Assayya.

I consult Y'ochanan on the best way to make my journey to Mitzrayim.

He tells me, "The best way would be to take the Derech Ha-Shur, Way of Shur and then from Hebron cut west and take the Way of the Sea, the *Via Maris*. That will take you to the Nile Delta of Mitzrayim."

"Y'hochanan, in my absence I put you in charge of affairs here," I tell him and prepare myself with spare clothing, water, dried food and money.

I set off in the direction of Bethlehem in the hill country of Jehudah.

---

[47] leprosy

It is the city where Dawidh was crowned Makla of Yisrael. The Derech Ha-Shur runs through Yerushalayim and Bethlehem where I join an orechah that takes me to Hebron, the traditional burial place of

Abba Avraham. Enquiring at one of the settlements in the outskirts of the city on how to get across the mountainous terrain to Gaza, I am told to go to Lachish a village between Hebron and the *Ha-yam Ha-Gadol*[48], Great Sea. Lachish was once a prosperous Yehudi kingdom city with a *báyith*[49] on a mound. It is now a ruin with only a small group of farmers. I spend the night with them.

I travel down the rugged hillslopes to reach Gaza. I read in the Mikra that Gaza was the place where *Shimshōn*[50] had died. After the city was destroyed it was rebuilt by the Kittim and given to Hordos the Great. It is a cosmopolitan city with Yavan, Kittim, Yehudi, *Maṣreyyīn*[51], *Pares*[52] and Nabateans. Amid prosperity there are many poor and sick beggars on the streets. Seeing them disturbs me.

I join another orechah on the Derech HaYam, the Via Maris or Way of the Sea to Mitzrayim. It is a very long way along the coast of the Ha-yam Ha-Gadol. It takes one day to reach Rafah about 30 milin south. It is a border town that crosses into Mitzrayim. At Arish, the orechah crosses the Wadi el Arish that originates on the highlands of the Shur desert. The landscape changes from desert to cultivated land. On reaching Pelusium we cut into the delta of the river Nile that spreads out into three major tributaries and lakes before flowing into the Ha-yam Ha-Gadol. The orechah then cuts into the delta to Tehpanhes. The Derech HaYam proceeds in a southerly direction. I get off here to

---

[48] Great Sea/Mediterranean Sea

[49] temple

[50] Samson

[51] Egyptians

[52] Persians

cut across the delta reaching Meniet and Samanud. I must go through many towns crossing rivers by boat. It takes several days to cross the delta to the west side to Alexandria and Lake Mariotis. It is marsh land interspersed with date palms, *shiqmah*[53] and eucalyptus trees. Alexandria, founded by its namesake about 300 years earlier, is the capital of Mitzrayim.

From Samanud I travel in a westerly direction and reach the shores of Lake Mareotis. After enquiring from the local people, who speak Yavan even if they are Yehudi, about the Assayya, I cross the lake by boat towards Alexandria. On a hillock by the lake, I find the community of Assayya. The journey is very long getting here.

There are small houses built of mud bricks plastered with mud and straw with small round holes for windows and flat roofs surrounded by shiqmah and eucalyptus trees and date palms. An unpaved dirt road leads to the colony. I enter a courtyard that also serves as an enclosure for farm animals. There are people around an oven of plastered mud built into the wall. I approach them and introduce himself. I am taken to meet the elders, for there are more than one.

"You have accepted our invitation and it is an honour for us to welcome the Moreh ha-Tsedek of Qumran," says one of them speaking Yavan. We sit on mud benches around a low table. Someone brings a jug of hot drink. While pouring the drink the elder says, "Please accept this beverage that we have learnt to drink. It is called tea."

There is also a woman among the elders. She says, "We have both men and women in our community. We meet but stay in separate quarters. Our life is simple, like yours in Qumran. We embrace poverty by renouncing ownership of property."

"I am very interested to learn all about you," say I.

---

[53] sycamore

33

"I hope you can stay with us for some time. We would like to hear you speak of life in Qumran," another elder invites.

"I am sure I will learn a lot from you, the Assayya," I respond.

"We are healers. The Yavan call us the Therapeutae. We have developed healing as a religious art."

"Our spiritual lifestyle is based on temperance, and through this severe discipline we develop other virtues. We spend six days of the week fasting and in solitary prayers, studying the scriptures and meditating on them in our enclosed cells, in silence. We read the Torah, the books of the *Nebim*[54] and the *Tehilim*[55]. In addition, we also possess writings of our own tradition like using numbers for interpretation. We take words as symbols, and search for the inner or hidden meaning behind them. We don't literally accept the words of scripture or give different interpretations as the Perushim and the Ṣĕdûqîm do."

Another adds, "For example, we see the history of Yisra'el as the grapevine taking root in different soil. We have drunk of the wisdom from faraway lands. Twice a day we pray at dawn and at eventide. I hope you will join us."

"I would like that," I nod.

"Let me show you where you can stay," says one elder and leads me through narrow footpaths winding between the cubicles. From the hilltop I admire the scenery. I can see the cluster of buildings.

"What are the things on the flat roofs?" I enquire.

"They are corn and cotton stalks and dried dung cakes used for fuel. Those cone-shaped structures of plastered mud are silos for grain storage. We are in between fresh water and salt water," pointing to a promontory he continues, "There is the port of Alexandria. We

---

[54] Prophets

[55] Book of Psalms

have people coming from all over the place for healing. We also have travelers over the sea who arrive in Alexandria to visit us. They also come overland from the far East. Please rest. You have travelled a very long journey. There is a jar of water on your table. Please let me know if you need anything else. The next sound of the bell will be mealtime. I will come and fetch you. Shalama aleikhem."

We all gather for the meal at the central building which is very spacious with high walls with palm-wood rafters supporting a flat roof built of layers of dried date-palm leaves. There are fireplaces built into the walls that also serve as ovens, keeping the place warm in winter.

The members are all assembled in rows where men and women are separated with a section for the children. The senior elder rings a hand bell for silence and introduces me, "Today we have a very distinguished guest. He is Yeshua, the Moreh ha-Tsedek of Qumran. He will share our life for some time, and we will listen to him talk to us."

The meal was simple, *matzo*[56] bread and *tahina*[57], braised lamb, diluted wine and fruits and nuts.

One of them tells me, "Tomorrow is the seventh day of the week, and we will all gather in this place just like this for scripture reading, prayer and meditation."

Noticing some strange people, I ask, "Who are those people?"

"They have come from a very faraway land called *Hodu*[58]. More than 700 years ago when our people were exiled to *Athura*[59] and

---

[56] A bland, cracker-like flatbread made of plain white flour and water

[57] a paste made from sesame seeds

[58] India

[59] Assyria/Aramea

Bavel[60], the Yehudim were already engaged in trade with people who came from Hodu bringing teakwood, sandal, rice and other merchandise."

"About 327 years ago when Tre-Qarnayia crossed over into Hodu, trade routes were opened up. Besides trade, other values related to religious beliefs and traditions also travelled along what is known as the Silk Route, which stretches as far as *Seen*[61], where they produce very fine silk and tea. One Malka, Ashoka of Hodu, sent emissaries to Ptolemy II, Malka of Mitzrayim, about 250 years ago. The wise men from Hodu came among them and some of them settled in with us here. They have integrated with the Assayya and have become part of us. They taught us, the Assayya, a new way of meditating and the art of healing, especially inner healing."

"You will hear them speak. Once in seven weeks we meet for a banquet where we serve one another because we do not believe in the idea of having servants or slaves, which we consider to be contrary to nature. After the banquet, we spend the whole night in a vigil singing hymns until dawn. During the general assemblies, we sit together to hear discourses on the topics of healing and different belief systems. Some of them will speak."

In one of the general assemblies, I am asked to speak. I speak about tsedek emphasising that tsedek should not be self-centred, but rather outgoing. Our acts of tsedek should reach out to those who have been deprived of their rights.

During other assemblies I get to know some of the wise men from the east. I am curious, "Did your people follow some leader in your land?"

"Yes, our leader was born more than 500 years ago in the land

---

[60] Babylon

[61] China

of Hodu in the foothills of very high mountains called 'the abode of the snow,' in a small kingdom of Shakya. He was a prince, son of Malka Suddhodana and his mother was a princess. His name was Siddhartha. Although his father ensured that Siddhartha was provided with everything he could want or need, the prince felt that material wealth was not life's ultimate goal. He was disturbed by the sight of people suffering from all kinds of illness. He lost all interest in the pleasures and privileges of becoming a king.

"One night, in his 29th year, he left home and became a *hasya*[62] seeking to find a way of deliverance from suffering. For six years he experimented with different religious systems, subjected himself to severe austerities but found that these practices did not bring him any closer to his goal. After sitting and meditating for a long time under a tree he found enlightenment."

"He discovered that neither sensual indulgence nor severe asceticism was the way. He saw a way in between the two extremes, a path of moderation. For him, this was a time of awakening when he had complete insight into the causes of suffering, and the steps necessary to eliminate this."

"The Assayya practise inner healing. Is this in line with that teaching?" I ask.

"Yes, indeed. Through this process one should be able to achieve a state of supreme liberation. The prince went about teaching what he learnt. He was a teacher, a moreh like you. He was given the title of 'the awakened one' or 'the enlightened one' and in our language, we call him the Buddha. His followers did not see him as Elahh or some god or a son of god, nor as a prophet bearing a message of divine revelation, but as one who had reached enlightenment.

"He and his followers formed a community of men and women who

---

[62] an ascetic

lived a very simple life, very similar to the life lived by the Assayya, an enclosed monastic life. They called it the *sangha*[63] and sought enlightenment through meditation."

In one of the discourses, another speaker who was a Buddhist monk explains methods of healing and medicine like natural and mineral substances in herbs, tallows, roots, astringents, leaves, fruits, resins and salts, prescribed for conditions ranging from 'wind afflictions' to joint pains, constipation, itches, boils, sores, eye diseases and many other common illnesses, and even poisoning from wrong foods and snakebites.

I learn that although the Assayya and the wise buddhas from the East share many practices, there is a fundamental difference between their worldview and that of Yahadut. They do not believe in Ellah or *Elohim*[64]; nor are they interested in the creation of the world or the universe. Unlike Yahadut, they are not preoccupied in worship, the liturgies, or the Beit HaMikdash. They do not speak of the supernatural realities of angels and demons. In Yahadut much is said about sin and punishment, and forgiveness and salvation. They speak of no such thing, only that whatever results from one's action is connected to the intention of that action. The results of such actions will bear fruit either in this life or in a subsequent rebirth which is foreign to Yahadut.

He continues, "We are only interested in the natural order of things. Human beings must study nature to attain personal wisdom regarding the nature of all things. For us, each human being has the capacity to purify the mind, develop infinite love, compassion, and perfect understanding. Our focus is not up in the heavens but in the heart, and solutions to our problems would come through

---

[63] A monastic community (Sanskrit)

[64] gods

self-understanding."

I find great depth in such thinking. Despite basic differences, their teachings are acceptable to the Assayya. By assimilating their teachings with Assayya's own tradition, the Assayya became known as the healers or 'physicians of souls'. They profess an art of healing superior to that practised in the cities. People come to them to be healed. I am determined to stay with the Assayya and learn from experience.

So, I move with the momentum of life in the community, participating in all their activities. I become an Assayya myself learning the skill of herbal remedies. Before I realize it, one whole year has gone by. I learn that the Assayya Way is to live in peace and harmony with ourselves, others, animals, plants, the environment, the *adamah*[65] itself.

Although I know that Qumran is in good hands under Yochanan, it is time for me to return. I bid farewell to the Assayya, collect a good sample of herbal medicine and return taking the shorter way with a camel orechah through the Shur desert. This is the desert that Aba Moshe crossed. It brings me to Beersheba and Hebron to Bethlehem from where I make my way to Qumran.

Before entering the settlement, I go to the spot under the date palm and sit down, drink some water, and ponder.

Reflection

I can find peace in quiet meditation and live in harmony with nature. I have grown accustomed to this life here or even in Mariotis. I have learnt so much from them who focus on the very basic needs of the people. Tsedek should be the enlightenment they speak of.

---

[65] earth

In all the towns and villages, I see poor people sick and suffering. My idyllic life is an escape from reality. We claim to have the right interpretation of tsedek. So do the people in Yerushalayim. What is the true interpretation? Even the scriptures themselves are contradictory and do not point a clear direction. Tsedek must be a response to the people who have a right to it. It must be selfless. I have been teaching tsedek to the wrong people. It is the kohanim, the Perushim, the *Soferim*[66], the Beit HaMikdash authorities, the Malke, the Kittim authorities, the landlords and tax collectors who need to receive the message of tsedek. It is the rich and powerful people who need to understand tsedek. I want to walk among people living in poverty and destitution, overburdened by debt and taxation, and besieged by malnutrition, physical impairment, disease, and illness for which they know no medical remedies.

Back in Qumran I share my insight with Y'hochanan. Y'hochanan also believes the message must be proclaimed to the world outside.

Towards the end of my seventh year Y'hochanan comes to me.

"I want to discuss something with you."

"Come, let us go outside." We go up to the very top of the sand hill and sit under the date palm.

"Yeshua, we have been living an austere disciplined life that will bring salvation in the form of a proper ordering of society. We have done that through a life of penance and repentance, but we must reach out to the larger society. They too must be called to repentance, especially the Perushim, the Şĕdûqîm, the Soferim, the kohanim and even Malka Hordos Antipas. We are too comfortable here; I am going out into the wilderness and call for change, for repentance. The end time cannot be too far away, and I am going to cleanse them in preparation for salvation. What do you think?"

---

[66] Scribes (Sofer-singular)

"I think you are right. You go and do what you feel you are called to do," I advise him.

Y'hochanan leaves the community.

Y'hochanan too has received some enlightenment. More than just repentance for those who have been abusing the system, I believe in changing the system and its leaders and compelling them to bring justice to the poor whom they are oppressing.

I have spent seven years in this cloistered life and gathered a comprehensive knowledge of the scriptures and the historical and religious foundation of Yahadut. I spent the early years observing all the rules and regulations wholeheartedly. As I read more and more of the scriptures I became less and less convinced. When I read Yavan philosophy and mythology, I fiund that Yahadut had a narrow perspective of the world. My travel and sojourn in Mitzrayim have opened new vistas. I am planning to resign from the position of Moreh ha-Tsedek.

I cannot leave at once. I must prepare the community and consider a suitable person to propose as the next Moreh ha-Tsedek.

After the installation of the new More ha-Tsedek, I collect my meagre belongings of a change of clothes consisting of my close-fitting loin cloth and a spare inner tunic wrapped in a bundle with my head cloth, food, and water.

Part Two

Followers

Ha Yam
Ha Gado
Ha
Galil
Beth-tsaida
Base
Camp
Magdala
Yam
Chinneroth
Tiberias
Nasrath
Har Tavor
Ha 'Emeq
Beit She'an
Ha Yarden
Pella
Beth-haggan
Shomron
Har Gilboa
Ha Yabboq
Sebaste
Sychar
Har Garizzim
Perea
Shiloh
Bethel
Yeriho
Yehuda
Yerushalayim
Ain Karim
Beth-ania
Qumran
Beth Leham
Yam
Ham Mavet
Murabba'at
Hebron
Ein Gedi
Moab
Masada
Mitzrayim

Map 4

Scenario 5 - Y'hochanan ha-mmatbil

Yeriho

I look back at Qumran with a degree of sadness and walk to Yerusha-layim and straight to the Beit HaMikdash. I see people lining up to make offerings at the altar.

Raising my voice I address them, "What's the use of making offerings at the altar? Ask yourself if your heart is clean. Have you violated the commandments given by Aba Moshe? If you have, first repent. Make shalama with your neighbour. Your religious leaders, the Perushim, the Ṣĕdûqîm, the Soferim and the kohanim all tell you to love your neighbour and hate your enemy. Who is your neighbour? You are told that the Yehudim are your neighbour and the goyim are your enemy. Your love must reach out to all people. If you have this love in your heart you will have no problem keeping the commandments. Go first and be reconciled with those you are not at peace with. Make shalama with everyone and don't be like your leaders. They oppress the poor because they do not make shalama with them. To make shalama you must have love."

This makes the religious authorities very angry, and they send the Báyith guards to chase this audacious preacher out of the precinct. I walk out by myself.

Having no place to go, I visit Ein Karim to pay my respects to my aunt and uncle, the parents of Y'hochanan. I brief them about Y'hochanan and what he has gone to do. There I meet a woman.

"*Rabbi*[67], my name is Marta. I was at the Báyith where you spoke up at the altar of sacrifice. I have never seen anyone who challenged the authorities. I would like to invite you to our home in *Beth anya*[68].

I get to know her and her sister Maryam and brother El'āzār[69]. Marta is obviously very impressed with me and asks me where I come from.

"I am from Naṣrath in HaGalil and I am going back there now," I say.

"Can I come and visit you sometime?" Marta asks to which I replied that she is always welcome.

On my way home in the outskirts of Yerushalayim, I meet Yehudah and Shimon.

Yehudah says, "We heard what you said at the Báyith. You have said something that has touched our hearts. We want to learn more from you. Can we come with you?"

"I am going home to my *kfar*[70]. Yes, you can follow me," say I.

Shimon says, "We are on the way to *Yeriho*[71] where our brother Y'hochanan is preaching on the banks of *Ha-Yarden*[72]."

"I'll be glad to pay him a visit," I say and the three of us stop in Yeriḥo for a meal and enquire about Y'hochanan.

As we travel towards the river there are people coming and going.

---

[67] Master/ teacher of the Torah/ rabbim – rabbis

[68] Bethany

[69] Lazarus

[70] Village

[71] Jericho

[72] River Jordan

Ha-Yarden originates way up north beyond Yam Chinneroth in the mountainous peaks of *Har Hermon*[73], and from there comes down in a straight line covering about 244 milin, dipping to below sea level into the Yām HamMáwet. Having lost its force, the river flows calmly and at a bend on a sandy bank, we find Y'hochanan addressing a crowd.

The riverbank is carpeted with a dazzling array of wild flowering plants and shrubs. We sit under a eucalyptus tree on the grass, a short distance from the crowd where we can hear Y'hochanan.

Y'hochanan's voice is deep and loud. "Those of you who have transgressed the law of Aba Moshe and have done harm to your brothers and sisters, repent now and clean yourselves. Change your lives and do good to those who are worse off than you. If anyone has two tunics, he must share with the man who has none, and the one who has something to eat must do the same.

"You who serve in the army, don't intimidate or extort from the ordinary people. In other words, do not rob people using violence or make false accusations. Do your duty and be content with your pay.

"You tax collectors, be considerate to those from whom you collect. Don't be corrupt. Exact no more than what is due.

"Ah, you too have come." He points to some Perushim and Şĕdûqîm. "Have you come to be cleansed or have you come to pass judgement on me? If you have come to repent and be cleansed, you are welcome. Repent and produce the appropriate fruits, good fruits. If you fail to do so, remember the axe is already laid to the roots of the trees so that any tree that fails to produce good fruit will be cut down and thrown on the fire. If you remain stubborn and claim Avraham as your Aba, let me tell you that Elahh can raise children for Avraham from the grains of sand on this riverbank.

"If you are genuine, come, join my other brothers and sisters. If in

[73] Mount Hermon

your heart you have repented, come, step into the water of Ha-Yarden. The clear continuously running water of Ha-Yarden represents a perfect miqva'ot. Come, immerse yourself in this water and regain purity."

None of them make a move. Y'hochanan continues, "But I know what you are. You only judge others and not yourselves. You are a brood of vipers, and you will not be spared the judgement of Elahh."

As the people come to him, Y'hochanan baptises them. He becomes known as Y'hochanan ha-mmatbil.

By the time Y'hochanan has finished with his baptisms the sun is already setting. Y'hochanan comes over with some of his close followers and meets us under the tree. We cousins embrace each other, and I ask him, "Why are you dressed like this in camel hair?"

Y'hochanan wears a short knee-length tunic made of camel hair over an inner tunic of sackcloth belted at the waist. His hair is long and wiry, and he is barefooted.

"I want to show my rough garment as being different from the Perushim and their long garments. Men in fine clothes are found in the courts of Hordos. They even come here dressed like that. I am different."

Yehudah and Shimon also renew their acquaintance with Y'hochanan and meet his followers.

Y'hochanan tells his followers, "Yeshua and I spent many years together in Qumran. He is a great moreh and a great leader. He is the one you should be listening to."

"It's alright, Y'hochanan. They should be listening to you also. Your preaching is very powerful. I hope the baptism and change in them will be lasting. Although there are some good Perushim and Şĕdûqîm, most of them are hypocrites and you told them off. The tax collectors too needed reprimanding. Before telling the soldiers to be content with their pay you should find out if they are being paid a fair wage. Know your people better," I advise.

"You are right. Tell me, what are you going to do?" asks Y'hochanan.

"I want to get to know the people. We have been out of touch with them. All I can see is that the rich people are very comfortable while the poor are struggling to get enough food to eat. Many of them are sick and disabled and are told that this is the punishment of Elahh. I have learnt a lot about healing from the Assayya and I want to heal them. They have also been made mentally sick by the teachings of the Báyith. The authorities from both the Báyith and the palace have been bullying the people for far too long. I hope I can improve the lives of these people.

"I too hope to confront Hordos Antipas when I get the chance," agreed Y'hochanan.

"Do you have something to eat?"

"You can share what we have," answers Y'hochanan. His followers unwrap some bundles containing dried grasshoppers and locusts. They fetch some river water and mix in some wild honey.

"This is the food of the poor, and we want to live like them," says Y'hochanan.

"That is very well and good and praiseworthy, but you need strength to do your hard work, so at least once in a while you must eat good food," I advise him.

"I have some fish, but it is hard to convince our preacher to eat it," says one of the followers who introduces himself. "I am Pilip."

"Your name, a common Yavan name?" I query.

"Yes, my family members too, have Yavan names. My parents must have thought highly of them. This is my sister, Miriamne. Her name too is the Yavan version of Maryam. She is accompanying us in our travels."

Miriamne bows her head and smiles. She sports short hair and dresses like a boy.

His companion comes forward, "I am Andrea."

"What do you do and where's your home?" Ask I.

"I am from *Kfar Nahum*[74]. We are fishermen from HaGalil. We were sent to Yerushalayim and other places to find new markets for fish," says Andrea.

"I'm from *Beth-tsaida*[75] and I work for a fish merchant," says Pilip. "Let's have the fish," he says to Miriamne.

They share the locusts, honey and fish from which Y'hochanan abstains.

"Where do you stay?" I ask Y'hochanan.

"Anywhere; in a cave or under a tree close to the water. Will you join me in prayer and meditation, like we used to do in Qumran?"

I agree and we sit on the ground, the others following suit.

We spend a while in perfect silence except for the sound of the flowing river water.

Then Y'hochanan begins and I join in unison:

In peace I lie down, and fall asleep at once,
Since you alone, Elahh, make me rest secure.
I say this prayer to you,
For at daybreak, you listen to my voice;
And at dawn I hold myself in readiness for you,
Explain to me how to respect your Law!
And how to observe it wholeheartedly.
Yahweh is Tsedek and El malei Rachamim[76],
Our Elahh is tender-hearted.
Elahh defends the simple.'

---

[74] Capernaum

[75] Bethsaida

[76] All Merciful God

51

These are some verses in the Tehilim that we used to recite as night prayers in Qumran.

We all stretch out our long head cloths and sleep on them, wrapping ourselves up with our long tunics.

The next morning, we are all up early and share a frugal breakfast. Y'hochanan is getting ready to welcome a new wave of listeners as word is fast getting around about this charismatic preacher.

Yehudah and Shimon are also getting ready for their journey and so are Pilip, Andrea and Miriamne.

Y'hochanan addresses them, "Stay close to moreh Yeshua and listen carefully to what he has to say. He has a strong message for the people. I am a voice in the wilderness, but his message will reach all people. I baptise with water, but he will baptise with fire. Follow him."

We bid farewell encouraging each other in our works ahead.

Ha Yarden

"Which way are you going?' asks Pilip.

"To HaGalil," said Shimon.

"We're also going to HaGalil," says Andrea.

"We can all go together, then," adds Pilip.

"We'll be going through the hostile territory of *Shomron*[77] and we can be stronger in numbers," says Shimon.

"We do not have to go through Shomron. I can show you a way we can avoid it by crossing Ha Yarden. It may take us a little longer, but it is safer. We can make the crossing right here," points Pilip.

The water is shallow and strewn with rocks. They hitch up their tunics and cross over including Miriamne.

---

[77] Samaria

"We have crossed into the territory of Perea which is also under the jurisdiction of Hordos Antipas. If we walk up along the river for about 15 *milin* we will reach the *Ha Yabboq*[78]. We can easily make it before nightfall." Says Andrea.

The Galileans are familiar with this route. We walk through a fertile piece of narrow land, the East bank of Ha Yarden valley where shepherds are tending their flocks of sheep and goats.

"Let us meet them," say I.

"Moreh," says Pilip, "shepherds are outcasts and sinners. They are known to be dishonest and unclean according to the standards of the law."

"Pilip, there are good and bad people in all walks of life, even among fishermen. Don't be as blind as the *rabbim*[79] who despise and label the shepherds as sinners because they don't observe all the meticulous hand washing and rules and regulations. They think they are a class above and have even banned the shepherds from pasturing their sheep and goats in Yisra'el and driven them to the deserted places on the plains and valleys. Yet they accept the lambs and kids for sacrifice. Don't be like them. Don't forget that Yisra'el's great leaders, like Avraham, Moshe, *Yiṣḥāq*[80], *Ya'akov*[81] and Dawidh were all shepherds."

A small group of shepherds sit at a well-constructed tent with their families and children. As I and my companions approach, the men grab their staffs and stand up. The staff is their protection against wild animals and thieves. They are wary of strangers.

"Shalama aleikhem, we are travelers. May we rest a while with

---

[78] River Jabbok

[79] Plural of rabbi – rabbis

[80] Isaac

[81] Jacob

you?" I speak.

They remain silent. The women gather the children together.

"We are from Yerushalayim on the way to HaGalil. We come in shalama and friendship," says Yehudah.

"We don't have anything to give you," says one of the men.

"We don't want anything," I respond.

"I have some fish and bread and we would like to share with you," offers Pilip.

They relax and invite the strangers to sit. "Thank you for the offer. We have enough good food. While we look after our sheep and goats, they also look after us. We eat lamb and mutton, and drink goats' milk. Our clothes are made of wool, and we use the hides to make our tents. How do we call you?" says one of the men whose name is Caley.

"I am Yeshua and my friends here are Yehudah, Shimon, Andrea and Pilip. Pilip introduces his sister. They are surprised for they had mistaken her for a boy.

Why do you not live in a permanent place?" asks Yehudah.

"We are not hirelings; we own the sheep and goats. We move because they need fresh pasture especially in the dry season. Sometimes the flock is attacked by wolves, and we too get robbed by a band of thieves. We are not sure of who you are," says Orna, one of the women.

"Your tent looks like you have been staying here quite a while," remarks Shimon.

"That is because my oldest son is unable to walk," says Caley.

"What's wrong with him?" I enquire.

"He injured his leg and is not able to stand up."

"I may be able to help. Can I have a look at him?"

Caley and his wife Orna take me and the others into the tent. The young man is lying on a goat's skin with his leg propped up.

"Alvan, Yeshua and his friends would like to help. They want to look at your foot," says Caley.

Orna lifts Alvan's right leg and rests it on a basket. Below his big toe is an open sore, a deep gash, red but not bleeding with flies buzzing around. His whole left foot, particularly his big toe is swollen and turning black. I quickly assess it to be badly infected.

"You have good food, but do you also have honey?" to which they answer, "Yes, we collect wild honey from the rocks," says Orna showing us a jar containing the wild honey which doesn't look very nice.

"Heat the honey over a fire and when it is soft strain it through a clean cloth. While you are doing that could one of you, please fetch some clean water from the river?" I request. "Alvan, can you move slightly towards the entrance of the tent where there is better light?"

The others help him sit up and shift him out. I pour the water over the wound and with a clean piece of cloth clean all around it. Then I drip the purified honey into the wound while it is still warm. Miriamne helps. Alvan twitches a little. The honey is flowing down his foot. I tear a smaller piece of cloth and soak it with honey and lodge it into the open cut and then loosely wrap the cloth around his foot.

"You should not bandage it too tightly to let the air get in but keep the flies out. On the way here, I noticed some wildflowers white and pink in colour. They have a strong sweet smell. The goats eat them. I don't know what you call them here, but they are known as the nettle of *satana*[82]. Pick the flowers and crush them into a paste. When the swelling has gone down stop the honey and apply the paste on the wound. Change it every day. Don't eat any sweet food but eat a lot of mutton fat. The healing will take place," I instruct.

---

[82] satan

The shepherds are impressed.

"We are roasting a lamb tonight and invite you to share a meal with us and stay the night," offers Caley.

I turn to Pilip, "How far have we travelled?"

"We are very close to Ha Yabboq. If we stay the night here, we can cross it in the morning."

We accept the invitation and hospitality. Some young men and boys have already started the fire and the lamb had already been slaughtered and skinned and cleaned. As night was falling, we hear sheep. The other family members round up the flock and corral them around the tents and rope off the enclosure to prevent the sheep from straying. The sheep are used to that and settle down calmly after they have their drink of the river water.

The other shepherds are introduced as extended members of the family. They wash themselves in the river and settle down on mats.

I tell Pilip, "You see, they do wash and clean themselves. Now you see how wrong the rabbim are?"

"Yes, Moreh," agrees Pilip.

It is a starry night and our gastric juices surge at the smell of the roast. The roast is served with abud, a rough Bedouin bread baked over an open fire. Pilip also shares his fish and taboon bread and wine.

The shepherds tell stories of their nomadic life, and hardships of the weather and wild animals and thieves.

After a restful night we wake up to a fresh morning.

To the surprise of everybody, Alvan stands at the entrance of the tent balancing on his staff. He is able to put his bodyweight on the heel of his left leg. The swelling has subsided, and he has a smile on his face.

Caley and Orna come to me and hail me as a great healer.

"Your son is a strong young man. It is important to keep the wound clean and the flies away. Continue with the honey for another two days until the swelling has gone, and then apply the paste."

We take their leave to move on. Orna gives us some roast lamb to take along.

We bid farewell and are on our way. "People are good," I remarked.

After walking for ten minutes, we come to Ha-Yabbok, a tributary of Ha-Yarden. At a shallow spot we manage to wade across.

We walk north along the east bank of Ha Yarden in the valley of Aulon. On the west bank is Shomron. By midday we decide to stop on the bank and have lunch.

"There is a rich growth of herbs along the river. Many of them are suitable remedies for healing," I say as we eat the roast lamb when Andrea asks, "Moreh Yeshua, what did Moreh Y'hochanan mean when he said that you will baptise with fire?"

"Both fire and water can be used for cleansing. I hope what I say will shake the hitherto unshakable foundations of our faith. There is so much that needs to be done in life to make life worth living, instead of worrying and fretting about the life hereafter. The people must stand up against the authorities that oppress them. I will set fire to all the unjust laws and rules and customs and traditions and wake the people up to peace and freedom. Will you help me do that?"

"Yes, but you must teach us how," says Yehudah.

We continue our journey and by evening we come to the outskirts of the metropolis of Pella. We rest.

"Look how they have built this magnificent city, choosing the beautiful surroundings beside the spring on the foothills of the Yarden valley. They were scholars and mathematicians. We don't build cities like that," I tell them.

"They also have taverns where they get drunk, and baths where men and women bathe together and brothels, all forbidden by our laws," adds Shimon.

"We do not have to follow all their ways. What they do openly our people do behind closed doors. Are we any better? Alright we don't have to go into the city. Pilip, what is the direction to Naṣrath?" I change the subject.

"We have to cross Ha-Yarden again and make our way towards Beit She'an along the valley of Jazreel. We will be entering *HaGalil HaTahton*[83] and no longer in Shomron," says Pilip.

"Let's go."

We walk through green, fertile pastureland approaching the city of Beit She'an, another magnificent example of Yavan architecture. This is also one of the *Decapolis*[84], the only one west of Ha-Yarden. The Kittim leader, Pompey, rebuilt this city and made it the capital of the Decapolis, renaming it Scythopolis, the city of the Scythians. We enter the city along buildings made of dark basalt blocks of stone, quarried from *Har haGilboa*[85]. Beit She'an is a metropolitan city but Jewish in character. We feel quite at home here.

We pick up some food at a stall and spend the night in the outskirts of the city, in the open. Looking at the walls of Beit She'an, I say, "In the Mikra it is written that when the *Plistim*[86] fought the *Bnai Yisra'el*[87] on Har haGilboa, the bodies of Malka Šā'ûl and his son Yonatan were hung on those walls."

---

[83] South Galilee

[84] Ten cities

[85] Mount Gilboa

[86] Philistines

[87] Israelites

Scenario 6 - My Objective

Nasrath

The following day, we go up the Ha-'Emeq valley skirting *Har Tavor*[88] towards Naṣrath. My family is completely taken by surprise, seeing me suddenly after seven years.

"Yeshua, look at you. You have grown bigger, and your beard has grown longer. What a pleasant surprise," says Maryam pulling him towards her in embrace. The other family members quickly follow, all talking at once. One new member stands behind them all.

I bow and kiss Aba's hand. "Who are these?" he asks.

Before I can introduce them... "Ah, Andrea, Pilip, Miriamne, we know your families, you are not strangers," says Ama.

"This is Yehûdâh Ish-Kerayot and Shimon Qan'anaya."

"Come inside, you are all most welcome," invites Maryam.

I notice the new member, looking enquiringly at her. Ama explains, "Yeshua, this is Arsinoe from Japha. She is staying with us and is one of the family now."

"Oh... it's a Yavan name, common in Mitzrayim. Good name, it means "woman with uplifted mind," say I thinking to myself that I

---

[88] Mount Tabor

59

would find out more about her later.

In typical Galilean hospitality we all sit around the taboon oven and share a meal. They have plenty of questions about Qumran and I explain.

The one most interested is Ya'aqov. In the end he says, "Most interesting, perhaps one day I will go and pay them a visit."

"Why did you leave and decide to come back? And are you clear now as to what you want to do with your life? Asks Aba.

"Yes, living a hermitic life in Qumran was a good experience for me. It was a peaceful and sheltered life. I had plenty of time to think things over. Having experienced what happened in Magdala, I kept thinking of the people, especially the poor who are oppressed by the rich and powerful.

"The religion taught by our rabbim is meaningless and leaves these people helpless. They are told that their misery is punishment for their sins, and that it is the will of Elahh. I want to see change in the people and in the authorities who determine their lives," I declare.

"How do you hope to achieve this impossible task?" asks Tabby, my second sister.

"I would like to meet some people who think like me and can help me achieve this task, which I think is possible. Remedies and solutions must be sought and experienced in life on earth, rather than after death," I state.

"We await the coming of the kingdom for liberation and salvation," asserts Yehudah.

There is silence for a while. Arsinoe fixes her gaze on me.

"Look at the seed, the soil, the trees, the birds, the fish, the sea and the sky – they are all connected. If we live in peace and freedom, happy to be part of all things in the world, we need not expect the kingdom to come. The kingdom is the world, and the world is the kingdom. Our time in this world is very short and that is why, all the more, we must value our life and the world.

"We live under oppression, yes. We must struggle for that freedom, even fight for it. We should start by looking for that freedom and peace first within ourselves and bring about a healing. We see people sick and maimed, real disease in the people but there is also an illness in society that needs healing. When society rejects a *tsa'ra'at*[89] as unclean, society is sick. Many of the teachings of the rabbim also bring illness to society. To bring about change is a difficult but not impossible task, Tabby."

"When would you start this work?" asks Andrea.

"Well, I've already started it. Now that I am here, I would like to visit Magdala. That is where I saw the power of oppression in action. Now I want to have a close encounter with the people there. When Hordos Antipas sent his troops to destroy and kill the people, I wanted to run away because I did not want to have any part in that situation of injustice. I realise now that there is no such thing as being neutral. If you do not resist you are on the side of the oppressor. That's what you taught me, Aba. I will always remember it."

"To resist violence, you also have to be violent. How then do we live in peace and harmony with the world?" questions Shimon.

"A very good question. We must be wise and calculate the strength of violence. If the oppressing force is too powerful, we will lose more lives. Although the people of Magdala knew that passive resistance meant death, they fought back. The enemy was too powerful, and they lost many more lives.

"We are taught that justice means an eye for an eye and a tooth for a tooth. In that case they lost more eyes and teeth than the enemy. The soldiers were carrying out orders but the real evil one is Antipas. There are many kinds of violence and different approaches

---

[89] leper

61

to violence, and we will learn more as we go along," I conclude.

"So, you want to bring about a change," remarks Aba.

"You know, Y'hochanan, son of Aunt Elisheva and Uncle Zachariah. He was already in Qumran before me. We were together and became very involved in the community life there. Only about a month ago he left and became a preacher in the wilderness calling for repentance and baptising the people in Ha-Yarden. He is known as Y'hochanan ha-mmatbil."

"Yeshua, I was thinking about you all the time, wondering when you were coming home," says Maryam and continues, "I know you are wondering about Arsinoe. She was betrothed at an early age and married to a middle-aged man when she was only 12. He beat her and treated her like a servant. She has a mind of her own and enough courage to break tradition and run away. She came here a very broken person, and we took her into our home. She is like a little sister to your brothers and sisters. She was very angry when she came. She has settled well and is a very determined person."

The next day Pilip says, "Miriamne and I have to go to Beth-tsaida and report to my employer on my mission. I generally work with Andrea and his band of fishermen in Kfar Nahum. We must get back. Moreh Yeshua, you should come and visit us sometime."

"Yes, I will. I am going to Magdala first."

Yehudah and Shimon say, "Can we come along?"

"Do come."

After they depart, Shemayon, Yeshua's fourth brother says, "I thought Yeshua had come home to throw his weight with the rest of us in our family trade."

"Yeshua seems to have a higher calling, a mission to the people," responds Maryam.

Scenario 7 - Tax Collectors

Magdala

I lead Yehudah and Shimon through the fortress into the busy streets of Magdala, which was merely a fishing village when I was last here. We approach Mariam's family house next to the pickling shed.

Mariam's mother meets us at the door. She recognises me and welcomes us.

"We heard that you had gone away," she says.

"Yes, I'm back now. These are my friends, Yehûdâh Ish-Kerayot and Shimon Qan'anaya. Where is Mariam?"

"She must be in the pickling shed. She is running the business now. I can send for her."

"No need. Please stay. I'll go and surprise her," say I.

Mariam is busy sampling the fish pickle in a jar. When she sees me approaching, she almost drops the jar but manages to save it.

"Yeshua, I thought you had gone forever," exclaims Mariam. She puts away the jar. I hold her hand and give her a friendly hug.

She discards her apron, and we go to the house.

Mariam says to Yeshua, "You suddenly disappeared one day without telling us and we never saw you again for such a long time. You must tell us where you went and what you did during all those years."

"Yes, it's a long story. I will explain little by little. These are my friends who have followed me from Yerushalayim. Has there been any more trouble from Antipas?"

"Yes, there have been a couple of small clashes and a big one. Every so often he sends his troops especially if the payment is slow. Taxation is indeed a recurring problem and a burden on the people and on business."

"I would like to meet the tax collectors."

"I know one of them. He is a reasonable man. His name is Mattithyahu bar Halfay. He works here now although he is from Kfar Nahum. He is employed by the Kittim because he is skilled with numbers. Would you like to meet him?"

"Yes, indeed."

"It is about this time before noon that the tax collectors meet up. Mattithyahu is a *Levi* who should have been a priest serving Elahh. He is not very happy doing this kind of work. Come, let's go."

Yehudah and Shimon are hesitant but decide to go along. Mariam takes them to a small alcove on the beachfront.

"You stay here while I try to locate him," says Mariam venturing into the place where women are hardly seen. Mariam is too well-known a person in Magdala. She comes out with Mattithyahu.

"This is Yeshua, the man I have been telling you about," she tells Mattithyahu.

After a briefing by Mariam, Mattithyahu says to me, "Are you sure you want to meet the tax collectors?"

"Yes, I'm sure."

"I don't think that is a good idea," intervenes Yehudah. "Most people stay away from them because they are publicans, they are sinners and traitors who have become rich taking our money, robbing us of our livelihood."

"We despise them as much as they despise us," adds Shimon.

"It is Hordos Antipas who takes most of the wealth, but the tax collectors also take a big cut. Yet, there are also good men among them who carry out their duties honestly," defends Mattithyahu.

"There are all kinds of people in our society who are ready to pass judgment on others. I think taxation is a good topic to discuss with them. Taxation affects your life, and you can express your feelings to them. I would like to meet them. If you don't feel comfortable, you don't have to come," I respond to Yehuda and Shimon.

When Mattithyahu walks in with me, the other two also follow but Mariam did not join us. Those who know Mattithyahu well make room for us and call for drinks to be served.

Seeing that they are rather formal and hesitant I begin by saying, "How is work these days?"

"Prosperity is in the air and business everywhere is good, therefore our work is good," says one of them.

"Yes, you are right, Zippori that was totally razed to the ground when I was young has been rebuilt and is expanding. The new city of Tiberias on the lake has become a great urban centre. My father and I used to go to Zippori and to Tiberias to work but I cannot say that we were well paid."

"Yes, tribute must be paid to Hordos Antipas for the great development," says another publican.

"I am surprised you pay tribute to Hordos Antipas. Seven years ago, I was here when he and his mercenaries and the Kittim soldiers massacred the people here. Of course, you were not on the receiving end," I remind them.

Mattithyahu intervenes, "I will not be too quick to pay tribute to Antipas because he takes the money collected from the grand bath houses and theatres. With the construction work and the labour provided by our people, he levies more taxes on top of that."

65

"And you are the people who fleece us of our earnings," interjects Shimon without hesitation.

"Alright," I join in, "Some of you who do the collection may not even see the big picture. You may be only collecting the taxes and keeping records for someone else. What I know is that your bosses are the tax farmers who have procured contracts from the state. These tax farmers would bid against each other to get the contract, and the highest bidder would obviously get the contract. He would pledge or pay in advance to the state, and then collect money beyond the contracted amount, which he keeps for himself. I am sure you too collect more than what you pay your bosses."

"Yes, we have to impose a surcharge which is our income," claims another publican.

"Ah, but we do not know how much more you collect," says Yehudah. "And we also do not know how you assess the value of our products."

"The evaluation is left to the tax collector and the surcharge is also what he considers reasonable, as long as he hands over the stipulated amount to the tax farmer," responds the publican.

"The fisherfolk have to apply to receive fishing rights and become indebted to you, the brokers, responsible for the harbours and for fishing leases. If they fish without a contract or sell to unauthorised middlemen, the fishing police go after them. Most of the fisherfolk do not even own their boats; these are possessed by the brokers. They have little money left after paying taxes, hardly enough to buy flax for nets, cut stone for anchors, wood for boat building and repairs, and baskets for fish. This is what I understand to be the case," I explain.

"Every male, because he is a man, is expected to earn a living and has to pay an additional head tax. Every step of the way it is tax, tax and more tax. It is the same everywhere. We have no say in the control of taxes. We live like slaves in our own country," asserts a frustrated Yehudah.

"Have you come to pick a fight with us?" asks an irritated publican.

I go on, "This is what *Yehuda ben Hezkiyahu*[90], the hero of HaGalil, fought for and was crucified. Yes, we must find a way to minimise taxation, and the place to start is here with you men. I know it is a job for you, but you can be reasonable in your charges and reduce the burden on the people.

"This whole system of taxation is open to abuse and brings an enormous burden to the people and because some of you abuse it, you all get a bad name, and the people call you sinners and traitors. Of course, this abuse goes up the ladder. Your bosses collect more than what they pay Antipas and Antipas takes all he needs and apportions a fixed amount for his Roman bosses calling it the civil tax. This civil tax amounts to a quarter of all produce and income, a severe burden on the people who work on the farm and live on the edge of poverty. They call that the land tax.

"You must see the big picture in which you are cooperating in the injustice of oppressing the poor. The rich among you get richer and the poor get poorer. Labour, produce and money in the form of taxes like the salt tax, crown tax, grain tax, tax on fruit and nut trees, poll tax, besides tithes, rents, tribute, or confiscation are all taken in the name of surplus to the benefit of the aristocratic families. Am I right?" I ask.

There is no response.

I continue, "This oppressive system also forces some of the poor to become dishonest. They develop ways to evade taxes by lying and hiding their goods and when they are caught, often by you people, they are severely punished. Of course, a major part of taxes becomes

---

[90] Judas the Galillean

the annual revenue of Hordos Antipas, who loves to live in luxury."

One of the publicans says, "We are not really tax collectors, we are toll collectors. We collect customs tax on the harbour here in Magdala where fish and goods are landed and sold."

"What is the difference! When our people are down and out because of taxation, they go to you to borrow money. You lend them money, but you also charge very high interest rates. I know this to be a pattern everywhere," says Yehuda of Kerioth.

"Make the surcharge a reasonable amount enough for yourself and your family and charge no more. If you lend money, do it with a good conscience. People's lives are already difficult; don't make it more difficult," I tell the publicans.

While they are carrying on this exchange, some of the Soferim and the Perushim, having heard of this gathering, come, and stand at the entrance of the house. Mattithyahu goes out and invites them to join in the conversation.

One of the Perushim tells him, "We do not keep company with despised folk. How is it that your moreh eats and drinks with publicans and sinners?"

Turning to them I speak loudly for everyone to hear, "You, Soferim and Perushim, you consider yourselves too good to make friends with these men. You hypocrites, you are no better. On top of all the heavy burden of taxes on the people you add on the Báyith tax. You impose this two-drachma tax on all men above nineteen years of age and that is equal to two day's wages for a working man."

"But this is prescribed in the Torah, and the money is used for the upkeep and maintenance of the Beit HaMikdash in Yerushalayim and for the daily sacrifices." they say.

"You quote the Torah, but why then are the rabbim exempted from paying the tax? Are they above the Torah?"

They keep quiet.

"Moreover, in the Bet HaMikdash you only accept the half silver shekel coin which is no longer in circulation. Cunningly you require that money to be changed and charge a fee for the exchange. Where does that money go? Has the Beit HaMikdash ever accounted for the money it collects? In the name of the Torah, you cheat the people and make them poor, and like that fox, Hordos Antipas, you live a life of luxury while the poor people struggle to survive." I am venting my anger at them.

Even before I finish speaking, the Soferim and the Parushim begin to move away. They are unaccustomed to being spoken to like this. The tax collectors are shocked and some of them take to heart what I am saying. One comes up to me and says, "Moreh Yeshua, I am a tax collector. My name is Zakchaios and I am a superintendent of customs, a chief tax-gatherer. Having heard what you have said I realise that I have become rich through cheating the poor. I am going to give half of what I own to the poor and to those I have cheated I will pay back double the amount. This is a promise."

"Zakchaios, you are a humble man; may you and your family be blessed for your repentance," say I. My followers and some of the tax collectors clap their hands and praise Zakchaios. We bid farewell to the publicans and returned to Mariam's house. Mariam and the women have prepared a meal of fish cooked with leek in milk and eggs.

"Moreh," says Shimon, "today you made both friends and enemies."

"Oh, what happened?" asks Mariam. The men explain all that happened with the tax collectors and with the Soferim and the Perushim.

Mariam says, "I have prepared beddings in the factory for you, if you don't mind the smell of salted fish." They retire for the night while Mariam and I sit talking and reminiscing the time I worked here repairing boats, our time together on the tower, and the massacre by Antipas' soldiers.

Let us take a walk on the beach," says Mariam.

The cool breeze from the water is refreshing on our faces. Mariam pushes back her long hair from her face.

"The smell of dried fish does bring back memories," I say.

"I thought we were developing a close friendship when you suddenly went away," says Mariam.

"In all the time I have been away I learnt a lot and reflected on many things."

"All you are doing now is upsetting the people. What's your real purpose? What do you hope to achieve?"

Seeing a large rock, I say, "Come let's sit a while."

"I've been trying to answer that question myself. Our people are taught to see religion as more important than politics. They are told that politics does not concern them, but religion does. People in politics then use religion to control the people. They are easier to control by the fear of being punished by Elahh in *gehenna*[91] for eternity, more than the fear of being crucified by the Kittim.

"I don't believe that the afterlife is more important than this life. You have a good life. You have built up your family business, but you too are taxed. When the poor are taxed whatever little they have is taken and they must scrape the bottom of the barrel to survive. What kind of a life is that? Yet they live in the hope of a tax-free life in *shamayin*[92]. Someone will have to make the people aware that they have the right to a decent living and to stand up against exploitation."

"What do you plan to do about that?"

"I'll go around and awaken the people to the truth and expose the

---

[91] Hell – desination of the wicked

[92] Heaven

injustices of the authorities."

"You know that's risky. There are very powerful people out there and they could arrest you and kill you."

"Then those who follow me will have to carry on my work until there is change for the better."

Mariam takes my hand and holds it in hers. We are silent for a while.

"Don't you ever think of settling down, getting married and having a family? You need someone to take care of you. I will take care of you."

I look at her with love. We hold each other close and kiss.

"I must travel and meet the people and do what I must do while there is time."

"I will always be with you."

We walk back to the house.

Beit k'nesset gathering

That night itself, some of the Soferim and the Perushim in Magdala ask the hassan, the caretaker of the local synagogue, to call for a meeting. The synagogue in Magdala was only recently completed and the flagstones have not yet been laid on the sand floor. The hassan informs the rabbim, law experts, local elders, some priests, and Levites, and other Soferim and Perushim.

At the appointed time in the evening on a weekday, these people begin arriving at the synagogue. They walk past the miqva'ot outside, scoop some water and wash their feet before entering the synagogue through one of the three open doors at the front façade. They take their seats. The elders and the Perushim sit on stone benches while the others sit on mats on the floor.

A *Parush*[93] by the name of Ehud, who was one of those at the shed where I met the publicans, sands up and addresses the gathering.

"Friends, today some of the Soferim, the Perushim and I met this man Yeshua eating and drinking with the publicans. He was confronting them on the issue of taxation, accusing them of exploiting the people."

"Well, let the tax collectors deal with that. That is not our problem," says Efraim, one of the elders.

"But then, he turned on us and accused us of doing the same thing by our Bet HaMikdash tax. He called us hypocrites. We told him that the Bet HaMikdash tax was prescribed in the Torah," says Ehud.

"Did he tell the people not to pay the Beit HaMikdash tax?" asks Efraim.

"He didn't say it in so many words but said it is a burden on the people and that we use the Torah to cheat the people," says Ehud.

Another Parush by the name of Hafetz Hayim says, "I don't think we should get all worked up by him. Yeshua is just a small-time itinerant preacher with hardly a following and from an insignificant place as Nasrath. Like so many others like him, he too will soon be forgotten."

"Since we do not have much power of action here in Magdala and we are not going to get the cooperation of the Kittim forces, all we can do is to send word to the elders in Yerushalayim to inform and warn them of a possible rebellion; but let's keep an eye on him," concludes Efraim.

---

[93] Pharisee

Scenario 8 - Word spreads about me

Nasrath

We are back in Naṣrath. To my surprise, Marta from Beth anya is here.

"Hello Marta, what brings you here?"

"I said I'll come and visit you. I came sooner than I expected. My brother Elʿāzār who was sick has died. My sister and I were looking after him. I was lost and did not know what to do. I thought of you and came to see you."

"You are welcome. I hope the family has been good to you. Tell me, what happened to Elʿāzār and how did he die?"

"There is a colony of HaGalileans living in Beth anya and a poor-house is established to care for pilgrims who come to Yerushalayim from HaGalil. It is run on charity assisted by some of the Assayya with their healing skills. It cares for the sick and destitute, and even the untouchable tsa'ra'at. Elʿāzār was helping the sick people there. Through his close contact with the tsa'ra'at he succumbed to the disease and became a patient there. Elʿāzār was feeling very poorly, and he had asked about you."

"There was temporary relief but the tsara'ath had spread from his legs to different parts of his body. We were all at his bedside when he died. My sister Mariam said that if you had been there Elʿāzār may not have died," says Marta with tears.

"I am very sad to have lost a good friend.

"Yehudah and Shimon, we will spend a few days at my home. Would you like helping out with the work along with my Aba and brothers?"

"Yes, we have no plans except to follow you on your next move."

Aba Yôsēp̄ is happy to have extra hands with their work.

In the meantime, Pilip begins to talk about me to the family that runs the fishing business in Beth-tsaida. They are all sitting down having their evening meal. The father of the family is *Zebadyah*[94] and his wife, *Shlomiī̄*[95] Their two sons are Ya'aqov and Y'hochanan. Pilip's sister, Miriamne, is also there at the time.

"On the way back from Yerushalayim, I was listening to the preaching of a great leader, Y'hochanan ha-mmatbil. His preaching was revolutionary. It was like thunder. He called the people to repent and be cleansed by the waters of Ha-Yarden. I have been baptised by him. I also met another great leader who was there. He was talking about bringing a change to our people. Y'hochanan pointed to him that he will cleanse the people with fire. I have never seen two such great leaders in one place. If one is the thunder, what follows is the lightning, even though the lightning, like fire, comes before the thunder."

"We have heard of Y'hochanan ha-mmatbil. Who is this other one?" asks Ya'aqov.

"His name is Yeshua, and he is from Naṣrath. Andrea, Miriamne and I accompanied him and his two friends to Naṣrath. He speaks quietly but his message is powerful and challenging. A new wind of change is blowing in our land. You should meet him. I have asked

---

[94] Zebedee

[95] Salome/ Salma

him to come to Kfar Nahum where we all work."

"You should have asked him to come to Beth-tsaida," says Shlomiṫ.

The whole family is interested in me especially Miriamne who says, "I can hardly wait to meet Yeshua again."

Like Pilip, Andrea is doing the same thing in Kfar Nahum telling his band of fishermen about me. "You have to meet him, Shemeyon" says Andrea to his brother.

One day, in Naṣrath, Ama says, "The day after tomorrow there is a wedding in *Kfar Kanna*[96] and we are all invited."

"The bridegroom is a relative of ours," adds Aba.

"Most of our friends will be there. Everyone knows everyone in this small place. In fact, people from the surrounding towns and villages in HaGalil are sure to be there. Yeshua, you and your companions are also invited. Would you all like to come along?" asks Maryam.

I look at Yehudah and Shimon and they nod their heads.

---

[96] Cana

Scenario 9 - Talitha koum

Kfar Kanna

The family takes some small stoneware as wedding gifts, along with bread and wine. We set forth early to walk almost ten milin through the fertile Bet Netufa Valley north to Kfar Kanna, which is on the road to Tiberias.

Many people from the surrounding areas and the lakeside towns of HaGalil HaTahton are there with more arriving. We greet the bride and groom and mingle among the crowd.

Mariam from Magdala is there and she brings along a friend by the name of *Shoshana*[97]. They bring with them a generous supply of pickled fish, fish sauce in clay jars and fish oil. Mattithyahu has also come with them. Pilip and Miriamne come with Andrea and his brother Shemayon and the family from Kfar Nahum. The whole family of Zebadyah has come from Beth-tsaida with gifts carried by the brothers, Ya'aqov and Y'hochanan.

We sit down to eat. Pilip brings Ya'aqov and Y'hochanan to meet me. They take the seats on either side of me. Andrea introduces his brother Shemayon.

---

[97] Susana

"Andrea has not stopped talking about you, *Marya*[98] Yeshua," says Shemayon.

The women are grouped together and among them is Joa'ana from Tiberias.

The master of ceremonies is Natan'el bar Tôlmay, a close friend of the bridegroom, a local man. He is busy attending to the wedding couple and making sure the guests are all well accommodated. He has a frown on his face. There are so many people, beyond expectation, and they are running short of wine which is being served in half-measures.

Wine shortage

Ama notices this. She whispers in my ears, "There are more guests than they expected. They seem to be running out of wine."

I reply, "What do you want me to do about it? This is a wine growing area and there should be plenty of wine."

"Just telling you about their predicament, it is very embarrassing," says my concerned Ama.

As we are discussing this there is some disturbance in one corner among the guests. There is whispering that the young daughter of one of the neighbours has taken ill and her condition is serious. To avoid spoiling the festivity, some of them decide to leave quietly.

Ama tells me, "That seems to be a more serious situation. Let us go and see what we can do."

As the maidens are singing the wedding songs of Malka Sh'lomoh, I leave together with Maryam my mother and Mariam of Magdala. The others who were around me also follow. Before we reach the house, a woman comes running out to announce that the little girl

---

[98] Lord/ Master

has died.

Nevertheless, we go into the house. The wailing has started. I enter the room and find the girl's parents and siblings gathered around the bed. Ama tells them gently to make way for me. I see the little girl lying still and apparently not breathing. I hold her hand and it is still warm. I hold it tighter and lean over with my face almost touching hers. I detect a very faint noise. I turned my ear towards her nose, and then begin furiously rubbing her face and shoulders.

Turning to the others I say, "Quickly rub her hands and feet. I start to shake her and pat her back and her upper arms with hard thumps, then lift her head. She suddenly coughs. I make her sit up, saying, "*Talitha koum*[99]!" She begins to breathe again.

I tell Ama, "Please go out and tell them to stop wailing. The girl is not dead."

I address her parents, "She has a fever and a bad cold that has blocked her air passage. Give her some water to drink."

All the people crowd at the doorway shouting "Miracle! Miracle!" and the word spreads.

The parents fall down before me. I lift them up, "Bow to no man, your daughter could have died but she didn't. Sponge her body with wet cloth to keep her cool. When she has rested, give her some milk to drink and then some food to eat. Take good care of her."

"What can we offer you?" asks the father.

"Do you have wine?"

"Yes."

"Take as much as you can spare to the wedding house. They have a shortage of wine there."

Wine skins and jars are carried from this house to the wedding house and given to Natan'el who asks, "Where did this come from?

---

[99] Little girl, arise!

Who has sent this wine?"

The bearers say, "The man, Yeshua told us to bring the wine to you."

Natan'el meets me, "Thank you for sending the wine."

"Don't thank me. The wine is from that house. How is it that in this rich wine-growing area you are short of wine?" ask I.

"The crowd is bigger than we expected."

"Well, then, send word to all the neighbours to contribute whatever wine they can spare."

"My family produces wine. We have plenty. I will send word to have them brought," says Natan'el.

Soon the potential wine embarrassment is contained. The guests are not even aware of the shortage. After the wedding rituals are over the merrymaking continues into the night.

Those who came hoping to meet me, now want to meet with me separately, away from the hustle and bustle of the wedding.

Natan'el joins this select group. He says, "My job here is finished. Everybody is well settled and happy with the flow of the wine. If you would like a place to meet, come to my house. It is quiet there and we can talk freely."

We take the road gradually sloping towards the west where the village houses are on terraces. The cool east wind from the Ha-yam Ha-Gadol blows in our faces as we look across the stretching verdant valley of Bet Netufa with its luscious grapevines. Natan'el leads us to his house on the terrace. His father, Tôlmay, is already home and busy cleaning his ploughs. He comes forward and welcomes us. We spend some time there admiring the village while Natan'el, with the help of Pilip, offers some wine.

Looking across the valley I remark, "You have beautiful vineyards there."

"Yes," says Tôlmay. "We take good care of them, but we don't own them. We are the tenants."

Due Collectors

Mariam of Magdala points to some men going from house to house and asks, "Who are those men and what are they doing?"

"Oh, not again," laments Natan'el. "They are the servants of the landlords who own the vineyards. They are like tax collectors. They have come to collect the dues for their master."

When they come to Tôlmay's house they are surprised to see so many people there. They demand the account of the grape harvest. They claim more than half of the takings. I turned to them, "You take the bulk of the produce and the tax collectors come after you and make more demands. Where is the incentive for the tenants to work harder?"

"We are just doing our job and why are you questioning us?"

"To you it is a job. How much more than the stipulated amount do you collect for yourselves?" I enquire.

"That is none of your business. We have our rates, and we know what we are doing," says one of them.

"It is the tenants here who work hard to nurture the plants to bring them to fruit. They deserve a fair share of the produce," I insist.

"You have to discuss that with the landlord."

"If your landlord is unjust, do you also have to be unjust? The tenants work hard for a good yield only so that they might get a little extra in the end. If you and your landlord are more generous to them, don't you think they will work even harder for a better yield? In all fairness there will be a better deal for everyone. You tell your masters what I have said," I say sternly.

"Hordos Antipas controls our roads, harbours, fisheries and natural resources like the mines, forests, our vineyards and agriculture which are a major source of tax revenue for him. The people who help to finance the huge cost of his luxurious living, his ambitious building projects, his elaborate administrators are his cronies, and you help them to become rich and make our people poor," says Natan'el.

These collecting agents of the landlords were surprised at the level of social awareness of these men. "We will come back later," they say and leave without inviting further discussion.

"It will take more than just advice to move the landlords or their servants," says Tôlmay.

Natan'el invites us to sit in a wide-open verandah with wood-panel flooring raised above ground. I address this group of people, "Many of you, including our hosts are wine growers, but you don't own the vineyards. You work for the landlords who take the bulk of the produce, and you are taxed on what is left with you. The crop tax used to be 10 per cent but now it has risen to 20 per cent in the case of wine, fruit, and oil. You don't even have enough for yourselves, so much so you must go to the landlord and buy back the wine you have made. In an event like today at the wedding, there was not enough wine. You must resist the system of taxation. The Kanna'im have already made complaints against the Kittim over this tax, and you should support them by raising your voices too against the landlords. The winegrowers everywhere also face the same dilemma."

"I will, with the help of my father, organise a meeting of winegrowers and discuss what we should do, and how to approach the landlords," says Natan'el.

"That would be a good start. Now that we are here, I understand that some of you know each other very well and others not so well. Let us get to know each other better," I propose.

Scenario 10 - The Followers

Kfar Kanna

The host is the first to start. "I am Natan'el bar Tôlmay. I did my schooling in Zippori and now I help my father who is a long-time vinedresser."

"I am Mariam from Magdala on Yam Chinneroth. My family owns a dried fish business. I met *Rabboni*[100] Yeshua many years ago in Magdala. We got to know each other well before he disappeared. Now we meet again after so many years."

"I am also from Magdala, and my husband was a merchant. He died at sea. I have no children, but I am self-sufficient. Mariam has told me a lot about Yeshua," says Shoshana.

"It was Mariam who brought Yeshua to me. My name is Mattithyahu bar Halfay. I am originally from Kfar Nahum, but I did not belong to the group of fishermen like Shemayon and the others. I have been working in Magdala. I am a tax collector employed by the Kittim because I am good with numbers. Yes, don't look at me like that. I know what you think of tax collectors. I have decided to leave my job and follow Yeshua."

---

[100] An endearing name for rabbi – beloved teacher

"I am Andrea bar Jona from Kfar Nahum. I first met Moreh Yeshua when I was baptised in Ha Yarden by Y'hochanan ha-mmatbil. Most of you know me and my brother Shemayon. We are fishermen."

"Andrea told me so much about the mysterious Yeshua that I couldn't wait to meet him. I am Shemayon bar Jona, a professional fisherman and a leader among them. I was born in Beth-tsaida but live in Kfar Nahum. Our father Jona was also a fisherman. My wife, Rebecca and our three children live with my mother-in-law, Abigail, in Kfar Nahum."

My name is Pilip and my sister and I were with Andrea when we met Moreh Yeshua. We too were baptised by Y'hochanan ha-mmatbil who told us to follow Yeshua and listen to him."

"My name is Miriamne, Pilip's sister."

"It was Pilip who brought news of Yeshua to us in Beth-tsaida. Many of you know the family of Zebadyah and Shlomīt my parents who run a fishery in Beth-tsaida, in the north of Yam Chinneroth. My name is Ya'aqov bar Zebadyah."

"I am Y'hochanan bar Zebadyah from Beth-tsaida, Ya'aqov's brother."

I am Arsinoe from Japha. I am now staying with Yeshua's family. Maryam and Yôsēp̄ have accepted me as one of the family, and I would like to consider myself as a sister to Yeshua just like Bethanna and Tabby.

"My name is Marta. I think I am the only one not from HaGalil. Moreh Yeshua visited my home in Beth anya, close to Yerushalayim. He stayed with us, my sister and brother. We became close friends. Recently my brother El'āzār died of an illness. I have heard Moreh Yeshua speak in the Beit HaMikdash. I have come to visit him."

"You are not the only one not from HaGalil. I am Yehudah bar

Shemayon from Kerioth and they call me *Ish Kerioth*[101]. Kerioth is in Yehuda on the west of Yām HamMáweṭ, way down south. I have met Moreh Yeshua several times before. I am a Kannai. I hope for a better Yisra'el in Moreh Yeshua."

"I am also a Kannai. I was from HaGalil and a fisherman, but I went south and joined the Kanna'im and moved with Yehudah. My name is Shimon. They call me Shimon Qan'anaya. Maybe my family has some roots leading to Cana'an, the son of Ham or the people, the *Kenaani*[102]. As Kanna'im we try to keep our faith pure."

"I am Joa'ana from Tiberias. My husband is a household steward of Hordos Antipas, the Tetrarch. I am quite disillusioned with the way the people live in the palace. My husband's name is Chuza, he is stuck there and not very happy. I am looking for a more meaningful life with the people.

My name is *Tauma*[103] and I am from Tarichea on the west bank of Ha Yarden, south of Yam Chinneroth. I am related to the wedding couple and their family. I have tried my hand at being a naggara but I've not been very successful. I am wondering why you were all gathering here. I just joined out of curiosity."

Tauma was not quite 30 years old and although he has little education, he has a very questioning mind and is good with his hands.

The HaGalileans are theocratic in their outlook, in so far as they believe that they are ruled directly by Elahh and they also have a tradition of political autonomy. Elahh is Yahweh of the Old Testament, full of power and might, an authoritative voice in the sky, a rolling thunder, a pillar of cloud by day and a pillar of fire by night, a commanding voice in battle, a ruthless slayer who led the

---

[101] Man of Kerioth

[102] Canaanites/ Phoenicians

[103] Thomas

people to the *Ha'Aretz HaMuvtahat*[104]. Just as they are frustrated with the political leaders, they are also disheartened by the fact that their promised liberation is not a reality to experience.

"*Rabboni*, these people are really interested to know more about you and your plans to bring change to our people," says Mariam.

Tell us about yourself Marya Yeshua," says Shemayon.

"Please, please don't call me Marya. We are all the same. I am just like one of you, a peasant of HaGalil who grew up as a naggara in Naṣrath. I have travelled and lived with scribes and scholars and learnt a lot from them. I will tell you about them some other time. But, please, from now on call me Yeshua and not Marya."

"Marya, you are different from us. You are learned, you know so much. It is like Elahh speaking from inside you," insists Shemayon.

"The difference is only in the way we see and understand things," say I.

"Some people call you Marya and expect you to deliver us from all evil," says Pilip.

"Others say that you are the evil one; that you are a magician and a satana worshipper, a follower of *Ba'al HaZvuv*[105], the prince of demons," says Mattithyahu.

"Mattithyahu, evil is in the hearts of men born out of selfishness. This bad thing has even crept into the hearts of the Beit HaMikdash leaders. People cannot see that because they are looking towards those leaders for a renewal and the restoration of the twelve tribes of Yisra'el," I try to explain.

"Some call you nebi, like Nebi Amos, a social *nebi* who will restore the Beit HaMikdash, and who will defend the poor against the rich." says Andrea.

---

[104] The Promised Land

[105] Beelzebub

"Most of our people in the whole of *Peleshet*[106] are rural peasants, like us. The small group of rich people in the cities get richer by taxing the people. So naturally the poor are angry and want someone to lead them to rise against the rich. Those who tried that were called Kanna'im but for sure we have to find a way to establish equality by just means," say I.

"Because you speak like this some are saying that you are subversive and dangerous." says Marta.

"Marta, it is true that when you criticise the powerful, you are considered a subversive. They don't like that and feel threatened," I respond.

"Some people say you are the moreh, who is going to change our society," said Shimon.

"Because of the wisdom and knowledge, you impart, they call you a *hakham*[107] and *hasid*[108], the holy man from HaGalil. They call you a thinker, a mystic and a mystery man," says Tauma.

I just listen and say nothing.

"Others say you are like one of the *kuvikoi*[109], a friend of freedom, and you speak with courage against oppression." says Shoshana.

"Well," I say, "There are so many of these travelling *kuvikoi* who are known either as philosophers or madmen. They are considered radical individuals who advocate the avoidance of worldly entanglements and defiance of social convention. They are non-conventional and stand for individual liberty in an oppressive society.

Perhaps, I'm like them but I am not one of them. We should also

---

[106] Palestine

[107] Wise man

[108] Pious Jew, member of a Jewish sect that observes a form of strict Orthodox Judaism also a holy one

[109] Cynics (Greek)

listen to them. They may appear to go against all forms of tradition in the way they live but they are wise people who are trying to convey a different message."

"Then there are others who say that you are just another Parush," said Mattithyahu.

"The Perushim are learned men and there are good men among them although they are self-righteous who think they are above the others in observing the law. I don't want to be a Parush because I do not want to be above others," say I.

"The Perushim have also spoken about the coming of the Mshikha[110] who will save us all, and some people are wondering if you are the Mshikha." says Shimon.

After hearing their views, I say, "Alright, I don't know where you hear all these things about me. Let them all call me what they want, and you can tell them that I have a godfather who looks after me; but who do you say I am?"

"You are our leader, and we follow you. We expect that you will regroup our people, set up a militant force and drive the Kittim out of our land," says Yehudah of Kerioth.

"We need a leader who will bring us freedom from the Kittim," adds Shimon Qan'anaya.

"Shimon and Yehudah you are part of the fanatical Jewish Nation-alists who are the defenders of the faith, devoted to the Law. You hate the Kittim occupation. You are Kannaim and you want to change our society. You are looking for a leader who will bring about a change. Change is indeed what we need, but not necessarily in the way you want it," say I.

"I don't really know who you are; but you are different from the rest of us. What you teach is different and even against the teachings

---

[110] Messiah

87

of Beit HaMikdash. There are rumours that the Beit HaMikdash authorities want to set you up as a trouble-maker and let the Kittim deal with you." says Ya'aqov.

"Whatever is said about you, the people want to listen to you talk," said Shoshana.

"I talk because our people are confused about the unfulfilled promises made by Elahh and the nebim in the Mikra, and how our leaders are working with the Kittim to oppress the working people, and also because you all have many questions you want answered, although I do not have all the answers. I would like us all to think for ourselves, and that is why I often answer a question with a question." I tell them.

"Moreh Yeshua, what are your plans?" asks Ya'aqov.

"I want to travel to all the towns and villages of HaGalil and beyond. If you want to travel with me, you are welcome. I have no place to stay."

"Moreh Yeshua, if we travel with you, we will have to find some place to stay," says Y'hochanan.

"We can sleep in a cave or under a tree, as long as we are near the people. If we travel as a group, we should be able to retire somewhere every now and again, to rest and reflect on our work with the people," I am thinking aloud.

"I know a place where we can retreat to and be by ourselves. We can set up the place as our base camp," offers Shemayon.

"That sounds interesting," say I.

"The place I have in mind is on the shores of Yam Chinneroth, not far from Kfar Nahum, a bay between *Ganne Sarim*[111] *and Ein Sheva*[112] and about five milin from Magdala. It is a little bay and the beach

---

[111] Aka Gennesaret

[112] Tabgha (another name)

is sheltered by the spreading boughs of shiqmah trees. It is safe, and my team of fisherfolk will keep an eye on the place when we are away," says Shemayon.

"Why don't we all plan to meet there?" asks Mariam.

"I cannot stay and travel with you all, all the time, but whenever I can, I will try to be with you," says Maryam, my Ama.

"Can we meet at the place indicated by Shemayon sometime soon?" I wonder.

"If we decide to follow *Rabboni* Yeshua, we must prepare ourselves, settle all our family affairs or businesses, and bring with us the necessary things to live like nomads," says Mariam.

"We need tents, cooking utensils, beddings and our own personal things," adds Andrea.

"What about food?" asks Marta.

We can always get boats and fishing nets from my friends. Most of us are fisherfolk anyway," says Shemayon.

"I am quite excited, and would like to be one of the followers," volunteers Arsionoe.

"Let us work it out among ourselves what to bring, so we don't all bring the same things or too many things," advises Pilip.

"I suggest we meet one week from today on the eve of the *ShA-bat*[113]," says Y'hochanan.

"Those of you who decide to come, you can come to Kfar Nahum because the bay is only two and a half milin away. If you have heavy things to carry, come by boat. Those in the south like Tarichea and Naṣrath and here can make their way to Tiberias or Magdala and take the boat. It is quicker by water.

"You are welcome to Magdala, then we can all go in one boat," says Mariam.

---

[113] Sabbath

"Take time to think this over and if any of you decide to follow me, it is like the plougher who sets the plough into the ground and does not look back," I warn.

With that we all disperse and those who came with me go back to Naṣrath.

Scenario 11 - Clean and Unclean

Base Camp

In Naṣrath I tell my family members, "The time has come for me to leave home again. For a start I will not be very far away, travelling within HaGalil. I will meet the people of Naṣrath too. All I need is a change of clothes and a staff."

"I will make you one," offers Aba.

"We too will need staffs," says Yehudah.

"I would also like to go," says Arsinoe.

"I too would like to, but there is too much work to be done here," says Tabby.

"I need some tools – a pickaxe, hammer and trowel. I want to build a taboon oven," say I.

"Before you finish building the oven you will need bread to eat. I have packed some bread for you all to eat," says Ama.

"I will bring some cooking utensils, ladles and drinking jugs," says Arsinoe.

"I have linen and towels and soap for washing," adds Marta.

"It would take you a few days to really settle down there. I know the place that Shemayon indicated. Your ama and I will come over and see you all in a couple of days," says Aba.

When the day comes, Yehudah, Shimon, Arsinoe, Marta and I say farewell to the family and are on our way to Magdala.

In Magdala, Mariam and Shoshana have packed dried food of pickled fish and dates. Mattithyahu joins them and all three carry a good amount of cash. "We will need money," reminds Mariam.

Tauma makes his way to Tiberias and meets up with Joa'ana. Natan'el joins them bringing two large skins of wine. Joa'ana too brings a fair amount of cash. They take a boat to Magdala.

Ya'aqov and Y'hochanan bring the heavy load, a large shepherd's tent, ropes and poles, and ground sheets. They pile them onto their boat and leave for Kfar Nahum.

In Kfar Nahum, Shemayon, Andrea, Pilip, Miriamne are busy folding another tent and other camping gear, and sundry cooking utensils. Shemayon checks his fishing net in the boat and makes sure there is enough oil for the lamps.

We all meet up in Kfar Nahum. All the basic necessities are loaded up in two boats, Shemayon's and Mariam's and we sail to the bay led by Shemayon.

There we anchor the boats, jump into the shallow water and walk up the beach to a spot above the high tide level. The level ground of sand with some grass is under the spreading boughs of one of the rare shiqmah trees. Further north of the lake there are fewer shiqmah trees, and no more grows beyond the lake into *Hagalil Ha'elion*[114]. This is indeed an ideal spot between Ganne Sarim and Ain Sheva, and midway between Magdala and Kfar Nahum.

"Is everyone happy with this place?" I ask. They all respond "Yes!"

"You have selected a very suitable place, Shemayon," I laud him.

"Come, I'll show you something," says Shemayon leading some of us to the right side of the bay into a rocky area where a spring water

---

[114] upper Galilee

flows out of the rocks. "There, fresh water," he says.

We unload all our possessions and carry them to the campsite. Mariam brought an extra hand on her boat. She tells him, "Take the boat back to Magdala. It is needed there."

Ya'aqov, Y'hochanan, Pilip and Natan'el select the spots for the two tents. Arsinoe and Miriamne help to stick the poles into the ground to hold up the canvas of the tent. Soon they pitch the tents and secure the guy ropes; one for the men and the other for the women.

Yehudah and Shimon go around to collect wood for a fire while Tauma and I select a place to build the taboon oven and look for rocks and clay to construct it.

There is an abandoned old boat on the beach. The women drag it, overturn it, and place it between the tents. It becomes the kitchen pantry, a storage place for food stuff and utensils. They have prepared a makeshift kitchen.

Shemayon says, "While you are all busy setting up camp, Andrea and I will go fishing."

Mattithyahu volunteers, "I will join you, after all, I once fished too."

Everyone is busy doing something to set up the base camp.

Tauma and I collect a good selection of rocks and construct a solid base for the oven. Yehudah and Shimon collect enough wood to build a fire. They store the rest under the boat to keep dry. It is already evening, and we have not eaten for the day. We were nibbling on the pickled fish brought by Mariam. Pilip and Yaaqov light up the oil lamps.

Shemayon, Andrea and Mattithyahu are sitting quietly on the flat-bottomed boat of cedar wood rocking gently on the water, the moon's light glittering on the waves.

"Let's pull the net," says Shemayon to his mates. They are using cast nets with lead weights.

"What a miserable catch!" moans Ya'aqov.

When they return, we are sitting around the fire. I am feeding the fire with the dried bark of the shiqmah tree.

"It isn't a very good catch, but we have enough for a meal."

"There you are, Joan'na." says Shemayon handing the fish to her. Joan'na and Marta begin preparing the fish. They go down to the waterfront to gut and clean the fish in the gentle waves of Yam Chinneroth.

"It is good to get away from the palace," says Joa'ana.

The remote hills on the mountainous region of the north are silhouetted against the moonlight while the plains flatten out towards the lake. Marta cut open the tilapia and as she pulls out the entrails, the stomach bursts and spills out dark green algae. Joan'na washes the fish in the water.

This region called HaGalil is long disputed.[115]

Although it is quiet, rustic and tranquil, it is not that peaceful among the people of the region. There is disquiet regarding the way this client-kingdom is run by the malka Antipas who is an absolute overlord. The Kittim *Keysar*[116] grants him a license to exact heavy taxes on the people so long as he keeps them under control. The Kittim forces are always present. Despite that, there were eloquent dissent among them from leaders like Yehuda ben Hezkiyahu and others who stirred up the people to protest.

"Andreia, Yaaqov, why don't you go and help the women with the fish?" I suggest.

"That's the women's job; let them do it," says Andreia.

---

[115] Originally inhabited by the Arameans or Syrians, the Maccabees who considered it to be part of the ancient kingdom of Yisra'el, seized HaGalil and forcibly converted it to Yahadut around 103 BCE.

[116] emperor

"You, fishermen, when you see the fish in the water do the women fish serve the men fish?" I ask.

"No, but we caught the fish so the women can prepare and cook them," says Shemayon.

"It's alright if you have a mutual agreement; but the women too can go fishing, no? We may be different by nature but aren't we all equal as persons?"

"No," said Shemayon, "women are not worthy of life."

"Shemayon, where did you come from? Aren't you born of woman? If the woman gave you life, how can you say that women are not worthy of life?"

"They are not equal to men because the rabbis taught us that in marriage the man becomes the master of the woman," adds Pilip.

I point out, "In marriage also the two, male and female, become one. Whatever the rabbis say, I am telling you that man and woman, although they may be different, they are equal."

At the waterfront cleaning the fish, Joan'na says, "Yeshua seems to have some kind of knowledge and wisdom. That is why people like to listen to him when he talks."

"He does not talk like the rabbis in the Beit HaMikdash. He says things different and against what the rabbis have been teaching us all this time," adds Marta.

"I'm afraid this is what will get him into trouble one day."

"But that does not seem to worry him."

"We have to be careful and warn him when we suspect danger."

"Ah," says Andreia walking down to the waterfront, "women, are you done with the fish?"

"Here, take them to the fire." Joan'na gives him the fish. Joan'na is from a noble lineage. She left her husband Chuza, steward of Antipas who manages the palace's income and expenditure because she was fed up with the way the women servants were treated there. She reacts to the male chauvinism of Shemayon and Andreia.

The two women wash their hands and rejoin the rest. I throw into the fire another handful of the dried bark of the shiqmah tree. Soon the flames of the fire subside, and the embers are red hot. The men wrap the fish in leaves and lay them beside the fire. We are seated on a mat spread on the ground.

"Let's have a drink," invites Natan'el and brings out the wine skins. When the fish is cooked, I tear the bread and pass it around.

Since we are all tired, we go to sleep in the tents while the fire is slowing dying out.

Clean and Unclean

I get up early and walk along the beach, sit on a rock and meditate. When the rest wake up and find me absent Mariam and Shemayon come along the beach looking for me.

"There he is," says Shemayon.

"Oh, he is either meditating or praying. He likes to get away on his own at times. Leave him be. He will join us later. We can prepare breakfast." They go back to the camp.

Fisherfolk have come to the bay early in the morning and are busy on the shore while some have already taken the net out to sea. The boat has taken one end of the dragnet that lay folded on the beach. Some men are paying out the net while others hold the ropes connected to the other end of the 300-foot long and 12-foot-high net.

Shemayon, Andreia, Ya'aqov and Y'hochanan join the fisherfolk who are actually their teammates ready to haul in the dragnet. The net is fully stretched with only the string of floats visible on the water, the boat circles around the bay in an arc and makes for shore. Another team takes hold of the ropes connected to the net from the boat and begin dragging. It is heavy because the bottom of the net has sinkers, and the top rope holds cork floats. The drag at the bottom would trap the fish hiding at the bottom of the lake.

The men and women spontaneously begin to sing a song with a rhythm keeping time with their hand and leg movements. Young boys and girls also participate in the dragging. I come down from the rock and join them singing along as the fish is dragged off the water by the net. The rest of my group have also joined in.

It is a big catch, and all kinds of fish are tossing and flipping up and down on the beach. Soon others come to skillfully extricate them from the net without damaging the fish or the net, and to sort them out. The small fish are thrown back into the lake. Some big fish are also being tossed back into the water because there is a distinction between clean and unclean fish. Fish with scales and fins are regarded as clean whereas fish like catfish and eel were slimy and considered unclean. The tax collectors are already on the beach counting and weighing the fish.

"Don't throw them away. There is no such thing as clean and unclean fish." I remark.

Everyone stops doing what they are doing and looks up at me.

One of them says, "How can you speak against the Beit HaMikdash teaching?

"All the fish in the water are products of nature. They are different just as we are different. They can be unclean only if they have dirt on them and they can be cleaned. They are not by nature unclean. We can cook them and eat them just like any other fish."

"Fish that is not kosher has no sale value, like that one," says one of the fishermen pointing to a sturgeon.

"Just because you cannot see the scales with your eyes, you consider that fish unclean. Look closer. You may still not be able to see the scales. If you put that fish into hot water, you can see the scales and you can also remove them. When you swim in the water among the fish you see some fish with scales but when they are caught and brought to dry land, they shed their scales. Other fish only develop scales when they are mature. There are various types of fish. You are fishermen, I don't have to tell you that. You have eyes but you see not. You are blinded by the Beit HaMikdash teaching of the Torah."

"We have to make a living."

Again, I interrupt, "If the merchants won't buy that fish, then keep them for yourselves and you don't have to pay tax."

That aroused their interest immediately.

"The taxes you pay to the tax collectors go to the wealthy friends of the king who has given them as a gift, the right to collect taxes. However, the bulk of collection goes to the coffers of Malka Hordos. They tax you on 60 per cent of your catch only after they have taken 40 per cent of the fish you catch in exchange for the right to fish in this lake. What you take home is not even enough to feed your families.

"This land and this lake are ours and nature has provided plenty of fish of all kinds for our benefit. Why do we have to buy the right to fish? Why do they call it the royal fishing rights? It is because Hordos Antipas, son of the Idumean, who governs HaGalil, is appointed by Roma as the territorial prince. We do not have the right to fish even as we live in our own land. Yet you throw away the so-called unclean fish after your hard work, only to give most of the fish away and go home with hardly enough for yourselves."

"Don't you think he is right? We never have enough for ourselves. We can keep that fish for ourselves and not pay such heavy taxes," says Shemayon who is a respected team leader among them.

"I think he is right. I have actually eaten catfish and found it quite nice," says one fisherman not too loudly.

"He is a madman, don't listen to him," shouts one of the tax collectors.

"Hey, you! Who gave you authority to speak against the Beit HaMikdash teaching? We will make a report against you for denying what is written in the Torah," says a middleman who is there to negotiate prices.

"All authority is assumed by powerful men who want to control your thinking. Think for yourselves. Look at how nature works. Do the birds in the sky look upon birds of different feathers as unclean? Do the lilies of the field look upon other flowers as unclean? These distinctions are only made by men to have control over other men and women," say I.

"Let's hear what else this man has to say." Some of them who are not directly involved in the activity start to gather around.

Shemayon's boat is partly grounded. I climb on the boat and sit on the prow above the people.

"When you drag the net, you catch more than fish, don't you? Catfish and eel are not the only creatures without fins and scales. You drag in shellfish like lobsters, crabs, prawns, shrimp, mussels, clams, oysters, squid, octopus and others as well. The Torah is quite clear in saying that you cannot eat any of these because they have no fins or scales.

"In the Torah many animals too are declared unclean simply because they do not chew cud and have cloven hooves. Even the camel is forbidden to be eaten because although it chews cud, it does not have cloven hooves. We don't eat camels because if we eat up our camels how are we going to travel? Now, if you eat any of these would that make you unclean?" I pause; there are murmurs.

"What is clean and what is unclean? If something is dirty and rotten and full of worms it is unclean in so far as it can make you unhealthy and sick. Eating clean food will not make you unclean.

Even creatures that scavenge and eat rotting food are themselves not unclean because what goes into the mouth passes through the stomach and is discharged into the sewer. Those creatures are superior to us in so far as they have a higher resistance to infection.

"It is not what goes into the mouth that makes a person unclean. Often it is what comes out of the mouth, like words, that do harm – words that come out of evil intentions within the person that are hurtful. Even words that come out of the mouth of religious teachers in the Beit HaMikdash who want to control our lives, can be considered unclean. The rules and regulations that rob you of the right to fish are unclean.

"Again, think for yourselves and don't blindly follow what you are told to do. Those who refuse to see the workings of nature and blindly follow the writings in a book or scribe oppressive rules and regulations for their own benefit are themselves blind. What happens if the blind lead the blind? Both will fall into the pit. Be on your guard against the teachings of the Beit HaMikdash especially of the Perushim and the Soferim."

The tax brokers and tax collectors talk among themselves that this man Yeshua is dangerous. The fishermen too begin discussing among themselves.

"It is easy for you to say all that but if we went against the rules, we will be punished by the contractors and the soldiers of Hordos and the Beit HaMikdash authorities. We will lose even what little we have," responds an older man.

"But then are we going to live all our lives as slaves? Our children will be worse off than we are if we do not stand up against this monopoly of the king," says another fisherman.

These are the views being further exchanged by the fisherfolk who are drying the nets on the rocks.

We retire to our camp for breakfast.

"*Rabboni*, by challenging the authorities and questioning the long-term religious and traditional practices, you have got the people thinking," says Mariam.

"This is the kind of message we have to spread among the people," say I.

Shoshana changes the subject, "Whether we remain here or travel, we need food to eat. We must stock up on provisions. So, we need money."

"I suggest that we all contribute whatever we can to a common fund. Shoshana and I have brought some money," says Mariam.

"I too have brought some money," says Joa'ana.

"Me too," says Marta.

"I have brought some of my savings," says Mattithyahu.

"Our parents have given us some money," says Y'hochanan.

"We are not rich people but I'm sure none of us has come empty handed," says Shemayon.

"I was hoping to be looked after by the people I meet. I really never expected all of you to join me. Since we are a community now, we cannot expect the people to look after all of us. Yes, we should be self-sufficient. The community I lived with gave me some money to cover my travels and necessities. It is not much. Here you are, that's all I have," say I, putting this in a small basket before placing it in the centre. Mariam unfolds the hem of her garment and takes out her money and puts it in the basket. Everyone else does the same.

"We need someone to handle this money and spend it wisely for the community," says Mariam.

"I propose Yehudah as our money-keeper. I know him to be honest and trustworthy," says Shimon.

I nod. Nobody objects.

Mattithyahu brings a pouch and fills it up with the money without even counting it and gives it to Yehudah.

We all start to clean up the place while Tauma and I go looking for more rocks and clay for the taboon oven. Others chip in. They select the rocks and shape them to be piled one on top of the other to build an arch over the foundation we have already constructed under my instruction. Others mix clay. The arch is completely covered with clay like a dome with an opening in the front and a smaller opening at the back. We set it to dry.

Shemayon says "Let's go to my kfar. We can walk along the beach or take the boat. We decide to walk the short distance.

Part Three

Travels

Scenario 12 - Meeting with Elders

Kfar Nahum

Led by Shemayon we go to Kfar Nahum in the north shore of the lake. We pass some fishermen and one of them taunts, "Why do you people follow that madman. He will only bring trouble to you. Don't you all have any better things to do?"

"Yes, we have, come and find out," calls back Ya'aqov.

When we reach Kfar Nahum, Shemayon takes us straight to his house. Before entering we wash our feet. Shemayon's wife, Rebecca, welcomes all of us and then takes Shemayon aside and whispers into his ear. Then they both enter the inner room. Shemayon comes out and says, "My mother-in-law is very sick, her body is very hot."

"Take me to her," I say. I touch her forehead and hold her hand at the wrist.

"Fetch some cold water, preferably from the well, and wet a cloth. Put it on her forehead and then her neck and other parts of the body. Boil some garlic and let her drink it hot."

Marta and Mariam help Rebecca to prepare the cold sponge while my Ama, Maryam, who was already there, and no stranger in Shemayon's house, prepares the hot garlic drink.

Andreia goes out to get buy food. The orechah has just arrived in town and setting up stalls with all kinds of food. Andreia, well known in his hometown, purchases some dates and other dried fruit like persimmon and figs, besides the usual fish. The other women prepare some food.

After we have eaten and sit talking, Shemayon's mother-in-law, Abigail, walks out of the room. The temperature has gone down, and she feels better.

"*Attha*[117], please, come, sit down and have something to eat," I invite her.

"You have a healing touch, Moreh Yeshua," says Abigail.

"Thank you and do take care of yourself. I think I'll take a little walk," say I.

I wander into the open market set up by the orechah merchants.

Marta and Shoshana discuss with Rebecca what to prepare for dinner. Ya'aqov and Y'hochanan say they are going to look for me, and Tauma and Mattithyahu join them. The rest stretch out and some begin to doze off.

When Yaaqov, Yhochanan, Tauma and Mattithyahu meet up with me, they say that some of the men among the elders of the town have asked if I would meet and talk to them. "Yes, take me to them," I say.

We go to a place not far from Shemayon's house. We enter a large room used as a prayer hall for they do not have a synagogue as such. The elders and many of the townsfolk are already gathered there. They greet me politely and invite me to speak. I tell them a story.

"A woman was carrying a jar full of grain. While she was walking along a distant road, one of the handles of the jar broke at the bottom and the grain spilt out behind her on the road. She didn't know this and hadn't noticed a problem. When she reached home, she put the jar down and discovered that it was empty except for a few grains."

---

[117] Woman

"What is your message?' asks one of the elders.

"You have been absorbing a lot of the ideas pouring out from the preaching of the Perushim and the rabbim. They fill you with a lot of nonsense. If you sit down and examine the contents of their preaching, you will find precious little that is worthwhile. Your pot is empty, and the birds of the air have eaten them all. Look for what is real in life."

They are shocked and angry with me, "How dare you denounce the teaching of the Beit HaMikdash?" Some of the townsfolk want to grab me, take me out and stone me. I calmly walk out, and no one touches me.

"Moreh, it is dangerous for you to say such things," says Natan'el.

"The rabbim speak of Elahh's punishment and the life hereafter. What do they say about taxation and the difficulties in your life?" is my reply. We return to Shemayon's house.

"The whole town will soon hear about this and there could be trouble," says Tauma.

"Perhaps we should leave Kfar Nahum tonight and come back when things have calmed down," says Shoshana. After the meal, we say goodbye to Rebecca and Shemayon's mother-in-law. My Ama decides to stay back.

"Perhaps tomorrow I will come by your camp and pay you a visit," she says.

We go to Ein Sheva an agricultural town by the lakeside. A large crowd of people are on the beach because it is the feast of *Sukkot*[118] celebrating the Spring harvest. It is also a time of thanksgiving and the fisherfolk are not catching. We find one of the fishing boats upturned on the shore with a gaping hole at the bottom.

"Shemayon, Yaaqov, look at that hole. Come let's fix it," I say.

---

[118] Tabernacles, a harvest festival treated as Sabath, also known as Tents or Booths

Shemayon asks the fisherfolk if they had any tools and some tar. I knock a piece of wood into the hole and seal it with tar. Some people see me and gather around. One of them asks, "Why are you doing that today? Don't you know it is Sukkot and you are not supposed to work?"

"The fisherman who owns this boat will not be able to catch tomorrow and he will lose a day's earning. Who among you will not untie your ox or donkey from the manger on the ShAbat and take it out for watering? Who among you will provide food for this fisherman and his family? The ShAbat was made so that we can have one day of rest in the week from the hard work of every day. ShAbat is for the benefit of humans; humans are not made to be enslaved by the ShAbat.

"Sukkot is a time for us to give thanks to nature for providing fruit and vegetable for food, and the sea for providing fish. Once a sower went out and sowed a handful of seeds. Some fell by the roadside and were eaten by birds. Some fell among the thorns, which smothered their growth and the worms devoured them. Some fell among the rocks and could not take root. Others fell on fertile ground and their fruits grew up toward heaven. They produced 60 and 120 units per measure."

"You are not telling us something that we do not already know, but what is your message?" asks one of the farmers.

"You understand the cycle of nature and sow at the right time of the year. You also know that if you want a good harvest, you must prepare the soil and sow the seeds where they will take root. The seed that fall along the roadside are like the taxes you pay. They are gone, eaten by the birds of the air or by the vultures of our society, and you get no returns. The seed that fall among the rocks are like people who welcome the words of the Perushim and the Soferim. They believe for a while but in times of trial and misfortune, they find these words unable to solve their problems because the teachings are not grounded. The seed scattered among the thorns are like those who become hampered by rules and regulations, like the rule of the ShAbat. They do not take root in real life.

"A good farmer will nurture his plot for a good harvest, and a good fisherman will take the full-grown fish and release the small fry back into the water for a better catch another day.

"The seed represents the bare necessities of life, and to safeguard good living in harmony with nature you have to use your wisdom and understanding. Think for yourselves rather than follow blindly whatever the authorities say."

They are perplexed by his new teaching that is so different from what they have been taught. They begin to think differently and ask him many questions. It is getting late in the afternoon.

"Let's take a break, the people too are hungry. Tell them to eat and share whatever food they have brought," I tell my followers who convey the message to the people.

Being a ShAbat holiday, the people always carry some food with them when they went out, like bread and dried fish, and wine and fruit. As it is customary, the families sit down along the beach and spread out their lunch. Others join them, and they share whatever they have with those who came empty handed. It is always surprising how food goes a long way when it is shared. Everyone, including our group ate well and rested.

We later make our way back to the base camp.

Scenario 13 - Bastard

Base Camp

As soon as we reach the base camp, we change into our inner garments and jump into the sea, even the women led by Miriamne. After a refreshing dip in the sea, we go to the spring of fresh water. The women go first and then the men.

I inspect the taboon oven. "It is dry enough. Let's build a fire inside."

Joa'ana kneads some dough, shapes it and I have the privilege of putting it into the taboon after pushing the fire deep inside.

We have pickled fish and almonds.

I look at the food, "We must eat some green vegetables. I know where to find some."

I go to the spring. Mariam follows me. "I remember seeing mulberry shrubs," she says. Soon we find them. The ripe fruits are almost black, others red, and the unripe ones, green. We pluck them anyway.

"The green leaves can also be eaten. We can cook them with the fish," say I.

"Ouch! The thistles are vicious," reacts Mariam.

"Look carefully, they are not all thistles. This is *Akkub*, a wild vegetable. You have to be very careful how you pick them."

I show her by reaching between the thorns and snapping the tender stems. "We can soak these in some wine and cook them in oil together with the fish."

"How do you know so much about wild vegetables?" asks Mariam.

"We lived in the wilderness and survived on all kinds of food."

"You are amazing, *Rabboni.*"

When we get back, fire is blazing outside the tents and the bread is done. Mariam and the women prepare the vegetables.

When all is ready, we eat around the fire.

Natan'el bar Tôlmay comes from a noble background. He knows letters and is able to read. He knows a lot more than the fisherfolk confined to Beth-tsaida and Kfar Nahum.

He has been wondering for a while if he should raise this question at all. Some amongst them would have heard about this but no one dares bring it up.

"Moreh Yeshua, forgive me, I do not mean to insult. There was one Sofer who called you a bastard," says Natan'el all of a sudden.

"Who is that sofer? I'll go and cut off his fingers and his ear." utters Shemayon.

"I heard a publican talking to his friends. He was telling them what he had heard from a sofer named Eleazar from Yerushalayim, who keeps historical records and says he has proof that Yôsēp̄ is not your father." declares Natan'el.

"Well, what did he say?" asks Mattithyahu.

"The Great Hordos became malka 62 years ago. After Hordos's death 29 years ago, our great hero Yehuda ben Hezkiyahu, grouped his band of Kanna'im to rebel against our rulers and the Kittim occupation. Yehuda ben Hezkiyahu captured Zippori, but the Kittim troops razed Zippori, raped the women and sold the rebels into slavery, and occupied the village. It was a traumatic experience for the Yehudim there.

"Moreh Yeshua's mother Maryam, he says, was there at that time. There were stories that Maryam was raped by a Kittim soldier named Pantera. Nobody knows where he is now, but you are the son born of Maryam," explains Natan'el.

"I know Maryam well and this could never have happened. It is nonsense gossip only to smear the good name of Yeshua. I refuse to believe it," says Mariam from Magdala.

"You can always ask my mother the truth. Yôsēp̄, my father, is a good man. Although he is a naggara he is also a great patriot who stands up for the people of Yisra'el. People have said very unkind things about my Aba and gravely insulted my Ama," say I.

"We all know and respect your family, Moreh Yeshua," assures Arsinoe.

Mariam says, "Maryam, our Moreh's mother, will be joining us later today. If anybody has any doubts, let us ask her and clear this matter once and for all. Maryam is an honest woman who will hide nothing from us."

They carry on talking and late in the evening Maryam arrives with a basket of fruits. She is quite tired carrying the heavy basket. Marta takes the basket from her and helps her to sit down.

"Ah, have you all eaten already? I have brought some fruits," she says.

Ya'aqov digs into the basket and pulls out a bunch of grapes, figs, ripe pomegranates, and freshly baked bread.

I take the bread, tear it, and pass it around. We eat and drink wine, and nobody is bold enough to bring up the subject of my birth.

Then I say to my mother, "Ama, my friends here have heard rumours about how I came to be born. They want to hear it from you. You have explained it to me, but please tell them so that they will have no doubts about it."

"Alright, I will tell you what happened. Zippori was a deserted ruin. Malka Hordos rebuilt and fortified the city and restored it to its former status as district capital. Zippori became the centre of trade for the whole area. Later the Kittim governor Varus destroyed Zippori.

Natan'el chips in, "Maryam, some people say that you were there in the city at that time,"

Maryam explains, "No, Natan'el, I was not there at that time. It is true that Zippori is where I grew up with my family. Zippori, a beautiful place even then, was a walled city on the hill. Although Hordos was responsible for making it beautiful he was not liked by the people because he did not care for the people. He was a cruel man.

"So, soon after he died, Yehuda ben Hezkiyahu, a tall handsome man, attacked the city, looted the royal palace and armed his men with Hordos' arsenal.

"Of course, there was an immediate response from the Kittim. The resistance was too strong for the local garrison of the Kittim, so they called for reinforcements from Athura.

"The Kittim governor of Athura, Quintilius Varus led three Kittim legions of 18,000 troops and brutally attacked Zippori, burnt it to the ground, raping and slaughtering hundreds of people and sold the living into slavery. There were 30,000 people living in Zippori at that time, but we had already moved out of Zippori to Naṣrath. I was holding the hand of a two-year old Yeshua in Nasrath from where we could see the black smoke rising on the hill of Zippori. Varus rounded up the revolutionaries and had 2,000 of them crucified in one day. Yehuda ben Hezkiahu was among them. The Kittim did that to put fear in our people.

"Now coming to the story of the birth of Yeshua, I was living in Zippori with my parents in a two-storey house that opened onto a narrow street. We shared the house with other families. On the

113

ground floor we had taboon ovens and underground water cisterns. They were constantly breaking and in need of repair. Skilled workers often came from outlying villages to find work in Zippori. One of the workers who came to fix our cistern was Yôsēp̄ from Naṣrath. As a naggara skilled in woodwork and stonework, he was like Yehuda ben Hezkiyahu, tall and handsome. That is when we got to know each other."

Because of the people's frustration over and hatred of Hordos, there were frequent skirmishes and attacks from the Kanna'im. Each time the Kittim retaliated with brutality. The women and girls were terrified of them. The narrow streets of the city were too dangerous to walk on, day or night. Kittim soldiers caught and raped women and young girls.

"Yôsēp̄ visited us often and we grew closer to each other," continues Maryam. "He spoke to my parents to take me away to a safe place. My father, Yoachim, was worried and reluctant but my mother, Hannah, had confidence in Yôsēp̄ and knew that Zippori was no longer a safe place for me. They both gave me their blessings. Yôsēp̄ knew well the inside structure of the city. There were natural springs outside the city and water was brought into the city from them. Aqueducts were built to transport the water from the springs to a reservoir that supplied water to the city. Yôsēp̄ had been working in the building of the water system, which had valves, vertical shafts, and support arches. In parts they could be navigated when the water was low.

"So, one night we packed some food and clothes, and Yôsēp̄ took me through the underground tunnel. He made me cut my hair and dress like a boy, just like you, Miriamne. There were two reservoirs and he led me down about 40 steps into one of them that was dry and still under construction. At the bottom, we went through the tunnel and squeezed through narrow shafts and walked up using another stairway.

"When we got out, we were outside the city. Yôsēp̄ took me to Naṣrath. Although it was walking distance, he had a donkey waiting nearby. We stayed the night in his home and workshop. Yôsēp̄ was living alone because his parents had passed on.

"Although Naṣrath was a small and poor agricultural village that was overpopulated, it was still not very safe because small Kittim detachments were dispersed throughout the area. Yôsēp̄ took me to a friend of his, a goatherd on the outskirts of *Iksal*[119] towards the slopes of Har Tavor. I was dressed like a boy, a goatherd, and looked after goats there. The hill slopes were patched with outcrops of rock and green pastures in between. In the springtime, it was brightly covered with flowers of different colours.

"Eventually Yôsēp̄ brought my parents to Naṣrath and we all lived there. Yôsēp̄ and I got married and a son was born to us. Yôsēp̄ saved me and my parents from the destruction of Zippori, so we named our son Yehoshua which means 'Lord who is salvation'. The short form of Yehoshua is Yeshua, spelled יֵשׁוּעַ, a very common name in our land."

"What about the story of Pantera?" asks Natan'el.

I take a drink of wine, clear my throat and set things right. "It is very simple. I was born two years before Hordos died, and only after he died did Yehuda ben Hezkiyahu and his men attack Zippori and occupy it. Fighting went on for some time until Varus arrived with his troops and burnt the city.

"My Ama and my grandparents had already moved out of Zippori. The Kittim soldiers committed atrocities like raping women and sending them to slavery. Thanks to my father, Yôsēp̄, my Ama was saved from those terrible crimes. This rumour is aimed to make me,

---

[119] A small village southeast of Nazareth

and my parents look bad."

"Maryam, thank you so much for clearing any doubts on the matter and thanks to your Aba Yôsēp̄ for what he did," says Mariam. The others too join in especially Natan'el.

Some of them continue talking while others prepare for themselves a place to sleep. When the camp is quiet, I get up and walk along the beach. I am always in deep thought.

Mariam of Magdala joins me and we both walk together.

On the same night in Kfar Nahum the elders hold another meeting.

Baruch, one of the rabbim says, "We heard Yeshua challenged the Torah that prescribes clean and unclean food. He told the fisherfolk and the people to eat unclean food. He has defied the word of Elahh."

"That is a serious offence. For violating the Torah, the punishment is *malkuth mardus*[120] with 40 lashes. However, the actual act of violation must be proven by at least two eyewitnesses. In this case, he seems to have only spoken about it rather than commit it," says Efraim.

"Not only that, but he also publicly broke the ShAbat on Sukkot in Ein Sheva. He was actually seen to be mending a hole in a boat," declares one of the Levites.

"The punishment for that would be by *sekila* – stoning. Again, he must be arrested and brought before the Sanhedrin with eyewitnesses. It would be a difficult process. We do not hold that much power here," says Efraim.

"Let us keep a watch on him and send a report to the Beit HaMikdash in Yerushalayim," decides Efraim.

---

[120] Lashes of rebellion, a corporal punishment

Scenario 14 - History

Base Camp

Another day, after breakfast, Ama says, "You are all well settled here ready for your mission. Stay together and be careful. I have to go back to Naṣrath."

"I'll accompany you back," offers Arsinoe.

"No, you don't have to. I know the way and the people along the way. I'll be alright," assures Ama.

After she leaves, we gather around, and more questions arise eager for my answers.

"Moreh, you seem to know so much about the scriptures and you interpret them differently from the Beit HaMikdash teachers. Where did you learn them?" asks Yhochanan.

"Naṣrath is such a small village that there is no school or beit k'nesset. The elders used to gather under the shiqmah tree for scripture recitation and prayer. We children also used to sit on the ground and listen to them. I was interested to know more about the scriptures." Then, I tell them of my experience visiting Yerushalayim when I was 12.

"Tell us more about these people who run the Beit HaMikdash," asks Natan'el.

"I am fortunate to be able to study history; I will tell you where in a while. If you are prepared to listen, I will first explain our history. Most, if not all, of our people who live in the countryside do not know the history of our people and our land. I too, coming from such a small kfar as Naṣrath, knew nothing except what we were told by the Báyith people.

"Our religion, Yahadut, is based on the behavioural codes embedded in the Mikra, which most of us cannot read or are not given the chance to read. Our land is really *Knaan*[121]. Aba Avraham came from the north and settled here and now we call this *Eretz Yisraél*.[122]

"Elahh cut covenants with Aba Noah and Aba Avraham, and later with Nebi Moshe at *Har Sinay*[123] when Elahh promised to make Eretz Yisraél a mamlekhet of kohanim and a holy nation.

"Our people were enslaved by the Maṣreyyīn. When Nebi Moshe led our people to freedom we came back here. We were not alone, there were other tribes here. "In the very early times our ancestors were wandering tribal nomads in a land that did not belong to us.

"Before we settled, the land belonged to many different peoples. We were strangers in their land. We wanted the land, so we built up our armies and fought the people who lived here. To justify our greed, we used the voice of Elahh's command. It is written that Elahh spoke to our people. He ordered us to listen to his voice and do what he says. He said that he will be enemy to our enemies and ordered our people to destroy all of them. There is no description of what Elahh looked like nor the sound of his voice. They became our enemies because they worshipped other gods. This happened way down in the south in Har Sinay. We went on a warpath and drove these people right up

---

[121] Canaan, Phoenicia

[122] Land of Israel

[123] Mount Sinai

to the coastal towns and took their land as *Ha'Aretz HaMuvtahat.*[124]

"Was our action, right? Was Elahh right in commanding us to do that? We were then no different from the Kittim today.

"The people all around us had malke. We had Elahh as our malka who was also the warlord who led our leaders into battle. But he was not like the malke of other people who were *adamim*, real human beings. So, our people wanted a malka like that. Our first malka then was Šā'ûl. After him came Dawidh and Sh'lomoh.

"Dawidh's reign was characterised by conquests whereas the reign of Sh'lomoh was an age of splendour. Now we long for the reign of Dawidh and Sh'lomoh. Dawidh tried to unify the twelve tribes without success. Yisraél became a mamlekhet. Then it split into two, Yisraél and Yehuda and our people became conquered and subjugated by the great empires.

"Today, although we have our own malke, they too serve the Kittim masters and maintain their positions by oppressing the people. Now we too live in the hope of liberation, salvation and redemption. We don't need malke who think they are Elahh. We need leaders who pursue the path of tsedek and guarantee us freedom to live in harmony with the world.

"The people of Eretz Yisrael are reminded to keep the law. This includes an elaborate sacrificial system through which atonement for sins can be achieved. The feast of the Paskha and *Yom Kippur*[125] are reminders of the practice of fidelity and obedience centred on the Beit HaMikdash.

"The first Beit HaMikdash refers to the one built by Malka Sh'lomoh in Yerushalayim almost 1,000 years ago. About 500 years ago, the Malka of *Bavel* destroyed this first Beit HaMikdash, and took our

---

[124] Promised Land

[125] Day of Atonement

people to Bavel in captivity. The Pares then defeated the people of Bavel, and the Malka of Pares, *Koresh*[126], let our people return to Yerushalayim. It was then that they built the second Beit HaMikdash and the outer walls of the city.

"Most of us speak Yavan and we must understand why.

"The empire of the Yavan was very big and extended into the whole middle eastern region. Their culture and civilization took deep roots inducing the people to speak Yavan. They created Yavan states. Their great leader was Tre-Qarnayia who died about 350 years ago. Many years later when Mithradates from Athura became King he changed his name to Antiochus. He restricted the practice of Yahadut even in Eretz Yisraél. He imposed the language of Athura, the language we speak today — Aramaic. Even though the Kittim have now taken control, the Yavan influence is still very strong. That is when the *Maqabim*[127] revolted against him.

"The Yavan Empire declined and about 80 years later the Kittim took control of more and more of the Yavan states. The Kittim had a great admiration for the Yavan civilization and did not destroy many of its features, maintaining the language and culture that became known as the Yavan-Kittim civilization. A great military and political leader, Pompey, extended Kittim control into Yehuda with the mission and vision of bringing the whole world under the influence of its culture. This was only less than 60 years ago when the Kittim Empire was established with Augustus Caesar as the Kittim Keysar. Hordos became the Great Malka."

"I hate the Yavan and the Kittim for imposing their goy culture on us and destroying our way of life," says Yehudah.

"We, kana'im, have always resisted them," adds Shimon.

---

[126] Cyrus the Great

[127] Maccabees

"We have been a subjugated people for a very long time. But they did not completely destroy our way of life. Yehudah, Shimon, we still speak our language and practise our religion. See what the rules and regulations of the rabbim and our own malke are doing to our people."

I continue to elaborate on the historical events right up to the time of the confusion created by the Perushim, and the Ṣĕdûqîm and the different interpretations of the scriptures.

"Our history is tied up with our religion," I conclude.

We attend to the chores of tidying up the campsite.

"We are running low on provisions," says Joa'ana.

Mariam says, "Yehudah, since you hold the purse, why don't you and a few others go and get some bread and wine and other provisions, now that we are going to stay here for some time?"

"I'll go with you, Yehudah," says Marta; and immediately Soshanna, Arsinoe and Miriamne volunteer to follow.

"Let's go to Ein Sheva, only a two milin walk from here. At this time of the morning the market will have an abundance of fresh food," says Yehudah. Turning to his mate, Shimon, "Are you coming too?" Sure enough, Shimon joins them. While the shoppers go their way, Tauma, Mattithyahu and Pilip pull out the mats and sheets and spread them out in the sun. After that they check out the tent and reinforce the guy ropes.

The fishermen, Shemayon, Andrea, Yhochanan and Ya'aqov check the boat and their fishing gear. Natan'el joins them.

Mariam and Joa'ana who are the main financial supporters of the group, think nothing of doing menial tasks. They take some clothes and utensils to the waterfront to wash and then rinse them at the spring. I join them after cleaning out the ashes in the taboon oven. "I shall leave you for a while. I want to go up the hill and be by myself."

While scrubbing the utensils with sand, Joa'ana, noticing Mariam washing Yeshua's spare tunic remarks, "Moreh has a special love for you, hasn't he?"

"Our friendship goes back a long way, Joa'ana. I got to know him when he and his father came to Magdala to work on the boats there. We are close and yet not that close. I believe we love each other but he does not want his love to be tied down to me alone. He feels he has an important task of preparing the people for a peaceful revolution, especially in their thinking.

"He is angry with the religious leaders for imposing their rules and regulations and heavy taxes on the people. He believes that there should be shalama and tsedek, and this cannot be achieved with fear of eternal punishment," says Mariam.

"His way of thinking is also very dangerous," adds Joa'ana rinsing the garments.

"He is aware of his dangerous position, of being perceived as a subversive element by the authorities. He keeps hinting that time is short and fears that something might happen to him. Perhaps that is why he does not want to commit his love to me. I am trying very hard to understand his teachings and I believe in what he says. I also have a feeling that he is preparing me to take over the leadership of our group," says Mariam.

"Are you prepared for that, especially with the men like Shemayon, who are so traditional in their thinking?"

"He is trying to prepare them also," responds Mariam.

In the meantime, I climb up the rocky hill to the source of the spring. Finding a flat rock, I sit, meditate, and reflect. Every encounter I have with the people sheds a different light to my own values. My mind is racing ahead of me changing my outlook on life itself. Am I becoming enlightened like the Buddha of Hodu! Some things are becoming clear but when I communicate with my followers, I only seem to confuse them. Perhaps I should go slow. Too much of a shock might defeat my purpose which is to change people. I sit motionless and concentrate on my breathing.

Tauma and Natan'el carry their bundle of wood and head back to camp.

They find Mariam and Joan'na drying the clothes on tree branches.

"Are you a changed person, now?" asks Tauma.

"I am changing. I am already different and will not be the same again," replies Natan'el.

Do you think people will change?" asks Joa'ana.

"Not all. Some will change, and hopefully more and more will change," responds Natan'el"

"Mariam are you a different person now after following Moreh?" asks Natan'el.

"I changed the very first time I met *Rabboni*," says Mariam.

Marta, pottering around with the utensils says, "It is difficult to change but I am changing. When I listen to the Torah now, I will question what it says."

"I believe that we have all changed after meeting and listening to Moreh, and living with him," adds Mattithyahu.

"Even though we have changed I doubt many people will change after hearing him. In fact, some people will become very angry and would want to destroy him and us for spreading such ideas," observes Tauma.

"Tauma, it has not been easy for us to change but we have changed. We too can change people, and when more and more people change, we will become a free people. Even if not completely free in everything at least free in our thinking," says Mariam.

"I am sure Moreh has a lot more to say that will be even more difficult to accept," says Pilip.

At the boat, Andreia begins to think aloud, "Have you ever wondered why we follow Moreh so faithfully when he is still not able to give us a clear vision of where we are going?"

"He hasn't told us everything yet. He is challenging us to think differently from the way we have always been taught to think. It is upsetting to us but more upsetting to those with power. What he says and does is good for us, the ordinary poor people. He is on our side defending us; he wants us to be free from oppression," explains Shemayon.

"When Moreh spoke about clean and unclean fish, that made a lot of sense to me. We were so conditioned by the words of the Torah that we discarded good edible fish. Even now when we are presented with eels, for example, we feel a revulsion against it. You cook it and give it to the people as fish, they enjoy it until you tell them it is eel and then they want to vomit. This has all been drilled into our minds by the Perushim and the Soferim. It is difficult for us to break out of this mentality," says Y'hochanan.

"None of us even dares to utter a word against the Torah. Moreh has opened our eyes to see that the words of the Torah are not *dabar*[128] Elahh," says Ya'aqov.

"He is attacking the Beith HaMikdash teaching, telling us to disregard the Torah teachings and even Elahh himself. That is what is difficult to accept. Even Y'hochanan ha-mmatbil did not teach such things. We have to ask him to explain more," observes Natan'el.

A similar conversation occurs at the marketplace in Ein Sheva.

"I really cannot understand what Moreh is trying to tell us," says Arsinoe.

Shoshanna adds, "I am also very confused especially when he says that the words of the Torah were written by men."

"Can you accept what he says about the Torah and about Elahh?"

"As I've said earlier, what he is teaching is completely different, but

---

[128] Word (of)

it is difficult to doubt the truth of what he says," responds Shoshanna.

"He said that they were written by men who did not understand women. I agree with him on that because if Elahh was the writer how could he say that women are inferior to men?" says Marta.

"He even challenges our understanding of Elahh himself," adds Miriamne.

"You see, whatever Moreh says, he grounds it in issues of real life. He does not simply say things. He had spent many years in Qumran studying the scriptures," explains Shoshanna.

"Yes, many things that Moreh talks about are real and not like the Beith HaMikdash teachers who throw the book at us," says Arsinoe.

"Moreh does not say very much against the Kittim who are really keeping us as slaves," says Yehudah.

"*Y'hudhah HamMakabi*[129] rose up as our great leader to drive the Kittim out of our land to establish a separate independent Yehudi nation, and a kingdom like that of Malka Dawidh. We are waiting for a leader to come, a Mshikha who will bring us shalama and tsedek. We are wondering if our Moreh is that leader," says Shimon.

"He does not care much about the life hereafter and talks instead about life here on earth. So, freedom from Kittim oppression is the way to go," insists Yehudah.

"But it's not clear to us how we are going to achieve this without fighting and paying a price for it," wonders Marta.

"I'm sure he has a plan," says Arsinoe.

"If the Kittim are gone, then what? More than the Kittim, the people who are oppressing us directly are our own religious leaders. The Malke, the Perushim and Soferim, and the tax collectors are the ones we are directly in contact with, not the Kittim. They only come in when there is trouble," explains Marta.

---

[129] Judas the Maccabaean

"I think we should address these issues to Moreh and ask him to clearly explain to us what his goals are," says Miriamne.

They buy green vegetables including cucumber, tomato, eggplant, and leek. They purchase matzo, taboon and barley and flour. At the fruit stall they pick pomegranates and apples, some nuts – pistachios and almonds, and some goat's milk. They buy some olive oil for cooking and peanut oil for the lantern. They also procure two live chickens.

"Let's not forget the wine," says Shimon. So, they collect two large goatskins of wine.

When the shoppers return with the provisions, they stack them underneath the overturned boat. I too rejoin them.

Scenario 15 - Elahh

Base Camp

"In Kfar Kanna we were questioning you on who you are. The Perushim teach that Elahh will send a Mshikha who will bring salvation to our people. We were wondering if you are the Mshikha and you never answered that question," said Shimon.

"Why should Elahh have to send somebody to save us when we should be working to save ourselves?" I declare. "I have indeed spoken of new and different teachings. I too have gathered my thoughts and will speak plainly."

They all move closer to me around the fire.

"The first people who lived on this earth dwelt in caves."

"Do you mean Adam[130] and Chava[131]?" asks Pilip.

"Well, you may be right because Adam is only a word that means man, or the human being made from the earth and Chava means the mother of life. If you want to give the first people who lived on earth names these could be them.

"Anyway, when this first Adam sits in his cave watching a storm

---

[130] man, humankind, a red, fair and handsome male

[131] Eve

lashing at its entrance he is almost blinded by a flash of lightning. He is scared and runs into the dark cave. He jumps at the explosive crack of thunder. Frightened, he runs further into the cave only to be followed by more flashes of lightning that illuminate the interior of his cave, bringing daylight into the darkness. He thinks, 'Wow, whatever is doing this is up in the sky and it is very powerful.'

"He crouches in fear with Chava. When the storm is over these people come out of the cave and look up into the sky. The sky opens and reveals something bright and beautiful. They conclude that whatever is up there cannot be all that bad and terrible. It can also make things good and beautiful yet be something to be feared. Humans have since lived in fear and awe of that great power in the sky.

"That is the beginning of the story of Elahh. Different people begin to tell stories about Elahh, taking possession of him.

"These stories speak about how the world began. To understand the world and nature, they attempt to describe the forces of nature by describing them as powerful humans and animals calling them gods and goddesses. They tell stories of how they become heroes and heroines. Images are made in human or animal forms, honoured and worshipped, and sacrifices offered to them for the preservation of life, the earth and crops. The stories become sacred narratives. Different cultures seem to have had similar stories.

"These stories are a clever and human way of explaining reality. There are observable *toqephs*[132] in the universe – not just one but several. These toqephs are personified in the gods and they reflect the cycle of life. They also reflect the pattern of human family life with hierarchies. There are marriages, births, deaths and rebirths or resurrections, and the struggle of life and death.

---

[132] Power, strength, energy

"Let me give you an example by telling the story that came from Bavel or *Birit Narim*[133]. It tries to describe the struggle between order and chaos through the natural cycle of the seasons. It is written long before the Torah. The world is in chaos and within the chaos the gods and goddesses are struggling for mastery. Tiamat is the goddess of chaos and disorder, but she is the wife of Apsu, god of fresh water. Ea, god of the sky, kills Apsu. Tiamat rises up in terror creating monsters to carry out her vengeance against the other gods. In the course of the struggle of the gods Tiamat is also represented as Winter and barrenness in the cycle of the seasons. Ea marries Damkina who gives birth to Marduk. Marduk is the god of Spring, bringing in the light of the sun and lightning in storm and rain. Marduk is also referred to as Jupiter, the 'wandering star'. He is the god whom the Knaani call Ba'al. Marduk is the patron god of Bavel.

"The council of the gods then enthrone Marduk as high king and commission him to fight Tiamat. With the *ruach*[134] as his weapon Marduk destroys Tiamat. He divides her body, which is chaos, using half to create the earth and the other half to create the heavens. He uses her saliva to make the clouds, her head to make the mountains, and the tears of her eyes to make the rivers, Tigris and Euphrates. He then goes on to create human beings. This story is known as the Enuma Elish.

"All that we see, the universe, is not the province of a single god. There is a hierarchy of gods and goddesses. Even though the writers of the Torah speak of Elahh, they also speak of the Elohim as God referring to his heavenly court of angels in substitution for other lesser gods.

"The peoples of all the lands we know have used the name El for

---

[133] Mesopotamia, land between the rivers

[134] Wind, breadth, spirit

God. It simply means power or the number one and the symbol used for that God was the bull, the god of power. Everyone claimed to possess the Most High God. Some called God *Adon*[135], others *Baal*[136] or *Malek*[137]. Because of the power in God, the male God was the most fearful and merciless. At the same time as father, he was also portrayed as benevolent and merciful. People have been told to fear and honour God with rites and rituals to such an extent that it has become religion.

"As fishermen and farmers, the people can predict the weather. They know the toqeph in the ruach that can cause havoc on earth, but they don't know why it happens and that is why they turn to the gods for help."

I elaborate on the Elahh of the Mikra and at the same time challenge their beliefs.

"A long time ago, people believed in many Elahhim or Elohim. Different Elohim control the sun, moon, stars, and earth with different natural cycles or seasons of the year like Spring, Summer, Autumn and Winter, to bring about some order in the world of so-called disorder.

"There are many Elohim who marry and have sons and daughters, and they too control different domains of nature like fresh water, the sky, the air, storms, thunder, fire, rivers, mountains, plains, cities, fields, farms, plants, and even ordinary things like pickaxes, brick moulds and ploughs.

"Then they begin to fight against each other as to who is stronger and superior. The naggara Elohim claiming to be the creators made plants, animals, and humans. The humans, us, said to have been

---

[135] Lord

[136] The Universal god of fertility

[137] Sometimes Molech associated with child sacrifice

made with clay, are created for the purpose of supplying to the Elohim food, drink and shelter so that they may be free to pursue their divine activities. Other Elohim who fathered many children claim to be Father El, and the father of all fathers was called *El-Elyon*[138]. Since there are different people believing in the Elohim, each wanted to claim El-Elyon for themselves. Elahh is what our forefathers called El-Elyon, but other people also claimed to have their own El-Elyon. This is clearly indicated in the Mikra."

Tauma interrupts, "How can there be two or more El-Elyon?"

"Even if there were, our Elahh defeated all our enemies and saved us. Elahh is indeed on our side. He is our Elahh. He even defeated all their Elahhim." says Ya'aqov.

"Ya'aqov, you say that Elahh defeated the people and their Elahhim and became our Elahh. Before our great Nebi Moshe led our people out of slavery in Mitzrayim, what were we?" I pose.

"We were children of our Aba Avraham," says Yehuda.

"Then Elahh gave Aba Avraham all the land that belonged to the tribes. We are his people and he is our Elahh," responds Natan'el.

"Yes, but there were other people on this land long before Aba Avraham came." I point out.

"But they are not Elahh's people. We are." insists Shemayon.

"If Elahh made a covenant with Aba Avraham promising to give all the land to his people, who, then are his people when all the other people also claim Avraham to be their Aba?" I ask.

"We are the chosen people of Elahh," says Y'hochanan.

I respond, "Ya'aqov, Yehuda, Shemayon, Y'hochanan, we were wandering in the desert like the many other tribes, and they all had their own Elahhim. Some of them also call Aba Avraham their Aba. Aba Avraham means 'Aba of many nations.' It is said that Aba

---

[138] Most High God

131

Avraham came from a country far away in the north beyond the hills from *Ur Kasdim*[139], city of the Moon God, in Birit Narim, the land between rivers. His people worshipped many gods and goddesses, the Elohim. The Elahh who spoke to our Aba Avraham was the Elahh of the mountain – *El- Shaddai*[140].

"The Mikra says that in Birit Narim, a Canaanite priest-king of El-Elyon, pronounced his blessing over Aba Avraham. He said: 'Blessed be Avraham by El-Elyon, creator of heaven and earth, and blessed be El-Elyon for handing over your enemies to you.

"This *Malki Tzedek* [141] worshipped El-Elyon and Aba Avraham replied: 'I raise my hand in the presence of the Most-High Elahh, creator of heaven and earth.' The El-Shadai of Aba Avraham and the El-Elyon of Malki Tzedek appear to be the same. The Most-High Elahh seems to have been called by different names," I say.

"Is he also the same Elahh who spoke to Nebi Moshe?" asks Miriamne.

"Elahh could have used different names depending on the different writers of the Torah, although some people believe that Nebi Moshe himself wrote them. For many hundreds of years, messages were handed down by word of mouth until they were written down on papyrus by different authors who had different understandings of Elahh depending on which tradition they followed.

"There was not only one tradition. When Elahh appeared to Nebi Moshe he did not present himself as El-Shaddai. Nebi Moshe wanted to know his name and he said *Ehyer asher ehyeh*. In the Mikra the Hebrew letters, הורי, are named *Yod-Heh-Vah-Heh*. This was only in written form never to be uttered. Elahh's name was considered

---

[139] Ur of the Chaldees

[140] God of the mountain

[141] King of righteousness - Melchizedek

too sacred to be spoken. It means 'I Am who I Am'," I explain.

"We say that, הוהי is our Elahh who led us through Aba Moshe out of bondage in Mitzrayim to the Ha'Aretz HaMuvtahat. Do you know what he did to the people of Mitzrayim, *Emori*[142], Plistim, and to all the seven nations so that we could possess this land?"

"Please tell us, *Rabboni*," says Mariam.

"If we follow what is written in the Torah, Yod-Heh-Vah-Heh is not a very nice Elahh. He easily got angry, became vengeful and ruthlessly destroyed people. Although he was merciful, most of the time he was fierce."

"Moreh, how can you say that of our Elahh?" asks Marta.

"Just listen, Marta," says Joa'ana.

"I am not just saying it; that is how they wrote about him. When we talk about Elahh are we still talking about our Elahh and other people's Elahh? There was a time when our ancestors did not deny that there were other Elahhim except that our Elahh was the Most High. Only about 600 years ago, our rabbim began to teach that all other Elohim are false and that our Elahh alone was the one and only true and supreme Elahh. If we agree that there should be a one and only supreme Elahh, should he not be the Elahh of all people and of all living things?"

"I think it is difficult to doubt that," says Tauma.

"In order to free our ancestors from slavery in Mitzrayim, Elahh brought very great evil upon the Maṣreyyīn, like the plagues. He turned their river into blood and killed all the fish, filled the whole country with frogs, mosquitoes, gadflies, and locusts. He killed the livestock of horse, donkey, and camel, herd, and flock. He infected man and beast with boils that broke out into sores. He sent down a hailstorm that destroyed all life and trees and vegetation, and blotted

---

[142] ancient Semitic people/ Amorites

out the sun for three days, plunging the country in darkness. Finally, he killed the first-born of all the Maṣreyyīn and their cattle. This is what is written."

"He did that because the Maṣreyyīn were evil and they enslaved our people," justifies Natan'el.

"True, it was the work of *Paro*[143], a bad malka but did Elahh have to punish all the innocent people, sending his angel of death to slay all the first-born children and animals? He also drowned the soldiers and the horses in the sea. Now we have made a feast of the Paskha to celebrate the Exodus with the *seder*[144] by retelling the story of the liberation of our people from slavery. We also at the same time praise Elahh for the destruction of the Maṣreyyīn."

"We celebrate because it was the day of deliverance and the birth of our Yehudi nation," rationalises Shimon.

"Yes, it is indeed a day of celebration. What I am trying to say is that if Elahh is universal, then all people are his children, and his actions must be seen to be just and fair. You remember the story of Aba Noah and the ark he built in which he saved his family and a pair of every species of animals in the great flood? He was ordered to do that by Elahh who then went and destroyed all the rest of living creatures. Is that justified?"

"Are you saying that our Elahh is unjust?" asks Andreia.

"Throughout the whole of the Mikra there is a bright side and a dark side to Elahh. Elahh is just as well as unjust. He fought with our people against all other people and tribes. He said he was leading our people to a land rich and broad, a land where milk and honey flow,

---

[143] Pharaoh

[144] Jewish ritual Passover Feast

the home of the Kenaani, the 'Emori, the *Perizi*[145], the *Khiv'va*[146], the people of *Heth*[147], the *Yebusi*[148], the *Girgasi*[149], and the people of *Midian*[150]. The Ha'Aretz HaMuvtahat belonged to all these tribes. He declared holy war against them. Our soldiers killed all the males and took the booty but spared the women and children whom they brought back as captives.

"Elahh was not happy with that, he was enraged. He believed that the women were the ones who perverted the sons of Yisra'el and made them renounce Elahh. So, he ordered: 'Kill all the male children. Kill also all the women who have slept with a man. Spare only the lives of the young girls who have not slept with a man and take them for yourselves'. Those women are our great great grandmothers.

"Elahh had a special preference for us," Shemayon finds an excuse.

"No. Elahh hated women and that is not the Elahh I believed in," says Mariam.

"Elahh spoke through *Shmuel* [151] to Šā'ûl: 'Now, go and strike down Amalek; put him under the ban with all that he possesses. Do not spare him, and kill man and woman, babe and suckling, ox and sheep, camel and donkey.' Elahh wanted nothing less than total annihilation. To obey this command of Elahh was an act of worship. Not only were the enemies of Yisra'el attacked, Elahh even got the tribes of Yisra'el to fight against each other. When Yisra'el and Yehuda had their malke, Elahh set one malka against the other,

---

[145] Perizzites

[146] Hivites

[147] Country of the Hittites

[148] Jebusites

[149] Girgashites

[150] Place in the north-west Arabian Peninsula

[151] Samuel

becoming vindictive, wreaking havoc on his own chosen people with vengeance, vendettas and family cleansing. Holy war was an act of worship," I emphasise this.

After I elaborated on this dark side of Elahh, Marta said, "We have been taught to fear Elahh because he is just and merciful. All his deeds were supposedly to punish the unfaithful, unjust, and those who disobeyed him. I now see a very ugly side to Elahh."

"Yes. The people betrayed Elahh and Elahh too betrayed his people. All the bad things were done by our people at the command of Elahh. It is very clearly stated in the book. Most of us are peasants and we do not have enough education to be able to read the scriptures. The Perushim and the Soferim would prefer it that way so that they can choose to tell you only what they want you to hear. I have had the opportunity to study the scriptures in detail from the ancient fragments. This is what I was doing during the years I was away.

"Reading through our scriptures, which is the only early history we have of our people, we learn that after we were liberated from bondage in Mitzrayim by Aba Moshe, we wandered in the desert before we eventually settled but first, we conquered these people who had their own malke and mamleket. The Mamlekhet Yisra'el only lasted about 200 years when it was overthrown by no other than the Mamlekhet Athura.

The greatest of all malke naturally became Elahh. The mamlekhet became the model and the greatest must be the Mamlekhet Elahh.

"We try to project the perfect mamlekhet in the Mamlekhet Elahh. That is our history and the Mamlekhet Elahh was created by our storytellers. It was not Elahh who created us. It is we who created Elahh and made him our malka.

How can we say, 'Blessed are the poor for they shall inherit the Mamlekhet Elahh? The Mamlekhet Elahh is wishful thinking. Even those who speak about it cannot imagine it.

"In the past our malke were decided by leaders who said they were chosen and anointed by Elahh. But now we have no choice in our malke. Hordos the Great was appointed as malka of Peleshet by the Kittim Senate, and the Kittim then divided our country among his three sons. They are his stooges. All they do is collect taxes and pass the bulk of it to their masters, the Kittim. Are we proud of our malke and mamleket?"

"The oldest religions of the world and the religions of the wise men from the east all talk about Elahh but they do not give as much importance to Elahh as in Yahadut. They focus more on the good conduct of living in the world."

My followers are utterly confused.

"What our Moreh is telling us is so shocking. No one has ever spoken about Elahh in that way. It is very dangerous," observes Miriamne.

"He is only telling us what is written in the Mikra," observes Pilip. I am having doubts about my faith in Yahadut," says Tauma.

Scenario 16 - Toqeph

On Yam Chinneroth

The following day I suggest, "Why don't we take a boat ride across the lake to Beth-tsaida?"

"Oh, great, my family will be very happy to welcome you," says Yhochanan.

"What do you say, Shemayon?"

"That will not be a problem, Moreh, but the weather does not seem very good. There is a strong wind," says Shemayon.

"Shemayon, you are the expert boatman. We rely on you," I say.

We do not really break camp because we are going to return before the day is out. People around there know of us and our camp. It is safe. Between the moving clouds, the sun is bright and hot. We all get into the flat-bottomed boat with the depth of four and a half feet with planks to sit on and plenty of room for the legs. Built out of cedar and oak, 26 feet long and seven and a half feet wide, the boat is big enough to hold 20 people. The large sail is unfurled. There are more than 200 boats on the lake, mostly fishing boats along with those ferrying people across the lake. The sun is shimmering on the water.

"You see Šemšā[152], so bright and warm. The oldest peoples on earth have worshipped Šemšā. The people of Mitzrayim worship the šemšā as their Elahh whom they call *Ra*. The people from the land between the rivers called Mesopotamia, from where our Aba Avraham is said to have come, worshipped the moon goddess and the sun god, Šemšā, whom they called *Shamash*. The Yavan call it *Apollo* and *Helios*, the Kittim call it *Sol*. The religion of Hodu known as Hindu also worship Šemšā whom they call *Surya*. There is great wisdom in looking up to Šemšā. If not for Šemšā we will have no life on earth.

"Šemšā heats up the air and makes it move. It gives toqeph to the ruach. That is what is pushing the sail and making us move. The ruach can be a breath, a breeze or the winds of a violent storm. They say that it is the Ruach of Elahh that created the world and everything. The Yavan call it *energeia* and the Kittim call it *spiritus* all meaning activity or operation – what makes things work.

"There are different kinds of toqeph in nature, always pushing and pulling. Šemšā was worshipped by all people because it gives out toqeph. Šemšā makes plants grow. Animals and we who eat plants absorb the toqeph that is in the plants. In turn animals eat other animals, and we who eat fish and animals, absorb more of that toqeph. We use this toqeph to do things like cook food and sail this boat. Everything we do is connected to toqeph in one form or another. This toqeph is all in nature and in this world and does not come from the Elohim."

Without us noticing, the sun has retreated behind the clouds, and the wind has picked up speed. Shemayon shouts from the back of the boat to lower the sail. Shemayon and his companions know only too well that such storms spring up suddenly on Yam Chinneroth. The cold winds that rush down from the northern hills and mix with

---

[152] The sun (Sun god)

the warm air on the lake would gather speed quickly. It begins to rain, and the boat is tossed about spraying water into it. Everyone is soaking wet.

"Please remain calm," say I. "We have experienced boatmen who know how to handle the toqeph. Let us do what they say."

Shemayon takes charge and gives orders about which side to row while he steers the boat to cut across the waves. The others are afraid and hold on tight to the boat. It is a passing storm and soon it is over.

"You see the toqeph can be very frightening. It is not Elahh who is trying to frighten us. The storm is a natural thing. If we did not have skillful boatmen with us, we could have perished. The toqeph is something we have to learn to handle carefully."

We do not have to fear nature but when the power of nature becomes destructive, we must move away from it like how Shemayon steered the boat away from the storm.

"The ruach is strong and the toqeph is powerful. It is something that touches us, and we can feel it. It is this ruach together with its toqeph that becomes known as Elahh.

"What I am trying to say is that the world and its natural wonders are the only reality with which we are connected. There is no other. We cannot make the ruach non-physical, belonging to the realm of the Elohim and souls, ghosts, angels and demons. Ruach is something we can feel, it is a basic force of nature and the bearer of toqeph. This is what we experience when a gust of wind sweeps across our face; if it is strong enough it will push us over. When a sail is spread against the wind it pushes the boat over the water. When we breathe in the ruach the toqeph gives us life, and to every individual a character.

"The Perushim, who are mostly the rabbim, have interpreted this ruach as *nephesh*[153], having a life of its own within us and lives on after death. We know that when we die the ruach leaves our body, but they say that it lives on and will be reunited with our body when it rises again.

"Toqeph is the activity we experience. It is very real and physical, and not beyond the physical. Which, do you think, has the greater certainty of existence? The natural or that which is not natural or above natural?"

"We don't know what the supernatural is. We cannot see it or feel it like the ruach and the ruach cannot be supernatural. The only real thing is what is natural," says Mattithyahu.

"I think you are beginning to understand what I am trying to say," say I.

"You say that this is a natural thing. If something had happened to us like the boat capsizing and some of us had died, we would say that Elahh was angry and was punishing us for our sins; that he had sent evil upon us. Is that not true, Moreh?" asks Andreia.

"It is not true, Andreia. This has nothing to do with Elahh. The toqeph just became strong and we were caught in it. There is no evil in the storm. There is no evil at all except in the hearts of men and women. Our religious leaders have made Ruach the breath of Elahh but the ruach is found everywhere in nature. We are part of it, and it is part of our world. It is toqeph that makes things work.

"In *Parthyaea*[154] over a thousand years ago, *Avestan*[155], a man of great knowledge, spoke about two kinds of toqeph, one good and another evil. Others like the wise men from the East also spoke about good and bad toqeph, in other words a good Elahh and a bad Elahh.

---

[153] soul

[154] Persia

[155] Zarathustra / Zoroaster

They say that the world and everything in it was created by the bad Elahh, and it is a kingdom of darkness. The good Elahh created all the spiritual and heavenly things, and that is a kingdom of light. It is another world, not physical, the world of the true Elahh."

"We must see the difference between the things we are connected with, things that we can control, against things that are not connected to us like angels, demons, souls, ghosts and even Ellah. They are not connected to us like blood, mind, intelligence, feeling, thinking, truth, love, breath, air, wind, force – the ruach and the toqeph. They are real, part and parcel of our life and the environment, all of which are connected.

"If only you look again at the ruach and the toqeph as something belonging to this world — not above this world — then we will experience a liberation from dabar Elahh."

The boat sails on towards the north of the *yam*.

Scenario 17 - Illusion

Beth-tsaida

Soon we reach the mouth of the Nehar haYarden. We proceed upriver a little. On the east side is Beth-tsaida. Ya'aqov and his brother Yhochanan take all of us to their home, which is one of the bigger buildings in Beth-tsaida. Their father Zebadyah owns a large fishing business with several boats and hired fisherfolk. Zebadyah is busy with the men so Shlomit, their mother, welcomes us into the house and showers us with hospitality. Drinks and cakes are served.

"Yeshua, I would love to join your group, but I have so much work to do here. I am happy that my two sons are with you. I hope they will find an honorable place with you," wishes Shlomit.

"I understand. Both Ya'aqov and Yhochanan are enthusiastic young men."

As the family begins to prepare lunch their Aba Zebadyah comes home and greets everyone. Ya'aqov and Yhochanan pay their filial respects by kissing his hands. The women volunteer to help prepare lunch.

Zebadyah asks me, "How is Nasrath and are your parents well? Why have you chosen to do what you are doing?" I explain to him as best I can.

We take a walk. Word immediately gets around that I am there. Some people bring a blind man to me hoping that I can cure him.

Both his eyes are swollen and almost completely closed. A yellowish sticky crusty discharge from the eyes is gluing the eyelids shut. I immediately understand that there is an infection. To avoid contaminating the others, I take the man aside and tell the others to stay back. I try to remove the crusty puss. Since it was all dried up, I used my saliva to wet the eyes of the man and massage his eyelids with a downward motion. The crusts begin to fall off and he can open his eyes.

"Can you see anything?"

"Yes, I can see people; they look like trees to me, but they are moving."

"Good. Now listen. You have not been taking care of your eyes. Go home and use a clean cloth with warm water and gently rub down your eyes like I did. That will loosen the dry crusts and you will be able to open your eyes wider and see better."

I bring the man back to the people and say, "He is not blind. He has not been taking care of his eyes. They were infected. He only has partial vision now." Turning to him I say, "Do what I told you when you wake up every morning and again at night. Keep yourself clean and your eyes will improve. You will be able to see clearly."

The people see that the man's eyes are partially open and that he can see and declare, "Yeshua has healed him."

"This man whom you call blind is not really blind. He has eyes that cannot see, and he is like most of you here. You too have eyes that do not see or see only what you want to see or made to see. You are told what to see and what to hear so much so that you become blind and deaf to the realities of this life. You are asked to see what you cannot see and close your eyes to what can be seen."

"What do you mean?" someone asks.

"That is because you believe what the authorities and the religious leaders say. They tell you that Elahh says this and commands that. Have any of them seen Elahh with their eyes or heard his voice with their ears? If not, aren't they themselves blind and deaf? I say it is all what they make up. They frighten you by saying that souls of the wicked will go to *sheol*[156] created by Elahh for satana and the other fallen angels, a place of everlasting fire, a place of torment where there will be wailing and gnashing of teeth. Have they seen that place or heard the wailings? Who has been there and come back to tell us about it?

"It is all an illusion created to put fear into us and keep us blind and deaf to the toqeph in the world that makes us see and feel the things that happen. See the lilies of the field, hear the birds in the air; that is reality. See the burden the poor people suffer under heavy taxation. That is reality. Open your eyes and you will see. Question what you see and don't accept blindly what they tell you."

We walk along the riverbank. Several boats are moored along the side. Some are under repair while fishermen are either mending or drying the nets. We return to Zebadyah's house for lunch.

"You have prepared lunch for so many of us. That is very good of you," say I.

"I have many hands to help me," says Shlomit.

After lunch I tell Shemayon, "Let's go along the eastern shore of the lake."

Bidding farewell to Zebadyah's family, we again set out on the lake. There was a fair northerly wind. We let down the sail and start moving fast.

"Such beautiful clear water coming down the river from the melting snow of Har Hermon!" Dipping my hands into the water with

---

[156] Hell/ Gehanna (destination of the wicked)

floating algae I continue, "The toqeph from the šemšā has produced these rich algae, and the fish flourish feeding on it. Nature provides us with such good things."

Unlike the western hills, the eastern side of the Yam Chinneroth was a plateau stretching for many milin. With only a few scattered towns it is not well populated.

Scenario 18 - Satana

Kursi

"With the speed we are doing we will reach the village of Kursi, which is also known as *Gergesa*[157], well within the hour. It is only five milin," says Shemayon.

Shemayon steers the boat to a mooring at Kursi. We all alight and take a walk. Some of the local people greet us. Someone is shouting from a distance making all kinds of noise.

"Who is that shouting? What does he want?" I wonder.

"Oh! he is a madman, possessed by the satana," says one of them.

"Let us bring him to meet Yeshua about whom we have heard so much," says another.

Some of them run to fetch him. When he sees them, he starts running? However, they corner him and begin to grab him. He struggles, and they start to beat him.

I raise my voice and shout, "Stop! Stop beating him and leave him alone."

"He won't come by himself, rabbi. He is possessed by many satanas. We have tried to restrain him with chains and fetters, but he always

---

[157] country of the Gergesenes

breaks the fastenings, and the evil would drive him out into the wilds among the pigs. All day and night he roams naked among the tombs and in the mountains, he would howl and gash himself with stones."

"What's his name?"

"We call him legion because he has many kinds of evil in him," they say.

"Please step aside," I say and walk up to him saying, "Come to me."

He moves away but I follow and again call out to him, "Come to me. Do not be afraid."

He stops and stands still, afraid, and hesitant. I go up to him and touch him on the shoulder. "Fear not. I will not harm you."

The people begin to gather around. Holding him I address them.

"This man is afraid and lonely because you have judged him and branded him as possessed by satana. You call him legion. Legion is a Kittim army unit of 5,400 soldiers. The Kittim are bad foreigners to you so when you call him legion, you make him an enemy. It is you who have driven him out of the community. Where is the evil? Have you seen satana? Why do you have to shackle him with chains? What harm has he done to any of you? He is only hurting himself.

"He is acting the way he is acting to catch your attention, but he is afraid of you and finds peace among the dead in the tombs and among the pigs. He wants to be free. He may be a little different but if you accept him for what he is, he will stop all his attention-catching behaviour. Who among you will spare his cloak?"

Nobody moves. One old man at the back comes forward and I ask him to cover the nakedness of the man who has calmed down appearing quite normal.

"Does anyone have some bread? Give him some to eat."

One woman comes forward with certain trepidation and gives some bread, which he receives and eats.

"We have legions of enemies who take away our freedom, there is no need to make enemies of our own people. Give this man a chance to be free. Stop hounding him. Let him find something to do in the community. Don't believe what the religious leaders tell you about satana." I lecture them.

To the man I say, "Do you have a home and family?"

"I do, but they don't want me."

"You go home now, and they will accept you."

The woman who gave him the bread says, "He is my son." She takes his hand and leads him home.

The people believe that some power or magic in me has driven the evil out of the man.

There were some Soferim who have come up from Yerushalayim and witnessed what has happened. They are not happy with me dismissing the belief in satana. They say, "Ba'al HaZvuv is in him. It is through the prince of evil that he casts satana out."

I hear that and respond, "How can satana cast out satana? If a kingdom is divided against itself, that kingdom cannot last. If a household is divided against itself, that household can never stand. Now if satana has rebelled against itself and is divided, he cannot stand either, it is the end of him. Satana is in your imagination because evil is only in us human beings, and especially in those who teach such things."

Again, I take the occasion to oppose the religious teachers.

Some of the women bring their children to me. It is a custom to bring the young to the Soferim to be blessed, instead they come to me. Yehudah and Pilip rebuke the parents saying, "Yeshua is not a sofer, why do you bring the children to him?"

I say, "Let the children come to me. Do not stop them. It is the children of today who are the hope of tomorrow. We must not spoil their innocence with ideas of angels and demons, and false hope of shamayim and sheol. I address the children.

"Love the good things of the world. Love and respect your parents. Love the flowers and birds and trees and animals too. Don't fight, but instead be friends. Grow up and think for yourselves." After spending some time here, we leave again by boat. We cross the yam from the east to west back to our rendezvous. It is late afternoon and as we approach the shore, we can see the spreading shiqmah tree and our campsite. Shemayon brings the boat to shore right in front of our camp.

Scenario 19 - Good and Evil

Base Camp

We light up the lamps, take out the provisions and prepare dinner.

There are several questions in the minds of my followers, and they start asking them even as the food is being prepared.

"Moreh, you were telling the Soferim today that there is no evil or evil spirits? But there are so many bad things all around us; how do we explain that?" asks Tauma.

"As I have told you, there is no evil anywhere except in the hearts and minds of people. We tend to see evil in everything that is not good for us. When we do things with bad intentions our actions are bad. Remember during the storm on the yam, it was the wind, the blowing air, the ruach and its strength was the toqeph. It was strong and powerful and dangerous but not evil.

"I spoke about good and bad toqeph, good and bad Elahh believed by other people. People gather ideas from the East, and from Bavel and Mitzrayim, and *Hellas*[158] and Athura. They also speak about two kinds of knowledge. One is by reason and the other is by personal

---

[158] Greece

experience. This is the kind of knowledge called *da'at*[159], which the Yavan call *gnosis*. It is supposed to be a deeper and superior secret knowledge that will bring enlightenment."

"Let's eat," call the women, laying out the food. Natan'el serves the wine.

"According to them we are material beings of this world, which makes us bad. To obtain that da'at we must reach out to the other world. I have spent a lot of time talking to people who give up riches, abstain from good food and sexual pleasures and pursue the path of wisdom. More and more, I have come to believe that the path of wisdom should lead us to where we are within ourselves and in the world around us. This world is not bad. This is the only world we know and experience the toqeph that makes everything work.

"Tauma, to answer your question of there being a lot of bad things all around us, it is we who are responsible for those bad things. Yes, we find ourselves trapped within this struggle between good and evil. Despite all the good commandments and directives in the books and in spite of the fear of suffering eternal punishment, we find people doing evil and getting away with it. Punishing the bad person for doing evil, even in this world, will not necessarily change that person. We can use the toqeph all around us to do good and stop the evil. We must place great value in a good deed enough to want it more than the bad deed. That should change the person.

"This cannot happen unless all people start to think that way," says Tauma.

"Absolutely right, Tauma. It is for us to change the thinking of the people. I cannot do this by myself. When I am no longer around, you must carry on this work of teaching the people the path of tsedek.

"I have already spoken to you earlier of all the past actions of Elahh

---

[159] knowledge/ spirit of knowledge, also ya'data

as written in the Mikra, and the evil things that he commanded his people to do. It is written in the Book of Yeshayahu that Elahh says, 'I form the light and create darkness; I make shalama and create evil. I, the Adon, do all these things.' I say, Elahh and evil cannot coexist. If they do, then that makes Elahh evil."

"All this is very difficult to understand, and it is very confusing to me because it is so different from what we have been taught to understand. We were never told that Elahh is evil. He is good, *El-Tsedek* and *El-Malei Rachamim*," says Shoshana.

"It will all become clear to you if you focus on the good things in this world, and not worry about reward and punishment in the world hereafter. If we have done wrong, we must correct ourselves, repent and change and if others have done evil things to us, we must forgive them if they repent. We have to be good for the sake of goodness."

"Good must overcome evil by preventing evil actions that harm and hurt other people and all life on earth except when we have to kill for food. The burden of taxation is evil; the destruction and rape of women is evil; the murderous actions of the *siqari'im* [160] are evil; the crucifixion of people by the Kittim is evil. Denying the people their freedom and independence is evil. Going to holy war at the command of Ellah is evil."

"How do we fight evil?" asks Yehudah. "What the Kittim are doing to our people is evil. To resist that evil, we have to resort to evil actions ourselves."

It would be difficult to confront the Kittim. We are simple people with no power," adds Tauma.

"Our power is in our numbers and in unity of purpose," I say.

"Moreh, we could build up a powerful force. There are many

---

[160] Bandits, Siqari'im -Sicarii - Latin plural of Sicarius – (Latin) dagger man, a contract killer. *Sicarii* comes from the Latin word for dagger *sica*

Kanna'im who could help to train the men to fight. We could build our own army," says Yehudah.

"Whom are we going to fight? I don't think we need an army to fight the Beit HaMikdash authorities. Our weapon against them would be resistance. Perhaps against Antipas we might need an army. Again, Antipas won't fight alone; he will call the Kittim. We won't stand a chance against the legions of the Kittim. Look what happened to Yehudah ben Hezkiyahu and his army. They crucified 2,000 men in one day. I would not want that to happen.

"It is people who do harm to others, and many get away with it. That is because we allow them to do so. Sadly, good does not always prevail even in the end. It is often evil that win. People who do bad things are often smart and powerful, and they know how not to get caught. Even the laws and regulations of the city cannot stop all of them.

"We cannot console ourselves by saying that the evil ones will be punished by God in gehanna, in the life hereafter. There is no eye in heaven watching the evildoers. We tolerate their evil doings because we are not powerful enough to stop them.

"The victims are usually weak and poor. Even though they are strong in numbers, the good people are not united enough to stand together. There are bad people even among the poor.

"There is no blessing in poverty. When we can find our strength in being united in tsedek, only then will we be blessed even if we remain poor.

"This world, the earth is all that we have. We live here for a short time, a very short time. Our children live on after us. It is for us to provide for them a better world. A world of tsedek. We must persevere in the way of tsedek even though we know that evil will always be there. Our strength is in our numbers.

"Religion tells you to be good and tsedek, and the scriptures have plenty of good words to say. Religion also condemns those who do not share your belief. If your religion tells you to condemn your fellow men and women what good is that religion? Religion actually divides people. Do not waste your time with it. Be single-minded in tsedek and look upon people of different colour and who speak different languages as one big family. The greatest culprits are the Yehudim who look down on the goyim as dogs. We must overcome this way of thinking by learning to love others as we love ourselves. The mind must tell the heart to love.

"Only we human beings are evildoers. The evil heart takes pleasure in hurting others and making them suffer pain. In the animal kingdom, we find pain when animals inflict pain on other animals when hunting them for food. We too do the same. The fiercest animal attack is nothing compared to the Kittim's act of crucifixion. Animals don't intend evil nor take pleasure in creating suffering. Only humans are capable of that. So, do not do to others what you would not want others to do to you."

On that note, we settle for the night; many of them confused and frightened. We had a long day and were tired. We get ready to sleep while, as usual, Mariam and I go for a walk on the beach.

"Mariam are you able to follow what I am trying to say?

"You are teaching almost the opposite of what we have been taught to believe all our lives. I think I understand where you are coming from after your vast experience of studying the scriptures, and meeting and discussing with different learned people. But we are simple people, all we know best is fish and fishing," replied Mariam.

"But you, Mariam, do you understand my message?"

"I am trying to understand. What you say makes good sense. If we have an open mind, it is impossible to disagree with you."

"Mariam, it has been hard for me too to change my thinking. Once you cross the bridge of traditional thinking you become liberated, and everything becomes clear. I think you are much more open to new ideas than the rest of them. I would like you to lead them across that bridge. Leave behind the unreal, fearful, threatening rules and regulations of the Beit HaMikdash teachings, and open up to the real issues of life here on earth. You may have to do that when I am no longer with you all."

"Don't say that *Rabboni*. Of course, we will always be together."

"I am already a target for the powerful people. My teaching is a threat to them, and they will want to get rid of me. We have to get our people to change their mind and there is not very much time."

"It is risky, but we will take precautions. No one has ever opened our eyes as you have."

"Once liberated from the supernatural we no longer need to fear the wrath of Elahh or seek to love Elahh. How can one love something about which we know absolutely nothing? The love of Elahh is a pious sentiment pursuing a myth. Love is something that comes from the heart and the mind. You cannot love something just with your mind only. I can love you Mariam, and you can love me because only we human beings can express love. Love is so powerful and full of toqeph that it becomes the moving force to do good."

We hold hands and listen to the gentle waves lapping on the beach.

Scenario 20 - Tsedek

Base Camp

As usual, at the crack of dawn, Shemayon and the fishermen go fishing and bring back some fish and get the fire going under the shiqmah tree. We go about our usual chores, especially getting the food ready. We pass the wine around while the fish is nearly cooked. The women bring out the bread.

"Ah, the fish smells good," I say.

At every mealtime we would gather and talk. They ask questions and I try to respond conscious of not upsetting them too much. Since we have decided to spend more days at the base camp, my idea is to prepare them with a good grounding of what is to come since they are not very sure of me or what my mission is.

Y'hochanan says, "Moreh, you said you would explain Qumran to us on another day."

I explain to them my first visit to Qumran and how I joined them 12 years later. I elaborate on my stay in Qumran and our preoccupation with the scriptures.

"Is that all you were doing?" asked Mariam.

"Qumran is also an agriculture-based commercial site. We trade our wares of pottery like vases, jugs, cooking pots, plates, drinking goblets and fibre-wick lamps. We have good quality clay to fashion the crockery. We also make baskets and mats from the leaves of date palms, and leather goods like water and wine skins, large bags, pouches, purses, sandals and garments. Fresh farm products are also traded. The trade is good income for our communities, which are more than self-sufficient.

"Nevertheless, it also believes in the physical deliverance of liberation from Kittim oppression. The people who are focused on this physical deliverance are the Kanna'im. The Hassidim, although pacifist in appearance, command an ideological influence with very strong undercurrents of militancy. It is their belief in the cataclysmic intervention of Elahh to physically liberate them from Kittim domination that inspires the Kanna'im to carry on the insurgency against their oppressors. Am I right, Yehudah?

"That is right Moreh, and we are waiting for that time," responds Yehudah.

"This is when from time to time, Yehudah and Shimon come to Qumran which provides a suitable hiding place.

They belong to the group of Kanna'im, who are theocratic nationalists. They proclaim that Elahh alone is the ruler of Yis'rael and urge that no taxes should be paid to the Kittim.

"We have Yehudah and Shimon among us who are Kanna'im. Tell us more about the Kanna'im," says Shemayon.

"Well, Yehudah, Shimon, why don't you explain," say I.

"The Kanna'im are freedom fighters who have vowed to liberate our people from the Kittim, but they do not generally resort to violence unless they have to. There is another group that also masquerades as the Kanna'im. This group, which also intends to get rid of the Kittim, uses violent means. They are known as the Sicara because the Kittim call them the Siqari. We call them the Siqari'im. The name comes from the small dagger they carry hidden in their cloaks. They are ruthless men who will kill the Kittim and anybody who sympathises with them like the wealthy Yehudim and the priests. They will even capture some of the enemies of the priests and collect money from the Beit HaMikdash or hold people under ransom. They are like mercenaries who will not hesitate to betray their own people," explains Shimon.

"Especially during the festivals in Yerushalayim, they mingle with the crowd and quickly stab their victims with their small, curved dagger before hiding this in their cloak and pretending to be shocked and alarmed with the rest of the crowd. In the commotion, they would slip away and come to Qumran to hide. We help Moreh Yeshua identify them so that the Siqari'im or dagger-men would not be admitted into the settlement," adds Yehudah.

"Several times Moreh Yeshua has mentioned Yehudah ben Hezkiyahu. He is the real founder of the Kanna'im. We do not follow the religious leaders, the rabbim. They condemn us for not compromising with the Kittim. Our concern is for the national and religious life of the Yehudim to be free from the unbelieving Kittim rule," says Shimon.

I explain how the Qumran community came about with the Moreh ha-Tsedek who broke away from the Perushim, Ṣĕdûqîm, Soferim and kohanim of the Beit HaMikdash because of the different inter-pretation of tsedek.

"The Qumran community believes that it is living in the last days struggling between light and darkness, represented by the Prince of Light or Truth and the Prince of Darkness or Falsehood, that is between good and evil. The ultimate triumph in eternal salvation would be in the end of days. Their objective is to prepare for the New Age of everlasting tsedek.

"As I was saying about Qumran's notion of tsedek, after the Moreh ha-Tsedek died they elected me the Moreh ha-Tsedek and I wonder about tsedek itself when both factions claim that their interpretation is the correct one."

I speak of my experience with the Assayya and my meeting with the wise men from the East.

"From Qumran I travelled on one of the orechah routes to visit the Assayya in Mitzrayim. They are even more strict than the Hasidim of Qumran and more contemplative. There are both men and women in their communities. They embrace poverty by renouncing ownership of property.

"When I met the wise men from the East there, my vision of tsedek opened wide. We are not the only ones who speak about tsedek.

"The men from Seen speak of tsedek which they call *dharma* as a moral disposition to do good completely. Dharma is the truth of the way things really are. In Hodu also, dharma is the central concept in their writings. Dharma includes rightness, goodness, morality, righteousness, and the natural way of living the path of rightness which is tsedek.

"They don't talk about the tsedek of Elahh. The Mikra makes tsedek the chief attribute of Elahh and we know there are two sides to the character of Elahh. The followers of Buddha say that dharma is the cosmic law and order.

"When I returned to Qumran, I began to wonder who has the right to claim that his tsedek is the correct one?

"Qumran provided me an idyllic life that was good for myself. We were secure and self-contained. We could live in harmony with nature and find peace in quiet meditation but that is an isolated life cut away from the daily struggles of the ordinary people. I loved that life, but it was an escape from reality.

"We lived by the rule of tsedek. That tsedek never left the confines of Qumran while in the rest of the country tsedek is denied the people. I was teaching tsedek to the wrong people. It is the rich and powerful people who need to understand tsedek."

"Moreh," interrupted Mattithyahu, "how do you know that your interpretation of tsedek is the correct one?"

"I cannot be absolutely sure. All I know is that people have rights. We have the right to live, the right to food and the right to catch fish for food, the right to live in a house, the right to own property, unless you choose to renounce that right, the right to drink clean water to survive, the right to healthy living, the right to speak freely like criticising wrongdoings, and there are other rights. It is not right to take away these rights or to tax the people on them. If tsedek addresses these rights it cannot be incorrect.

"It is not a matter of who is right or wrong about tsedek. Tsedek is not to be centred on the self. One must lead others in the path of tsedek where goodness prevails. I want to be Moreh ha-Tsedek to the people.

"There is only one way of looking at tsedek itself. It is either right or wrong. If wrong, then it is not tsedek. We cannot dress tsedek up to look right. We must look for the true tsedek in the teachings of our religious leaders and unmask the falsehood presented as tsedek.

"I resigned from my office as the Moreh ha-Tsedek and left Qumran. Now I want to get my message of tsedek across to the chief Kohanim, the Perushim, the Şĕdûqîm, the Soferim, the Beit HaMikdash authorities, our Yehudi rulers, the Kittim authorities, and to the landlords and tax collectors."

"Moreh, yesterday we spoke about the Kittim. They also say they are being tsedek when they crucify our people. Do we tell them our tsedek is the right way? Isn't justice the way of tsedek? How are we to fight for justice along the way of tsedek?" queries Yehudah.

"A good question, Yehudah. Sometimes, we may have to use fire and sword. The intention is to safeguard our rights that are violated by evil forces. When we resist with this intention to achieve tsedek, it is not wrong, it is justice."

"Would you say then that tsedek is done when we demand an eye for an eye and a tooth for a tooth, as we are taught that to be justice?" asks Shimon.

"No Shimon; that is a fallacy in Yahadut. If that happens then we will be like the blind leading the blind, and we will all fall into the pit and into deep darkness. This teaching will make us all blind to the truth of reality. If we can bring about a change in the enemy, we can seek tsedek and justice. Evil for evil will not necessarily bring about good.

At the same time there should be due punishment for evil deeds because some people will not repent without punishment. An eye for an eye may sound like equal punishment but that may not be appropriate. An appropriate punishment should aim at changing the bad person to a good person. The path of tsedek that I propose is also a threat to the authorities, but we must pursue the way we believe in.

"Moreh, you made your intention clear to us. It is also troubling because we are up against very powerful people," says Marta.

"Do not be troubled. We will find a way. Things are only becoming clearer to me. We must stand up to what we know is the right way. There will be obstacles because we are challenging very powerful people. I want you to hold fast to what I am trying to teach you so that you will carry on this struggle even when I am no longer with you," I reassure them.

They are further troubled by the thought that I may not be with them. Am I having a premonition that something was going to happen to me?

Scenario 21 - Group disbands

Tiberias

Early the next morning I am once again seated on the rock with the wind blowing in my face wondering if I have made my position any clearer. They leave me alone until I am ready to join them for breakfast.

Joa'ana says, "Moreh, we have not visited Tiberias which is now the capital city of HaGalil. I can lead you into the city."

Shoshana responds immediately, "I would like to visit Tiberias. I think we should all go."

Mariam is somewhat hesitant because it is set up as a rival city to Magdala. "It is the city of Hordos Antipas and *Rabboni*, you will not be welcome there. About 10 years ago Antipas developed the village of Rakkath to draw away the sea trade from Magdala. He makes it the capital of his realm in HaGalil, naming it Tiberias after the Kittim Keysar."

"I will go in through the gate and find out if the Malka is in residence or not," says Joa'ana.

"I will not let anyone come between me and the people. Where is Shemayon? I think we should take the boat," say I.

Shemayon and Andrea are busy folding the fishing net and cleaning the boat. Natan'el shouts out Shemayon's name and beckons him to come over. Shemayon readily agrees to take the boat.

After breakfast we put everything away neatly, secure the tent ropes and embark on the boat. We set sail moving south following the coastline and pass Magdala.

"Many of the ships now bypass Magdala because of Antipas," moans Mariam.

As we approach Tiberias, Joa'ana says, "Go past the harbour and approach from the south. The smaller piers there are not so busy."

Having secured the boat in the suburban village of Hammat, also known as Emmaus, we walk along the waterfront. The village has a spa that flows into 17 natural mineral hot springs. People are bathing in the hot pools.

Natan'el puts his hand into the water to feel its temperature. It is warm enough to bathe in.

Joa'ana says, "The waters in these pools are considered to have healing properties. Those people are sick and are looking for healing." Pointing to stone walled structures, she continues, "Behind those walls are hot baths constructed by the Kittim. The rich and those who are not Yehudi go in there. Further up there is a cemetery. When Hordos Antipas built Tiberias many religious Yehudi and the kohanim refused to settle here because they consider the cemetery to be ritually unclean. So, the malka brings in the goyim, or rather, the non-Yehudim, to settle here."

We walk through the South Gate under a stone arch along the street of paved stones. We skirt a huge Kittim theatre with steps descending to the centre.

"Most of the Yehudi here are poor farmers who face the same problems. They work for the rich landlords. Antipas makes it the capital of HaGalil. His palace is on the high ground, which the Yavan call the acropolis. He does not always stay here because he uses it as his lakeside resort spending his leisure time with his women friends."

"Does your husband still work at the palace?" asks Natan'el.

"Yes, he does, but I don't think he will be there long. We will go to the palace and try to meet him. Let me go ahead first into the palace and find out if Antipas is in," says Joa'ana and leaves.

I approach a woman holding on to her son in the water. "Why do you bathe him in the water?' I ask.

The woman replies, "My son gets seizures every now and then and when he bathes in the water, he becomes calm. It is healing but not curing."

I touch the boy, feel his arms and place the palms of my hands on both his cheeks. He is rather thin.

"That is good. Keep doing this and avoid stressful situations. Also try giving him *pegana*[161]. Do you know that herb?"

"Yes," says the mother.

"Boil it for a long time and give him the extract a little each time during meals. Give him chicken cooked with skin on and butter or cream with the food. He will become better."

Somehow word has gets around that I am in town. A court official from the palace comes up to me, "Can you please come and heal my son who is very ill and may not last the night?"

"You work for Antipas, don't you?"

"Yes, will you hold that against me?"

"No. Your malka is very close to the Kittim. I am sure you know that the Kittim have a public health system with Yavan physicians. Why don't you approach them?"

"Rabbi, those physicians treat only Hordos and his family, the people with power like the high-ranking military and the Ṣĕdûqîm. I

---

[161] rue

am below that level.

"Aren't there also physicians attached to the Báyith?"

"Yes, but they only attend to the kohanim."

"Alright, then. You go home first and have one of your men show me your house. I will come later," I say awaiting Joa'ana's return.

"Please come quickly before my son dies," pleads the official.

Joa'ana returns, "Antipas is not in, although his lieutenants will be watching you."

"Take us to the court official's house," say I to the man waiting to take me.

As we approach the house there are a few people, presumably family members and relatives getting ready for the worst to happen.

The official takes me to an inner room where his wife is sitting beside their son, holding his trembling hand. I immediately assess the situation. I try to steady his hand and notice several red spots. Putting my hand under the boy's tunic I feel his chest and stomach. "He is shivering with a burning fever. It is qaddachath[162]. First thing to do is bring cold water and with a cloth, sponge his whole body to bring down the burning heat."

"Do you know the herb called sheba or la'ana[163]? Its leaves are silvery blue in colour with yellow flowers. Pick those leaves, crush them and boil them with a piece of wild ginger and make him drink it four times a day. Keep the cold sponge going until his body heat has gone down," I prescribe.

"Rabbi, what sin has my son committed that Elahh should punish him? If not, it must be our sins, the sins of his parents. We are told that sickness is the punishment for the disobedience of Elahh's laws,"

---

[162] Malarial fever

[163] Wormwood, a very bitter herb indigenous to the Middle East, (Artemisia arborescens)

says the official.

"Your son's sickness has nothing to do with sin or Elahh's laws. Coming here, I notice several hot springs. Did you take your son to bathe in them?"

"We have done that several times until now when he cannot even get up."

"I also notice near the hot springs there are small pools and marshes where the water is stagnant with no drainage. It is a breeding ground for mosquitoes. Your son has been badly bitten by these mosquitoes. They put an infection into the blood of his body. That sets off a battle within his body causing the burning inside him. His good blood is fighting the infected bad blood. If he wins, he lives; if he loses, he dies. The sheba will weaken the infected blood and he will win the battle. Burn some incense inside the room. That will keep the mosquitoes away. Also keep the people away from him. Your son will live."

As we approach the palace gate Joa'ana meets the guards and asks to see the steward, Chuza. They walk into the foyer and some of the servants recognise her and greet her.

Chuza meets his wife formally, "You should not come here. It is known in the palace that you have become a follower of Yeshua." Then, looking at the man behind her he concludes that I must be me whom he has never met, he says, "Rabbi, you should not have come here with all your followers. Although the malka is not in residence, he has heard of you and keeps saying that he wants to meet you." Lowering his voice, he continues, "Antipas is planning to lay a snare for you. Please keep away, you and all your followers. He will surely come to hear of your visit."

"Thanks for your warning. If he asks, you can tell that fox to meet me in the streets with the people," I tell Chuza.

We admire the construction of the city as we walk back to the boat.

Antipas has established a court and administration in this city unlike the other cities of HaGalil. This city of Antipas is cosmopolitan and prosperous.

The court official meets me, "Rabbi, the fever has gone down, and my boy has stopped shivering. We prepared the tonic, and he drank some. He is now sleeping. You are a great prophet, Rabbi Yeshua. Thank you for saving my son."

"Follow what I have instructed and take good care of him," say I.

"I'm sure we are all hungry. I know a place here that serves very nice *falafel*[164]. It is on the waterfront," invites Joa'ana.

We all go to the place and sit down on stools while Joa'ana places the orders. She knows the owner of the fast-food street stall.

Falafel is served in pita stuffed with fried meat balls, fava beans with pickles, tahina, hummus and cut vegetable salad garnished with *harif*, a hot sauce.

While we are relishing this *ha-mitbaḥ ha-yisra'eli*[165], Mariam says, "It is that time of the year when we get ready for our business trip to Yerushalayim. *Rabboni*, can I take leave from the group for some time? I have to get back to Magdala and help to get all the products ready for the orechah to Yerushalayim for the Paskha."

"Of course, you have to be with your family."

"I have to go with her too," says Shoshana.

"Shemayon can you drop us off at Magdala?" asks Mariam.

"No problem," says Shemayon.

"Our father Zebadyah will also be expecting us to prepare for the same trip. Y'hochanan and I need to go back to Beth-tsaida to gather the fish, bring them back to Kfar Nahum and prepare them for the trip. Shemayon, Andreia are you also coming with us. This is the

---

[164] Pasta made from egg noodle dough

[165] Israeli cuisine

annual event we all take part in." says Yaaqov.

"Is that alright, Moreh, for six of us to go back?" asks Shemayon.

"Certainly, you must be with the family and do the traditional thing," I respond.

"Yes, it is also the time for us to get the wines ready in Kfar Kanna," enters Natan'el.

"My sister Miriamne and I will join you," says Pilip.

"This is the time when our group of Kanna'im will be having meetings on what actions to take during the feast in Yerushalayim. I think Shimon and I would like to be with them," says Yehuda of Kerioth.

"Why not? It is festival time and I used to follow my parents to Yerushalayim. We will wait for you," I reply.

"Please drop me off also at Magdala. I will settle some business and perhaps I could join your family and help out," said Mattithyahu.

"That will be wonderful," says Mariam.

"In that case, I will stay in Tiberius and see what plans my husband has," says Joa'ana.

"I will go to Beth anya and spend some time with my sister. I will meet up with you all in Yerushalayim," says Marta.

"It is a good time for us to take a break now and we will regroup after the Paskha Feast," I say.

This came rather suddenly. Did I say something to put them off? I must understand they have other commitments. My brothers are not happy with me travelling around and not helping in the family. I too will spend some time with the family, but I will continue to meet the people.

"We can all break up at Magdala," said Shemayon.

"No, I will go to Kfar Kanna from here. It is closer," says Natan'el.

"*Rabboni*, you are welcome to Magdala," invites Mariam.

"Thanks, Mariam. It is also shorter to Naṣrath from here," say I.

"Aren't you forgetting me? I am part of your family," says Arsinoe.

"I'm sorry, my dear sister. I wasn't thinking,"

"I am a naggara. Can I help you and your brothers in your work if that is alright?" offers Tauma.

"Our home is your home, Tauma". I welcome him.

"Before you go, Shemayon, on your way back stop over at the camp. Strike the tents and put everything away securely and take the provisions to your home. After the Yerushalayim trip we should all meet up again at our camp," say I, hoping my followers will stay on.

"The orechah from the north will be going your way, close to Naṣrath and we would like you to join us as we go to Yerushalayim," says Mariam.

"I will consider it, although I do not like Yerushalayim," I say.

Shemayon, Andrea, Yaaqov and Y'hochanan with Mariam and Mattithyahu head up north in the boat, while Arsinoe, Natan'el, Pilip, Miriamne, Tauma and I take the road to Naṣrath. Before Naṣrath, Natan'el and his companions branch off to Kfar Kanna. As we skirt Zippori, I say, "Since we have been to Tiberias, we should visit Zippori some time."

Scenario 22 - Family Tension

Naṣrath

We walk through an olive grove and some cypress trees but cannot not see much of the countryside in the dusk. We do, however, notice some grand houses that belong to Hordos's cronies who have their bigger homes in Zippori or Tiberias but come here at harvest time. I lead them to my humble home, part of which serves as a workshop.

As we entered the house Ama greets us. Arsinoe runs up to her and kisses her hand.

"Ama, where is Aba?"

"Oh, Aba and Yehudah have gone to Tiberias for work. They are on contract and would stay there for another two weeks," says Ama.

"Oh, we didn't know. We are just coming from Tiberias," says Arsinoe.

Bethanna and Tabby come out to greet them. "Ah, Yeshua, you decided to come home at last," said Bethanna. Arsinoe went and embraced them both.

"And I have brought along one of my friends too," say I.

"Where are the rest of your gang?" asks Tabby.

"You could have, at least, sent word so we will have prepared a meal," Ama complains.

"Where are my brothers?"

"Yôsēp̄ and Shemayon are in the workshop," says Bethanna.

"And Ya'aqov?"

"We'll let Ama explain." Tabby refrains from answering.

"Wash your feet and come inside, we will talk," invites Maryam.

Tabby offers us some spring water to drink.

"You may not believe this. Your brother Ya'aqov has followed your footsteps and gone to Qumran. You have left, and he has joined. Your other brothers are not happy about it and blame you," explains Ama.

"As the young birds grow up, they don't stay in the nest anymore," I try to be polite.

"Why don't you go and meet them?" Ama says.

I am quietly wondering why my two brothers, Yôsēp̄ and Shemayon, do not come to greet me. I go to the shed to meet them. I find them chatting away with Tauma. When I approach, they stopped talking.

"What have you all been doing?" I ask.

"Oh, the usual stuff," says Yôsēp̄. They are not very communicative, and I sense something is not right. I welcome Tauma to our house and even ask him to consider it as his home, but I myself feel not very welcome in my own home. I take a walk around with my eyes on the ground. I kick a stone that goes flying and hits an old broken cart. One of the shafts and the sides are broken but the wheels appear intact. I sit on the cart and ponder on the purpose of my life and what I am trying to achieve.

Bethanna come and sits beside me. "You were away for so long and when you came back to HaGalil, we thought you would be part of this family again. Instead, you left home once more and found your own family of followers."

"Bethanna, I am still part of this family. I have travelled widely and observed the way our country is being run by our leaders. We are not a free people. We are oppressed by our own leaders who use

172

religion to blind our vision. We are fed with the hope of a blissful life hereafter, yet we live in poverty and suffering here. I can stay home and help the family, but it will not change anything," I explain.

There's a call from the house to come and eat. We wash our feet and hands and enter the house followed by Yôsēp̄, Shemayon and Tauma. Food is served and we all sit down on mats. As the wine is being passed around Yôsēp̄ begins, "Yeshua, when you went away to Qumran, we thought you were never going to come back. When you did return, you have never stayed home and pulled your weight with the rest of us. Aba is still working hard to support the family. You are the eldest and you don't seem to care at all. Why do you even bother to come home once in a while?"

"And now Yehudah has followed you, and he too is gone and has left us," adds Shemayon.

"Yôsēp̄, Shemayon," says Ama, "Elahh has given me five sons and two daughters. Thanks be to Elahh. You can't all be doing the same thing all your life. Aba and I have talked with Yeshua and we allowed him to go because he believes he must do something for the good of our people. Later we let Ya'aqov also follow what he believes. With you both, and Yehudah and Aba, we are doing alright. Even when Bethanna and Tabby get married and leave we will still be alright."

"We are not doing alright. It's hard to get good timber, and to season it and make furniture is hard work. Also, the local market is too small, and we have to sell them at very low prices," complains Yôsēp̄.

"And Yôsēp̄ and I are expected to carry on working for the family, right?" protests Shemayon.

"Yôsēp̄ and Shemayon, you too will have to find your own lives. We are a family as long as we are together as a family but even if we are not staying in the same house, we do not cease being a family," says Maryam.

"What is so important that you have to convert the whole world to your thinking?" questions Yôsēp̄ addressing me.

"I am not trying to convert anybody. You can see as well as I can that the people's lives will not change if we continue to live under oppression. I am just trying to make the people aware of the reality and hopefully bring about a change."

"You don't care for the family now," accuses Yôsēp̄.

"Yôsēp̄, Shemayon, when you were still young, I went out with Aba and worked repairing boats and broken carts. We repaired cisterns and did stonework and any work we could get. At home we built tools, ploughs and yolks for carts, door and window frames, and even toys for children. We also taught you to make them," I say.

"Yes, we still make some of them," admits Shemayon.

"Now that I am home for some time, I don't mind doing some of that work again," I offer.

"That would surely be a great help, don't you think so, Shemayon?" Bethanna tries to change the mood.

The tension at the meal is somewhat relieved.

The next day we are sorting out some timber to work on. "I want to check on the tools. Yôsēp̄, can you please lay them out." I request.

Yôsēp̄ and Shemayon lay out the tools. First the axes. Then, there is the broad axe used for shaping logs for boatbuilding and timber framing, and the cleaving axe and the froe, both of which are used for splitting green wood lengthwise or cleaving wood by splitting it along the grain. There are also a few wedges of different sizes together with hammers and mallets.

Shemayon brings out the bucksaw used for cutting logs; then the adze used for smoothing or carving wood, and the drawknife, a blade with two handles used to shape wood by removing shavings.

"Ah, my favourite tool, the twybil," I remark. It is used for chopping out mortises with timber framing. I check the blade with my thumb, "The blade needs sharpening."

"They all need sharpening," says Shemayon laying out a collection of chisels and gouges.

"Do you still have the grinding stone that Aba made and mounted with a turning handle?" ask I.

"Yes, the handle is broken but can be fixed," says Shemayon.

Finally, Yôsēp̄ brings out the planes used to produce horizontal, vertical or inclined flat surfaces on work pieces. The smoothing plane is the last plane used on wood surface to do the finishing.

We sharpen all the tools and work on the meagre supply of wood. Tauma is happy to be of help.

It is the beginning of a beautiful sunny day in the isolated village of Naṣrath in HaGalil HaTahton surrounded by hill slopes and valleys with pools and lakes, a fertile land dominated by oak, pistachio, cypress, arbutus, and between outcrops of rocks, grapevines and olive groves. A herd of goats grazes among the scattering of Narcissus flowers, glowing white and yellow in the sun.

I say, "I want to take a walk into the village. Anyone interested in coming along?".

Arsinoe and Tauma said they would. Bethanna looked at Tabby and they said they would too. The brothers decide to carry on with the work in the shed. Ama says, "I'll come along too. I need to do some marketing."

We all walk down the Market Street to the old spot under the shiqmah tree.

"This is where I used to learn about the Mikra under the tree. The Mikra is in *Ivrit*.[166]The elder would use the *targumim*[167] to explain and expand it in our language, Aramaic.," I inform.

---

[166] Hebrew language

[167] Plural of targum, explanation of the Hebrew Bible in Aramaic

Meeting the elders of Nasrath

"Now there is a building here, not a Beith of worship but used as a beit k'nesset — a gathering place for the purpose of reading the Mikra and having them explained — a house of instruction," updates Maryam.

Some of the elders, recognising me as the bright little boy who was keen on learning the Scriptures, invite me in and everyone follows suit. They know of me as a leader and ask me to pick a scroll to read. Instead of picking from the Torah, I select one from the Mikra. Unrolling the scroll of the Book of Amos, I read the following passage:

Trouble for those who turn justice into wormwood,
Throwing integrity to the ground;
Who hate the man dispensing justice at the city gate,
And detest those who speak with honesty.
Well then, since you have trampled on the poor man,
Extorting levies on his wheat –
Those houses you have built of dressed stone,
You will never live in them;
And those precious vineyards you have planted,
You will never drink their wine.
For I know that your crimes are many,
And your sins enormous:
Persecutors of the virtuous, blackmailers,
Turning away the needy at the city gate.
No wonder the prudent man keeps silent,
The times are so bad.
Seek good and not evil
So that you may live.
Hate evil, love good,
Maintain justice at the city gate.

Let justice flow like water
And integrity like an unfailing stream.

I then roll up the scroll, give it to the assistant and sit down. All eyes in the beit k'nesset are fixed on me. Then I speak to them.

"Nebi Amos was a sheep herder and a shiqmah fig farmer. He experienced oppression under the rich landlords, and he spoke about them. The same kind of landlords are here today continuing their injustice against our people. By their heavy taxes and levies, they persecute and blackmail you. If you speak honestly for justice, they will hate and detest you and become cruel towards you.

"Many of you choose to remain silent because you are afraid. If you stand together and be firm in demanding justice, you need not be afraid. This evil of being denied a fair share of your produce is the evil you must hate. To seek tsedek, the good of justice, you must be united. Stand firm and you will win. Then it will be they who will be denied the pleasure of wine and living in grand houses."

I win the approval of all, and they are astonished by the courageous words that come from my lips although they know that such words are dangerous. Among them some are saying, "This is naggara Yôsēp̄'s son, surely. Maryam is his mother, and his brothers Ya'akov, Yôsēp̄, Yehudah and Shemayon. His sisters too, Bethanna and Tabby, are they not all here with us? So, where did the man get such wisdom and courage to speak like that?"

Another says, "It may be safer for us if he went away and not bring us trouble."

"No," objects another, "he has opened our eyes to the real poverty under which we are living."

They continue the debate among themselves while I and my group leave.

Ama looks at me, "You are just like your father. Yôsēp̄ says similar things to his working companions. Even the wood from the forest that they use for building the boats and other things, are taxed. Be careful, son, you are becoming a marked man."

"Ama, you are the one who quoted the psalm to me saying, 'He has pulled down the princes from their thrones and exalted the lowly, the hungry he has filled with good things, the rich sent empty away... '. When do you think this is going to happen?"

Ama buys some meat, vegetables, fruits and nuts. Many people come to wish me well, proud of the learned son of Naṣrath.

Joining the orechah

During the meal, I speak, "I have been thinking. May I suggest something?" Taking their silence as 'yes' I go on. "In a few weeks, the orechah from the north is going to Yerushalayim and our friends have invited us to join them. Why don't we start making some woodware and join the orechah with our own merchandise to sell there?"

"There would be a good market in Yerushalayim," adds Tauma.

"I think that's a great idea," comments Tabby. "We don't just join the orechah but be part of the orechah."

"If we are prepared to work, we can start building things right away," I propose.

"Aba and Yehudah will be back soon and together you can make a solid team," encourages Ama.

Yôsēp̄ and Shemayon look at each other and nod. "Yes, I like the idea. We can give it a go. Life is quite boring here anyway," says Yôsēp̄.

"Tomorrow we make plans about what we can produce. I saw a broken cart outside that we can soon fix and will list out the things to do. How much timber do we have?"

"Not much good timber. We can get some. If we want it quickly, we will have to pay upfront," says Shemayon.

"Take me to the merchant I will see if I can talk him into giving us credit," say I.

That night itself we begin itemising the merchandise.

"We can make door and window frames. If we can get hardwood, we can make ploughs and handles for hoes, scythes and harvest knives. I remember Aba used to make rattle toys for us. They are easy to make, and Aba will have more ideas for us when he comes," I say.

I can help with those," says Tabby with excitement.

The tension within the family has broken and the whole household is gripped with a new enthusiasm. Ama is very happy.

Yôsēp̄, Shemayon and I go to the timber merchant and make a deal, and soon the new batch of timber arrives.

"This is rough cut timber. We have to trim them to regular door frame sizes, then plane them down to even width and even thickness. For the side jams we can cut them slightly longer than regular length, and the same with the top jams. We can do the same for the window frames with top and bottom, and side wall plates. The specific dimensions must be regular. We could sell them just like that without assembling them. The buyers can then trim them down to their specific needs. This is not difficult to do, and the pieces can easily be stacked on the cart," I advise.

"We should bring the cart around and start getting it into shape," says Yôsēp̄.

"Tauma and I will bring it round," says Shemayon.

"It will take more than the two of you to do that," I say.

We are busy the next few days working away getting the frames ready, and Tauma is catching on fast.

Suddenly one day Aba Yôsēp̄ and Yehudah arrive. Bethanna and Tabby came out to greet them followed by Maryam.

"What's all the activity?" enquires Yôsēp̄.

"We are preparing to join the orechah to Yerushalayim to sell our merchandise," explains Tabby.

"Yeshua, when did you come home?" asks Yehudah. I greet my Aba kissing his hand, and then give Yehudah a hug. All of us take a break and go into the house for the afternoon meal. All the detailed plans are explained to Yôsēp̄ and Yehudah. Now we have two more experienced workers to join in and guide us.

From his tool bag Yehudah takes out a honing stone and tells us to use it for sharpening. Meanwhile Aba Yôsēp̄ watching us work sees Shemayon struggling to straighten the wood. He pulls out of his tool bag a chalk line that he has made himself. A string is wound in a small wheel in a box containing a chalk dye. He shows Shemayon how to use it.

"Shemayon, secure the box here and pull the string to the other end of the work piece. Wind the string around the nail and knock it into the wood. Make sure it is pulled tight across the rough surface. Good. The string is coated with dye. Take hold of the string, pluck it and let it go. The string will hit the wood and mark it."

Shemayon does as he is told. "Now remove the string and there you have a straight line to work on," says Aba Yôsēp̄ who then goes around and picks up the offcuts on the ground.

"We can use these to make toys," he says.

Tabby comes running, "Aba, teach me how to do it and I will make the toys."

Father and daughter sit down to work together. Aba Yôsēp̄, using the froe, split the wood into thin slabs. Using the smoothing plane, he gives the surfaces a clean finish.

"Tabby, draw an animal on one of these slabs leaving space at the bottom," instructs Aba Yôsēp̄.

Tabby draws a donkey. Aba touches up the ears and makes the legs more solid. "Now, using the small chisel and a knife, cut out the donkey. Cut out the space between the legs leaving the base. You must mount the donkey on to another slab. While you start cutting, I'll go look for something."

He comes back with an even straight branch. Using the bucksaw, he slices the stick into thin circular discs.

"These will be the wheels which we will attach to the base." He shapes the base by rounding off the corners and using the bow drill makes two holes in either side of the base. He then shapes thin wooden rods with a head on one end. The rods fit tightly into the holes. He then drills slightly bigger bores into the centre of the discs.

"Now you have all the pieces to put together. Cut and smoothen all the rough edges. Mount the donkey on the base with two nails from the bottom and fix the wheels. Make a hole in the front and tie a string to it so that it can be pulled. When you have put it all together, we will colour it with a dye, finish it with olive oil and paint the eyes. You can ask Ama and your sister to help you make them."

They also find straight branches which they use to make handles for hoes and sickles. By the fourth week they have compiled enough merchandise including a dozen of Tabby's toys, to fill the cart, which has also been repaired and made serviceable. They need another cart to travel in. Aba Yôsēp̄ borrows a cart and donkey from his friend and rents a mule. Next, they must gather enough food and provisions for the journey. Ama and Bethanna decide to stay home while the rest including Tabby prepare to join the orechah.

Scenario 23 - Orechah

Shomron

Two days later we sight the first carts of the orechah. There is a long string of carts and loaded camels. The carts belonging to Mariam of Magdala, Zebadyah, Shemayon and Tolmay stop at our house, while the rest of the orechah move on a little further to make camp for the night. They have already travelled about 32 milin from Magdala. The orechah travels an average of 33 milin a day and stops to rest the animals. The friends who went north are reunited with our family. Joa'ana has joined Mariam's family group. They are all surprised to find that Yôsēp̄'s contingent is joining them with their own merchandise. All together our group comprise seven carts all lined up. They do not pitch tents but share the space in our house. They also share a lot of stories about their merchandise.

Early the next morning, we set forth to meet up with the rest of the orechah that is also getting ready to move. Only a milin from our house is the route to Yerushalayim. There are orechah routes crisscrossing all over HaGalil, from Dimashqu in the north and to the Sea in the west. These are the roads built by the Kittim, mainly as supply routes for their forces. The Kittim are good road builders and their roads cut through rocks and spurs. Yôsēp̄'s carts, that's ours, are handled by me, Yehudah, Yôsēp̄, Shimmon and Tabby. The long journey begins, and we are going to enjoy it.

We set out on the Kittim road to Yerushalayim, first descending along the hill slopes into Ha-'Emeq, the plain of Esdraelon or the valley of Jazreel between two hills. Then we go through this fertile agricultural land to its south-most edge, which is the boundary between Shomron to the south and HaGalil to the north. On the outskirts of *Beth-haggan*[168] at the foothills of Har haGilboa on the eastern side of the valley of Jezreel, we set up camp beside a spring at the foothill of Har haGilboa, carpeted by the beautiful Irus Ha-Gilboa, purple iris blooms. Nighttime is like a carnival with each group having its own tent and campfire. That night around the campfire I relate the time Šā'ûl, the first malka of Yisra'el who leads his army against the Plistim, is defeated. It is on this Har haGilboa where the malka commits suicide. His son *Yonatan*[169] also perishes here.

We start moving very early the next morning, having fed and watered the animals. We plan to go right through Shomron in one day without stopping. Shomron is hostile territory. We must cover about 45 milin to track the southern border of Shomron. While pushing along the road we suddenly hear the sound of trumpets. The Kittim are on the move. They travel very fast with horse-drawn carriages. Very quickly the drivers steer their carts off the road. They make sure the children are off the road. The Kittim come galloping at a high speed. Without slowing down, they thunder through the orechah and are quickly lost in the dust.

Because of the hostilities between the Yahudim and the *Shom-ronim*[170], in ordinary times the Yahudim would take the roundabout

---

[168] Megiddo

[169] Johnathan

[170] Samaritans

route [171] to the Ha-Yarden and down along the river to by-pass Shomron. This route is 38 milin longer and would take another extra day of travel. The journey would become very difficult especially for a heavily loaded orechah with 24 milin of steep road that wound through canyons and cliffs. It is certainly worth the risk travelling through Shomron. Besides, we are more secure in a big orechah.

By the direct route, we can traverse the whole of Shomron in one day, but we would have to keep going past the towns of Sebaste, Sychar and Shiloh without stopping. Nothing untoward happens because the Shomronim are also busy at this time, making their pilgrimage to *Har Garizzim* [172] where only men participated in public worship.

By dusk we reach the outskirts of the border town of Bethel. We have crossed the border into Yehuda where we set up camp. Being so close to the border, the orechah people are on guard against any raid by the Shomronim or other bandits. The men take turns in keeping watch. Once again, I tell them stories of how Bethel got its name.

"Aba Ya'akov, grandson of Aba Avraham is supposed to have had a dream in this place. Elahh, it is said, promises Ya'akov in his dream that he would give him the land he was lying on, which would one day blossom into the nation of Yisra'el. Ya'akov immediately names the place Beth-El, the house of Elahh."

That night we rest the animals well and take it easy the following day. Yerushalayim is only about 20 milin away.

---

[171] They would have to climb from 812 feet below sea level to 2,600 feet above sea level in Yerushalayim. That was a difference of 3,400 feet of change in elevation. They would have to climb from 812 feet below sea level to 2,600 feet above sea level in Yerushalayim. That was a difference of 3,400 feet of change in elevation.

[172] Mount Gerizim

Scenario 24 - Paskha

Yerushalayim

When the orechah reaches the gates of the city each group has to pay a toll based on their merchandise. They must hurry and find the best place possible, given the huge crowd gathered around the Beit HaMikdash. Aba sends Yehudah and Shemayon ahead to book a good place.

Marta is walking up the orechah road looking for her friends and their carts. Not finding us, she moves down among the carts and this time sees Yehudah and Shemayon standing, guarding a vacant lot.

"Greetings, Yehudah, Shemayon, where are the rest of the gang?" asks Marta.

"They are coming, and we are reserving this place for them. Yeshua and we also have a cart this time," says Yehudah.

Soon the rest of us arrive, set our carts next to each other and release the animals to feed at the back. The carts are parked back to front. The back becomes the shop front. We also pitch tents on to the carts. Finally, we settle in and begin to display our merchandise. The whole place is a hive of activity and people from all over the country come overland, and the Yehudim from over the Ha-yam Ha-Gadol— the Great Sea — have also come in ships.

Pilgrims go up to Yerushalayim for the *Shalosh Regalim*, the three pilgrim festivals. They are Paskha (the Passover), the *Shavuot* (the Pentecost or Weeks), and *Sukkot* (the Tabernacles or harvest festival also known as the Tents or Booths). Now is the time of the Paskha that commemorates Aba Moshe liberating our people from slavery in Mitzrayim.

The month of Nisan begins on the night of the full moon. It is still five days before the 15th day of the month of Nisan, when the Beit HaMikdash feast of the Paskha would start. A week before the feast, pilgrims have already begun to arrive for the necessary rites of purification ordered by the Torah. It is not only the pilgrims who come to the city; the *goyim* come in great numbers too, mainly to shop for good things.

The crowd knows this is the time when all kinds of merchandise are brought to the city.

As we are briskly doing business, Yehudah of Kerioth and Shimon Qan'anaya find us.

"Ha, Moreh, you have become a merchant," greets Yehudah.

"Moreh, we have news. The question of taxation has been a hot topic every year during the festival and there has always been agitation. This year we are raising the issue once again."

Others come and join us to hear what the two kohanaim have to say. Shimon immediately says, "Let us not talk out in front here. Let's go behind."

There Yehudah tells us, "The people who come from outside generally have no problem with the atonement tax money of the *half-shekel* [173] coin. The people are against the Kittim tribute that is superimposed on the tithes and other taxes owed to the Beit

---

[173] The annual contribution every Jew was required to pay to the Temple, equal to 160 grams of barley

HaMikdash and the kohanaim. The people have never forgiven Marcus Pontius Pilatus for bringing into Yerushalayim the Kittim troops bearing their legionary standards with carved images of animals and deities. Pilatus's big project now is the construction of the aqueduct to bring water into the city. Since most of the imperial tax money is parceled off to Roma, Pilatus, it is strongly rumoured, is taking money from the Beit HaMikdash treasury, the qorban,[174] to finance his project. We all know that the qorban belongs to Elahh and not for any personal or secular use.

"This is the issue we are going to raise and call on the people to send a petition to the Kittim Keysar about what Pilatus is doing. Our kana'im will be well placed among the crowd to raise their voices in a call to stop using qorban money to finance the aqueduct project. We expect trouble. There will surely be a riot. If you and our friends are going to be there, please stay together. Others stay and protect your merchandise. The riot can get out of hand."

"You are raising a valid point regarding the misuse of the qorban. I would rather challenge the taxation itself. It is estimated that in the whole of Peleshet, the total of Yehudi and Kittim taxes has reached an annual rate of almost 25 per cent. It is also very unfair when all are taxed evenly. The system is unequal when the rich and poor have to pay the same amount. It is not a progressive system, so the gap between the rich and the poor has become extreme. The poor have become indebted to the rich. How are the poor expected to pay taxes? This is where the injustice lies, and I will raise the issue of tsedek about this. You, Yehudah and Shimon, can carry on with your protest and we will support you."

---

[174] Temple offering

Beit HaMikdash

Together with Shemayon, Y'hochanan and Mattithyahu, we sit on the Beit HaMikdash steps. Being lunch time, we take out some bread and eat, when a bent-over old woman balancing herself with a walking stick, comes up to us.

"We have heard of you, Marya Yeshua, and of your teaching in HaGalil. Some people have been hoping to find you here."

"Oh, what have you heard?" asks Shemayon.

I say nothing but look intently at the woman.

"They say that your teaching is different from what they teach at the Beit HaMikdash.

Mattithyahu offers her some bread when we are interrupted by two Perushim and a Sofer.

"We have been watching you. All of you are eating bread without washing your hands. You are defying the tradition of our elders," accuses one of the Perushim.

I look at them and then slowly say, "You learned men of the scriptures, tell me where in the Torah does it say that you must wash your hands before eating?"

"There are rules for hand washing," they say.

A few people have already gathered around listening to what is going on.

"Those rules are for the ritual cleansing connected to worship in the Tabernacle. It has nothing to do with hand washing before eating, although that is a good practice. It is you who have created such a tradition and imposed it on the people. You make your traditions more important than the word of Elahh."

They don't reply to me. I turn to the woman.

"Look at this woman with a bad back. What have you done for her?"

"She is a sinner, possessed by satana who is holding her bound," they say.

"You are obsessed with your rules." I beckon the woman to come close.

"Shemayon, Mattithyahu take hold of her hands and hold her steady. Y'hochanan, take her stick away."

"Lift your head up as high as you can." I feel her back, running my fingers down the spine. I keep feeling around the hip bone. "Attha, listen to me. Let the weight of your body go into your legs and let it sink into the ground. Stay still and be completely relaxed."

Standing behind her I placed my left hand on her left hip and my right palm between her spine and right hip. I give a sudden screw jab with my right palm. She cried out in pain and then a sigh of relief.

"Let go of her hands slowly. Attha, try to straighten up slowly."

She lifted her torso up, not right up but almost halfway up.

"Are you still in pain?"

"Only a little, but so much better," she says.

"Do you have relatives? Ask them to rub nutmeg oil or olive oil on your lower back and hips every day and try to straighten up little by little," I advise her.

"Marya Yeshua, you are more than a prophet. Thank you," she bows.

Sanhedrîn

Word gets around and my teaching reaches the ears of the Beit HaMikdash authorities. The elders are the leading citizens of the city and the chief kohana is the head of the guild of kohanaim. The Soferim are often associated with the Perushim. In one of the sittings of the Sanhedrîn, a body of 71, including the chief kohanaim, the elders and the Soferim, the high kohana chairs the session on the religious, legal and internal Jewish civic matters that do not pertain to the Roman governor. During that session, the question of me and my controversial teaching is raised.

The high kohana, Caiaphas, says, "We did receive news of this man from HaGalil. He does not have much of a following even in HaGalil and much less here in Yerushalayim. He should not cause too much of a problem although he does teach against our beliefs. We will get some of our people to keep an eye on him. I will also send word to the prefect."

Orechah

Back at the orechah site, business was booming although some locals are apprehensive of trouble brewing as that invariably happens every year. They have their own orechah security people always on the watch.

Pilatus's palace

Pilatus, the fifth governor of Judea, had his palace built on the north-west side of the mount on which the Beit HaMikdash stands, and overlooks a large square surrounded by a colonnade where the merchants sit to sell their various commodities. Pilatus summons his officers and the leader of his SA, the Special Arm of the Kittim guards who work undercover.

"I anticipate trouble during the festival as it usually happens with these unruly Yehudim. I want the Kittim garrison to be stationed along the colonnades and on the roof of the Beit HaMikdash. Stand by and keep watch. Look out especially for the troublemakers. When a commotion starts wait for the signal and then move in and arrest the troublemakers," instructs Pilatus.

Protest

As anticipated, the kana'im marshal their men and deploy them among the crowd in front of Pilatus's palace. Someone in the crowd shouts "qorban!" Others join in and their shouts increase in volume. A voice is raised, "We want the governor to tell us what has happened to the qorban. The Beit HaMikdash will not tell us. Who has been taking the money? Who is paying for the aqueduct?" The merchants begin to pack up. A riot is beginning.

At the given signal, the Kittim soldiers move in with shields and clash with the crowd. The people run in different directions, some are beaten, and others arrested. The agitators withdraw in fear. The riot is quickly quelled. The Kittim have been handling this year after year. They know what to do and the crowd expect it. Since this is a recurring phenomenon, which the merchants deplore, they are well prepared and very quickly things returned to normal.

By the end of the week, the orechah people are already packing up to leave. Our cartload of merchandise is all sold out. The others too make very good sales. They are all in high spirits and it is an occasion to celebrate. They have bought a variety of food at the stalls and share them around the campfire.

Everyone has new supplies of wine from different regions. They pass around grapes, figs, pomegranates, dates and nuts.

The women are preparing some dishes. They bring out *kneidlach*, the traditional soup of the Paskha, made of matzo ball, followed by *charoset*, an apple and nut dish generally served at the Paskha. Then Marta goes to another wagon and brings back *farfel,* small pellet-shaped egg pasta. With plenty of wine they all celebrate a successful business trip.

Mattithyahu says, "Moreh, what you did to that disabled woman was like a miracle. How do you know so much about the human body?"

For the benefit of the others, Mattithyahu described what had happened with the woman.

"I learnt all this from the wise men of the Eastern lands. They are experienced healers."

Before we retire for the night I tell my group, "It is nice that we can enjoy this freedom together, but our country and our people are really not free. Look what happened today. Our own leaders are greedy and selfish. They don't care for the poor and the suffering. For their own benefit they play a game with the Kittim. Pilatus does not really care for the rules and rituals of the Beit HaMikdash. He is prepared to shed the blood of the Yehudim, and our own leaders are not prepared to stand up to him and defend the people."

"The Kittim are so strong and powerful, what can we do? We don't have an army of our own to fight them," says Andrea.

"It is not the Kittim whom we should fight. We need to have good and strong leaders who understand tsedek and negotiate with the Kittim to safeguard the rights of the people instead of using religion to exploit them. The Kittim are here only to keep the peace and collect taxes. The kana'im are the only ones who are resisting but they too are more zealous for the religion than for the rights of the people," say I.

"Where is Yehudah of Kerioth and Shimon Qan'anaya?" asks Mariam of Magdala.

"Shimon has been wounded, but I think I know where they have gone. They are resting in Qumran and will join us later."

"What plans do you have, Moreh?" questions Natan'el.

"I have no plans. We must continue to resist and not be blinded by the religious teachings of the Beit HaMikdash authorities."

They do a final round of packing and after their celebration, they retire for the night.

The day after the week of the Unleaven Bread they break camp at midday, and the orechah from the north begins to move. Marta has rejoined the group. By late afternoon we reach the outskirts of Bethel and set up camp. This is an *orechahserai*[175], a station for travellers, which normally has food, water and shelter for the merchants, their servants and their animals.

That night they share more of the good food from Yerushalayim around the fire.

"Tomorrow we are going to go into the land of the Shomronim and the Yehudim look upon them as our enemies. Did you notice that they did not go to the Yerushalayim Beit HaMikdash for Paskha?" I ask.

"HaGalil is separated from Yehuda and Yerushalayim by Shomron. The Shomronim have their own Báyith on Har Garizzim. They refuse to accept the oral tradition of the Torah and reject the Beit HaMikdash at Yerushalayim. Although the HaGalileans are Yehudim, the close proximity of the Shomronim does not fail to influence them. I would like to see the Shomronim as friends rather than as enemies."

"They want to be different from us. They follow their own tradition of going to Har Garizzim where they have built their own Beith and offer their own sacrifices," says Mattithyahu.

"The Shomronim are forbidden access to the inner courts of the Yerushalayim Beit HaMikdash because they are considered to be goyim," say I.

My Aba explains, "When you were very small Yeshua, we heard that the Shomronim went to the Yerushalayim Beit HaMikdash during Paskha and spread human bones within the Beit HaMikdash porches and the sanctuary. It was considered a desecration.

"There were accusations and opposition from both sides. The Ha-

---

[175] Caravanserai - A roadside lodge where caravan travellers could rest and recover.

sidim were not the only ones who broke away from the Yerushalayim Beit HaMikdash over disagreement about worship. The Shomronim say that the Yahudim of Yerushalayim have changed Yahadut. Today we express animosity towards the Shomronim because every Yahudi does it without even trying to find out how it all began.

"This hatred goes back a long way even though both the Shomronim and the Yahudim call Avraham Aba. Avraham's sons Yiçḥaq and Yaʿakov, who was also named Yisra'el, had twelve sons whose descendants became twelve tribes. One of the twelve sons, Yôsēp̄, was blessed by his father and the territory given to the two sons of Yôsēp̄, Ephraim and Manasseh, is the fertile land that became Shomron."

I add, "After the exile the Yehudi who returned to Yerushalayim and started to rebuild the Beit HaMikdash. The Shomronim wanted to help in the rebuilding but were rejected by the Yehudi because of their intermarriages. The Yehudi considered themselves to be the pure ones, but the Shomronim did not think so. The Shomronim claimed that they were the true descendants of Yisra'el who had not been taken away in captivity but instead remained on the land. They both accused each other of tampering with the Torah.

"There are two versions of the Torah, the Shomronim and the Yehudi, and each claim that theirs is the original. The *Torah Shomroniyt* [176] identifies Har Garizzim as Elahh's chosen place for worship, and they built their own Beith on Har Garizzim. The Yehudi claim that Elahh chose Yerushalayim to establish his name. Yerushalayim accuses Shomron of idol worship while Yerushalayim was practising ritualistic prostitution. So, this mudslinging runs deep. Based on this long-standing collective animosity, we have remained separated and consider ourselves enemies when we are the same people who call upon the same Elahh."

---

[176] The Samaritan Torah

"What are we supposed to do? If we go into their land, they could refuse hospitality and even be hostile to us. How can we accept them?" asks Miriamne.

I say, "Let me tell you a story. We are travelling in an orechah with many people and feel secure in numbers. Let's say, one of us is travelling alone from Yerushalayim to Yeriḥo and falls into the hands of brigands. They take all that the person has, beat him up and run away leaving him half dead. Now a kohana happens to be travelling down the same road, but when he sees the man, he passes by on the other side. In the same way a Levi who comes to the place sees him and passes on the other side.

"But a Shomron traveler who comes upon him is moved with compassion when she sees him. She goes up and bandages his wounds, pouring oil and wine on them. She then lifts him onto her own mount, carries him to the inn, and cares for him. The next day, she takes out two denarii and hands this to the innkeeper. 'Look after him,' she says, 'and on my way back I will make good any extra expense you have.'

"The victim is a Yehudi and the one who proved to be a friend is a Shomron woman. She did not bother to find out who the victim was or where he came from. If we can look at people as people and not look for friend or foe, we become more human. We and the Shomronim are the same people divided by religion. Does religion serve a good purpose here?"

They wonder how I know so much history and yet remain unprejudiced.

"Tomorrow as we go through Shomron I want to get off and spend some time with the people there. I shall join you all back in HaGalil," I declare.

"They may not welcome you or give you a place to stay. It is not safe," objects Mariam.

"Let me worry about that."

"You all have work to do when you go back. I will go with Moreh," volunteers Tauma.

"I too will join you," says Pilip.

"That is fine with me," say I.

Scenario 25 - Shomron woman

Sychar

Early the next morning we strike camp and the whole orechah moves on into the land of Shomron. By afternoon, the orechah is moving along the outskirts of Sychar.

"We will get off here. You have a safe journey home," say I.

Tauma and Pilip join me. We walk towards Sychar.

"I will walk in that direction," I say, pointing to a settlement. "Why don't you go into town and buy some food?"

We part company and I keep walking until I come to a well. I sit down by the well to rest my legs. In a short while a woman comes along with a bucket and rope to draw water. She looks at me and immediately recognises me as a Yehudi. She hesitates, wondering if it is safe to draw water. I ignore her and look away. Seeing that I am not interested in her she takes courage to approach the well and draws water.

I look at her, "I am thirsty. Can I have some water?"

She is uncertain, "You are a Yehudi, and you ask me for a drink?"

"I know but I am only a thirsty traveller passing through." I look kind enough and there is nobody else around who might accuse her of talking to a Yehudi; so, she offers me a drink.

"Thank you, this is good water."

"Of course, our Aba Ya'akov gave us this well. He and his sons and his cattle all drink from this well."

"Ya'akov is also our Aba."

"No, he is not. You are foreigners."

"Ya'akov is the grandson of Aba Avraham who is the Aba of all of us."

"Then why do you have your own Har haBáyith with your Beit HaMikdash in Yerushalayim and do not allow us there?"

"You also have your own Har Garizzim and you worship there."

Just then Tauma and Pilip arrive with some food.

"Our Moreh is talking to a woman, a Shomron woman!" whispers Pilip.

"He is even drinking water from her utensil considered unclean." But they say nothing to me.

"Are these your men? Have you come here to make trouble?" asks the woman.

"No, they are my fellow travellers." I turn to them and say, "See, this kind woman has given me some water to drink even though she knows who I am. Isn't she like the good Shomron in the story I told yesterday?"

She continues, "Our fathers worshipped on this mountain, Har Garizzim, while you say that Yerushalayim is the place where one ought to worship."

"I do not say that. Believe me, attha, a time will come when you will worship neither on this mountain nor in Yerushalayim. We do not need a mountain or a Beit HaMikdash to worship at. Your heart is your Beit HaMikdash if you choose to make it so. It is out of the goodness of your heart that you give me water to drink. You have a good heart. Where you find goodness, you will find your Elahh."

Some men and women from her settlement come with their goats to the well. The woman is afraid, but it is too late to disengage.

"Who are you men? What are you doing at our well?" asks one of the men.

The woman says, "They are travellers passing through."

"Why do you entertain them? They are Yehudim and why do you give them water from our well?"

"That is because she is a good Shomron woman," I say.

"He is not like the other Yehudim. We should listen to what he says," says the woman.

"What do you have to say?"

"I say it is time for us to stop being enemies. The real foreigners like the Kittim are the ones who dominate us. We are the same people divided by religious differences created in the past. We don't have to say that we are better than you or you better than we or because we worship there, and you worship here. We are all the children of Aba Avraham. Can we not live in peace?"

They gradually calm down and listen.

I turn to my followers, "You may think that this tumbler given me by the woman is unclean. You are wrong. We are wrong. This is good water in a clean tumbler. The only thing that can be unclean is what comes out of bad and selfish thoughts which make the heart unclean."

After listening to me talk for some time, they invite us to stay with them. I have won the hospitality of the Shomronim.

As we gather in the house of one of them, I speak, "Do you know that the Yehudim call me a Shomron just because I come from Naṣrath in HaGalil, north of Har Garizzim? It is true that the malka of Athura had brought foreigners here to live among those of you who remained. They brought in the people from *Kutha*[177] and some of you are called

---

[177] city in the neo-Babylonian empire in the region of Mesopotamia, now Iraq

the Kuttim. Kutha is in the same region of *Kaldo*[178] or *Kasdim* in Makedonia where our Aba Avraham came from.

"There were intermarriages and most of you are the descendants of those marriages. The good thing about this is that you live together in peace, although you may worship differently, and have identified yourselves as Shomronim. The Yehudim consider themselves the pure descendants of Aba Avraham but in fact they too intermarried with foreigners. The bad thing is that all those who had foreign wives were sent them away with their wives and sons. They exiled their own people. They did not become united and live together like you people. So, who are the better people? We should stop accusing and maligning each other. After all, we are basically one people who have become richer with intermarriages. I do not believe in the concept of a pure Yehudi. Purity is in our hearts.

After spending two nights in Sychar, we take leave of our Shomron friends and proceeded to HaGalil.

Tauma says, "We are not far from Tarichea, my hometown. You know, Tarichea is like Magdala and we too make dried fish but on a smaller scale. My mother lives alone and I do not get along well with her. I will just pay her a short visit before re-joining you all. He takes off in an easterly direction from Har Tavor.

---

[178] Chaldea in southeastern Mesopotamia

Scenario 26 - Family approval

Naṣrath

By evening we reach Naṣrath. During the meal Pilip relates to everyone how I had won the hearts of the Shomronim.

"We are very much prejudiced and mistaken about them. They are really good people. One day in the future I hope to visit them. If you will permit me, I won't stay. I'll go on to Kfar Nahum and join my sister Miriamne." says Pilip.

"When you go by Magdala, please tell Mariam that I will see her soon and fix a date for a meeting at the campsite," I request.

I stay home to help my Aba and brothers do some work. We find that the orechah idea was good and profitable. We plan out what other artefacts we could produce for the next trip to Yerushalayim or maybe even to the coastal town of Tyre. We made enough money to buy more wood and start working on them. We learnt in Yerushalayim that people are looking for more than just the handles for implements, they want the implements themselves. So, we buy the metal pieces of knives, sickles and choppers, and make wooden handles for them. The whole family is very happy that I am spending time with them.

After about ten days, during mealtime I say, "Aba, Ama, it is good to be home and be together, but my heart is restless. The people need to be awakened to the reality of being deprived of a good life. We are relatively comfortable. We have a good life, but most of the workers, farmers and fishermen are being robbed of that good life. What is life if we cannot enjoy the goodness of the earth. What is life without peace, happiness and the freedom to love life. We only have a short lifespan, and so many people's lives are made even shorter by disabilities, sickness and disease compounded by leaders who are not tsedek. Time is indeed short and when that is over everything is over.

"I know you don't like me to leave but if I stay, I will not be at peace with myself. I want to go and continue talking to the people, heal their ailments, and challenge the authorities with whatever time I have left."

The family members listen and remain silent. Ama breaks the silence, "The last thing a mother wants is a separation from her child. However, Yehoshua, if you have an inner calling to save the people from injustice and oppression, I will not stand in your way." Ama set the tone for the rest of the family to ponder.

Aba said, "Yeshua, it is expected of the first-born son to carry on the work of his father. On the other hand, if I were not a naggara and had the education, I too would like to do what you are doing. You have my blessing."

"Whenever I can, I will join your group," says Ama.

"I am with you, my brother, Yeshua," says Arsinoe.

The others, including his sceptical brothers begin to understand my purpose.

"I will go to Magdala and rally the group together," say I.

The following day the family helps to pack the necessary things. I embraced Aba, Ama, sisters and brothers, and so does Arsinoe. Marta pays her respects.

Arsinoe, Marta and I leave Naṣrath.

Scenario 27 - Petition to reduce taxes

Kfar Kanna

Kfar Kanna is on the way, so we call on Natan'el. He and his father Tolmay welcome us. Natanel says, "Moreh Yeshua, we took your suggestion seriously and held a meeting with the winegrowers of Kfar Kanna. I explained to them that if we are to better our lives, we must do something. The wine growers were really taken up by what you said about taxation. They were excited and wanted to do something. They are overcoming their fear and ready to approach the landlords and ask for better treatment. We calculated the produce of grapes and its market value. What we are paid is nowhere near the market value. Even though we are paid wages as vine dressers, the taxes imposed take away most of our wages. As you suggested we projected that we would double our efforts to get a better yield if they reduced taxes and increased our wages. We set up a committee and listed our demands. The committee met the landowners and presented our petition. Now we are waiting for a response from them."

"Great work, Natan'el. What if they don't agree to your petition?" I ask.

"We told them we cannot guarantee a high yield," says Tolmay.

"I hope you are successful,"

"We are heading for Magdala and hope you will join us," says Arsinoe.

"Can we send word to Tauma in Tarichea and ask him to meet us at Tiberias or Magdala?" I appeal.

"Yes, we can do that. We have people travelling in all directions from here," says Natan'el.

"We will go to Tiberias and take a boat to Magdala. From there we can send word to the others to meet at our camp," say I.

At Tiberias we meet Joa'ana and together go to Magdala by boat.

Mariam is at the pickle factory. She takes us to her house for some refreshments and immediately sends word to Shoshanna and Mattithyahu.

"Is everything alright after the Yerushalayim trip?" I enquire.

"We are good. We made good money and the business is well established to carry on on its own. I am prepared to re-join the group."

"I think the break has been good for all of us, but Yerushalayim is full of corruption and the religious authorities are using the simple belief of the people in fulfilling the law to bully them. I do not see Yerushalayim as the great city of Malka Dawidh. It is a city run by the Kittim using the kohanim and they are only interested in collecting money," I remind them.

"I wonder if Yehudah and Shimon are alright," says Natan'el.

"When are we going to move to the camp?" asks the impatient Arsinoe.

"It is lunchtime. Let's eat," invites Mariam.

We wash hands and sit down to have fish and chicken with vegetables and bread. Natan'el who has brought some wine, as usual, says, "I will go ahead to Kfar Nahum and get Shemayon and the others to join us at the campsite."

"Take the boat. One of our boats should be leaving soon. It is quicker," suggests Mariam.

Arsinoe, Joan'na and Shoshanna with Mattithyahu who has joined us, wait for Mariam to settle some of her family business matters and we prepare some food, water and wine along with extra provisions to take with us.

On the way Mariam says, "*Rabboni*, I will always be beside you."

Walking along the waterfront on the way to Ganne Sarim, a man comes up to me and goes down on his knees. I immediately lift him, "Kneel before no man. What is it you seek?"

"Marya," he says, "take pity on my son, he is a lunatic and in a wretched state; he is always falling into the fire or into the water."

"Where is the boy?"

They bring him. He is not even 12 years old. He is burnt and bruised but defiant. I go down to his level and looked him in the eye. The boy looks away, then turns to see me eye to eye. Without saying anything I put my arms around him and embraced him. The boy calms down and all tension seems to leave his body.

I look directly into his eyes, "You are not a lunatic. You are a clever boy; you are a good boy. You don't have to believe any of the bad things, others say about you. You clean yourself up and put medicine on your wounds. You do not have to prove anything to anyone anymore. You can do good things and great things. So, do it."

The boy looks perfectly normal. I say to his father. "Do not call him a lunatic and pay attention to him. Listen to what he says."

After they go away Mattithyahu asks me, "How did you heal him?"

"I did not heal him. There is nothing wrong with the boy. He has been scolded and beaten by his father, and perhaps also by his mother. He has been called all kinds of names and made to feel useless and stupid. As a result, he thinks very lowly of himself so the only way

205

for him to gain attention is to act like a person possessed by a demon. If he is encouraged and taken seriously, he will be quite normal."

People hear this and begin to believe that I have indeed healed a boy possessed by satana.

Scenario 28 - Aseret Ha-d'Varîm

Base Camp

By the time we reach the base camp, the others — Shemayon, Andrea, Ya'aqov and Y'hochanan, Pilip and Miriamne — are unloading the boat of fresh fish and some extra camping gear. Natan'el is also with them.

The tents had been packed away by Shemayon and gang before we broke up. We pull the bedding material out to air them and start to pitch the tents. "There are a couple of rips in the tent, we will have to mend them," observes Mattithyahu.

Miriamne finding a needle and thread in Shemayon's fishing kit, uses this to sew the tear in the tent.

Pilip and Natan'el clean out the fireplace. I clean out the ashes in the taboon oven.

·The women restock the provisions under the boat, take out the utensils and prepare the meal.

Bread was baking in the taboon oven.

Yehudah and Shimon appear on the scene, together with Tauma. Everybody welcomes them.

"We go to Naṣrath looking for Moreh and Tauma is there too. Then we find out that you all decided to meet here," says Yehudah.

"Shimon, how are you? We heard you were wounded," enquires Mariam.

"I was slashed in the arm, but it is healing well now," says Shimon showing the scar on his left upper arm.

"We took refuge in Qumran where they attended to my arm with their medicines. Your brother Ya'aqov made us welcome and asked about you, Moreh."

"We also have some bad news," says Yehudah, "Yeshua, your cousin, Yhochanan ha-mmatbil, has been arrested by Malka Antipas."

"Why? For what reason?" asks Shoshana.

"Yhochanan had objected to Antipas's second marriage, which he claimed was against the law," says Shimon.

"I think I can explain," adds Joan'na. "Antipas is the youngest son of the great Hordos. He put aside his wife Phasaelis and took to his bed Herodias, who was not only the wife of his half-brother Pilip but was also his niece. Yhochanan ha-mmatbil considered that not proper and Herodias has been entreating Antipas to shut him up and urged her daughter to do the same. So now Antipas has given in to her wishes and arrested Yhochanan."

"Poor Yhochanan; in Qumran he was a strict observer of the law. He may be imprisoned, but he is stubborn and will not give in," I add.

"The authorities have been looking for you, Moreh, in Yerushalayim. There is also talk about you among the Beit HaMikdash officials. They are watching you and looking for a strong reason to report you to the Great Sanhedrin in Yerushalayim," says Yehudah.

"*Rabboni*, you have to be careful," Mariam says.

"Careful, yes; but I cannot be silent in the face of injustice. Yhochanan ha-mmatbil was not afraid to speak against that fox even though he knew he could get into trouble. He is a man of great courage. We also must have courage and be prepared to face the consequences of what we say and do. When more people become aware of what is happening, we too will find strength in numbers," I assure.

"Yes, Moreh, we'll walk with you, but we don't want to lose you," says Pilip.

"What are your plans, Moreh?" asks Tauma.

"I want to continue meeting the people in the towns and villages and talk to them," I repeat.

"Malka Antipas is also watching your reactions to the arrest of Yhochanan ha-mmatbil whose followers are very restless. Antipas inherited the magnificent palace at Machaerus on the Eastern shore of the Yām HamMáweṭ. This was built by his father Hordos who had also constructed a formidable fortress on top of the hill to intimidate and control the troubled area between Peleshet and Petra, the capital city of the *Nabataeans*[179].

"It was at the gates of this palace that Yhochanan ha-mmatbil was preaching. When Antipas' troops apprehended him, the people rallied in front of the palace gate and demonstrated. Yehudah and I joined them. The people were shouting 'Sin, Sin, Sin' at Antipas. We were also denouncing the Perushim and Soferim for remaining silent.

"They are the great defenders of the Torah and quote the Torah saying it is an offence for a man to marry the wife of his brother or to uncover the nakedness of his brother's wife. Yet when a malka does that, they remain silent. Yhochanan ha-mmatbil also knew the law and he denounced Antipas," says Shimon.

Yehudah adds, "During the protest the troops came out and arrested six of Yhochanan's followers and detained them. The rest

---

[179] Arabs of Nabatene, borderland between Arabia and Syria, from the Euphrates to the Red Sea

of us dispersed. We learnt that these six were later released. But they took Yhochanan up the hill into the fortress.

"The kohanim and Perushim are watching your statements against the traditions of Yahadut and the Torah while the Kittim are watching if there will be instigation against the empire as they always keep watch over the kana'im."

"Pilip, Natan'el, help us to pitch the tent," says Mattithyahu. Together they put up the tent again and secured the guy ropes and flap and suspend the lantern.

"I shall leave you for a while. I want to go up the hill and be alone for some time," I tell them.

Pilip says, "He seems to be upset."

"Well, it is nothing new. He often goes away by himself to meditate," says Natan'el.

"Moreh is not very communicative. His eyes seem to look far away. He is upset by what happened to Yhochanan ha-mmatbil, I think," says Mattithyahu.

"Perhaps he is planning something though till now he has not revealed any of his plans. Almost everything he says appears contradictory to what we have been taught," says Tauma.

"Can you accept what he says about the Torah and about Elahh?" Shimon throws the troubling questions.

"As I've said earlier, what he is teaching is completely different, but it is difficult to doubt the truth of what he says," responds Tauma.

"Moreh is trying to change the people and hopes that by forming our minds we will be able also to influence others. Although his views are so different, it is also refreshing to leave behind the old ideas and look towards a happy and fulfilling life," answers Mariam.

On the hilltop after contemplating and missing my cousin, I am wondering where I am leading my followers. They may be expecting something spectacular to happen. At best there will be a change in the people. At worst we will be hunted down and destroyed. I must make them believe strongly on this new way of looking at reality... I go back as they are getting lunch ready.

"*Rabboni*, are you alright?" asks the worried Mariam.

"Yes, yes, Mariam, I am alright, I just needed time to gather my thoughts. What are you all discussing?" I ask.

A lot of us are still not clear regarding what you have been telling us," says Ya'aqov.

"Come, dinner is ready, let's eat," calls out Shoshanna.

During the meal Shemayon says, "Moreh, we have spoken to different people about your new way of looking at tsedek. Many people are not convinced because they believe that the Torah is the way of Elahh and cannot be questioned at all. We are wondering where you are leading us and what plans you have."

"They always invoke the Torah claiming that it was written by Elahh. The Perushim and the Şĕdûqîm do not agree on the Torah and the Shomronim have their own Torah.

"Now the rabbim who interpret the words have also added a lot of their own codes of conduct, all based on the fear of Elahh and his punishment in sheol. To please Elahh they drew up religious observances like ethical rules, prayers, proper clothing, holidays, the ShAbat, pilgrimages, the reading of the Torah, and dietary laws."

"Do you mean to say that we need no law or rules to follow?" asks Mattithyahu.

"I have come not to destroy all law, because there is good counsel in some of them. Since the writers were also using the so-called dabar Elahh to make people good, there are indeed many good teachings in the Torah. Some laws are necessary to maintain good order and moral conduct of the people. There are, however, far too many unnecessary rules and regulations."

YESHUA

"We are told that Elahh gave Aba Moshe the *Aseret Ha-d'Varîm*[180]. Are they also not necessary anymore?" asks Shemayon.

"The writers of the Torah say that Elahh wrote the commandments on stone and gave them to Aba Moshe. When they say that these came from Elahh, it puts fear into people not to go against Elahh. The first four of the commandments were for this purpose, and to make you observe the ShAbat. They are not necessary. Only six commandments are:

Honour your parents, don't kill, don't steal, don't commit adultery, or bear false witness or covet what is not yours. Except for the one to honour and respect your parents the rest tell you what not to do. I shall put it this way. Love and respect life as something good. Be committed to faithfulness in marriage and develop a partnership in love. Everyone has the right to own property, unless you choose to renounce that right, and we must accept and respect that right. Finally, always be truthful in everything. This is the way of tsedek."

"These fundamental rules are based on the two pillars of love and tsedek, and tsedek is born out of love. If we remain faithful to these two principles all else will fall into place.

"Love is also the root behind the golden rule that Hillel, the great Yehudi religious moreh spoke about. I am fortunate to have met him when I was a boy when my parents took me to Yerushalayim. Moreh Hillel was not only a learned Torah scholar he was also a naggara like my father Yôsēp̄.

"Moreh Hillel was discussing with the Yehudim scholars in the Beit HaMikdash when one of them asked him, 'Can you explain the Torah while standing on one foot?' and Moreh Hillel, standing on one foot, said, 'What is hateful to you, do not do to your fellow: this is the whole Torah; the rest is the explanation; go and learn.' He summed

---

[180] The Ten Commandments

up all the law in that one golden rule of Love. Moreh Hillel recognised brotherly love as the fundamental principle of Jewish moral law.

"However, he was not the first one to speak about love in this way. I learnt from the wise men from the East that in the far eastern land of Seen about 450 years ago the philosopher Confucius said, 'What you do not wish upon yourself extend not to others.' But even about 50 years before him in the land of Hodu, it was written in their sacred writing called the Mahabharata, 'This is the sum of duty. Do naught unto others what you would not have them do unto you.'

"Love must be understood clearly and practised seriously. You have heard it being taught that you shall love your neighbour and hate your enemy. It is the common belief among the Yehudim that the neighbour is one who has accepted the Berith of Elahh, that is, the Yehudim and you are not bound to love those who are not Yehudim. But I say to you show love even to your enemies, bless those who curse you, do good to those who hate you and mistreat you. If anyone grabs your coat, let them have it if they need it more than you. If someone slaps you on one cheek, slap them back on one cheek unless you did something to deserve it. Do you remember the story I told you about the person from Shomron who did good to a Yehudi? Like that every man, every woman and every child is your neighbour."

"Moreh, you are asking too much from us. The enemy is never forgiven let alone shown love. We hate the enemy who oppress our people and we must fight them or else we show that we are weak, and they will oppress us more," says Yehudah of Kerioth.

"For years and years, we have been under oppression because the enemy has never changed and never will," says Shimon Qan'anaya.

"I understand your feeling. When we are in a critical situation of destroy or be destroyed, we have no choice but to destroy the enemy. It is by no means an easy task, Shimon. Destroy the enemy we must. However, isn't changing the enemy better than fighting the enemy?

"Our malka is so full of evil. What can change him?" asks Pilip.

"There is room for change in everyone. If the body is the temple the heart is the altar. Find the enemy within and sacrifice it at that altar. Destroy the 'enemy' within the oppressor. Bring about a revolution that will bring the oppressor around by eliminating the enemy that is within them. Once that enemy is destroyed the oppressor is no more.

It is like removing the scales from the enemy's eye, that is blinding them. As long as the scale is there like a broad beam, they cannot see the good in you and this also applies the other way around. We must not be blinded by our hatred.

"Since the core message of the Aseret Ha-d'Varîm is love, we must want to do good not out of fear of Elahh and his punishments if we fail to do good. As I have already said earlier, we should do good for the sake of goodness and not out of fear of Elahh. To love not only your neighbour but all people is worth more than all the burnt offerings in the Beit HaMikdash.

If your brother sins, warn him. If he listens to you, forgive him. We must first try to change them and if all our efforts fail then we must fight for tsedek. If you love those who love you, what merit is there in that? After all, even sinners love those who love them. And if you do good to those who do good to you, what merit is there in that? After all even sinners do as much. The sun shines on the bad and the good and the rain falls on those who are tsedek and also on those who are not tsedek.

"People in power use evil ways to remain in power by taxing the people and oppressing the poor, making life miserable and unhappy. This must change through tsedek ways. When we call for tsedek we threaten the powerful people.

"They will not listen to our voice. We cannot stand up and resist powerful people without a powerful army," repeats Yehudah.

"The voice that calls for tsedek must be a united voice from all the people. The Kittim are behind the religious authorities, and we are not equipped to fight the Kittim," says Shimon.

"I am sure there are some good people in the ranks of our leaders. We can try and make them change," says Mariam.

Grabbing a fistful of sand and letting it run through my fingers I continue, "This is what is real; this is Adamah; this is Adam; this is what we are made of, and this is what we will return to. You see the leaf that falls from the tree. In a short time, it becomes Adamah. We have only a short time to live on earth and if our life is not good and free and happy then what is the meaning of life?

My followers spend the following days pondering on this new angle of my teaching, trying to absorb its core message.

Scenario 29 - The Wise Perushim

Kfar Nahum

Shemayon's wife Rebecca and her mother were used to seeing me and my followers turn up without prior notice. Before we reach the house, Mariam tells Shoshana and Joan'na to go to the market to buy some fish and provisions. She also tells Yehudah to give them money for this.

They buy fish and vegetables including cucumber, tomato, eggplant and leek. They also purchase barley and some fruits, pomegranates and apples, and nuts, pistachios, almonds and some goat's milk. These resourceful women do not want to burden Shemayon's family.

They get busy preparing the afternoon meal. Shoshana cleans the fish while Arsinoe washes the vegetables, and Rebecca works on baking barley bread.

The men are outside the house having a drink.

We are visited by a close associate of Shemayon, a fisherman by the name of Addai. He takes over the leadership of the fishing team from Shemayon and has travelled widely transporting and marketing fish. "Hello, Shemayon, it has been some time since we met. How have you been?"

"I am alright. How is the fishing business?"

"That is doing quite well. There are some Perushim here who want to meet Yeshua," he says.

"Oh, not again!" exclaimed Ya'aqov. "They always want to argue and find fault."

"These Perushim seem to be different. They want to meet you, Yeshua, quietly at night and don't want to be seen in public meeting you," says Addai.

"Alright," I say, "bring them to me tonight."

Quite late that night Addai comes with some of the Perushim. They walk with their heads covered and ask if they could meet inside the house. Shemayon goes out to meet them and brings them in. They unfurl their hoods and reveal themselves. There are three of them. They offer greetings in the customary manner. The Perushim generally don't bother with formal greetings with ordinary people, but these Perushim were different.

Shemayon says, "Blessed be he who cometh."

The three of them bow their heads and say, "*Shalom alekem*[181]".

Shemayon replies, "Alekem shalom."

"Shalom be both to thee and shalom be to thine house and shalom be unto all that thou hast. My name is Nikodemos, I am a Parush and a member of the Sanhedrin. We have travelled from Yerushalayim to meet Moreh Yeshua."

They are surprised to hear a Parush address Yeshua as Moreh.

"I am Yeshua. You have a Yavan name, are you a Yehudi?" I ask.

"Oh, yes I am. My parents had great admiration for Tre-Qarnayia and gave me the name Nikodemos, meaning 'victory of the people'. Although Tre-Qarnayia brought victory to his people by his conquests, he did not bring victory to our people. However, my parents

---

[181] Hebrew for peace, same as shalama in Aramaic

took the meaning of the name to bring our people's victory. My parents were learned Yehudim and I studied and became a Parush. I believe in the victory of our people."

"I am Yôsēp̄ from Harimathea, also a member of the Sanhedrin."

"And I am Gamaliel, also from the Sanhedrin, and I am the grandson of Moreh Hillel."

They bow and sit on the floor mat while Rebecca offers them some water.

"I understand you have important positions in the Sanhedrin. Are you an official delegation the Sanhedrin sends to interrogate me?" I ask.

"Oh, no. Do not misunderstand our visit. We have heard a lot of people saying different things about you and what you teach. We would like to hear from you your views, your purpose and your message," says Nikodemos.

"Gamaliel, I was very fortunate to have met your grandfather the elder Moreh Hillel when I was a small boy, and I was fascinated by his teaching," say I.

"We too are fascinated by your teaching, but we find it very confusing. You say many good things, but you also disregard our traditions," says Gamaliel.

"You are the guardians of our traditions. You guard them well, too well, indeed. By your teaching we are made to accept all of them as true. What if they are not all true?"

"You cannot question them because they have been revealed by Elahh."

"As good intelligent learned scholars are you not trained to question life and its reality?"

"Yes, of course…"

"But then, why do you make an exception when it comes to the scriptures?"

"It is because we believe that the words of the scriptures were given to us by Elahh through the mouth of the prophets."

"I too was brought up believing that. I worked for a number of years in Qumran studying the fragile fragments of the scriptures. Over the centuries there have been copies made of copies and added on by commentators replete with errors. I am convinced they were written by men to keep the people under control. Those in power try to solidify their position by quoting selected verses of the Torah out of context to suit their arguments and force blind obedience with what they call the rules of Yahadut. You are scholars, surely you cannot be blind to that."

"But surely there is much wisdom in the scriptures."

"I will not deny that. But sometimes even that wisdom can be questioned. We can only question our traditional beliefs if we are born again."

"How?" asks Nikodemos, "are we to reenter our mother's womb and be reborn?"

"You see, when a child is born, their mind is like a blank slate, and they learn from life and their parents. They build their knowledge and beliefs as they grow up. We, however, have grown up filled with all the traditional beliefs and been told that these must be impressed in our brains. We are stuck with that knowledge and beliefs. The only way is to start with a clean slate by being born again. Nature is our teacher and the toqeph in Nature is our instructor."

"Are you asking us to wipe away all our beliefs? This is something very difficult to do," says Gamaliel.

"No, we look at our beliefs with new eyes. If they are reasonable, good and things that we are in touch with, we can absorb them. Life is meant to be lived in peace and happiness and doing good. I like your grandfather's teaching of doing good as basic to the Torah.

"The Torah contains the Law that guides us in the path of tsedek," says Yôsēp̄.

"Look up to the heavens and see the stars. They are guided by the law of the universe. Nature is the mother of all law," say I.

"If there were no laws to control our lives there will surely be trouble and chaos and insecurity," says Nikodemos.

"Some laws are necessary to safeguard the common good of life and property but there are too many unnecessary laws drawn up by men that only restrict the freedom of life. Moreh Hillel was able to see basic law in the Torah beneath all the added laws and regulations as

love which is expressed in doing good. Good life is living in this world doing good things for a short time only and what we leave behind is only memories nothing more. We come and we go and hope to leave the world a little better than we found it. There is nothing more," I asserted.

"How can there be nothing more? The Torah says, 'And the Almighty formed Adam of dust from the ground, and He blew into his nostrils the *neshamah*[182] of life and Adam became a living nephesh. The neshamah is part of Elahh's essence. Since Elahh's essence is completely spiritual and non-physical, it is impossible that the nephesh should die," declared Yôsēp̄."

"Let me ask you what is it that Elahh blew into the nostrils of Adam? Is it not also called ruach and is not also called Ruach Elohim?"

"Yes."

"Ruach is wind, breath, mind, spirit – all of that. In the Torah, all that breathes is also referred to as the nephesh and applies to all living things, Adam and all other creatures, and they eventually die. The ruach is something physical. Nothing we know is non-physical except an idea or a memory that is in our heads, and even that dies

---

[182] spirit

with us. The whole idea of Elohim is something created in our mind," I explain.

"We do not know everything in this life," says Nikodemos.

"That is true indeed, we have so much to learn," I acknowledge.

The others, finding the discussion rather deep, just listen.

"That is why we look to *Olam HaEmet*[183] – the next world, the world of truth where we will understand the real purpose of life," declares Gamaliel.

I make a comment, "It is refreshing to be able to talk frankly, but forgive me, my learned friends. There is very little in Yahadut that teaches about Olam HaEmet, the afterlife. Wisely so. Who really knows anything about it? Many of the concepts of afterlife are opinions of the rabbim and these concepts have been developed by scholars like yourselves.

"With Olam HaEmet in the distant view, the primary focus of Yahadut is to obey the *Mitzvot*[184], the divine commandments given by Elahh in the Torah. But the rabbim have combined their own rules and laws, in the *halakhah*[185], to be obeyed simultaneously. There are more than six hundred of them if I am not mistaken. These are the burdensome rituals and religious observances for the benefit of the Olam HaEmet that the people follow to avoid punishment. The Torah emphasises rewards and punishments that are physical and immediate rather than something happening in the future in another world.

"There are many differing opinions among our spiritual leaders. The Şĕdûqîm, for example, who maintain the Báyith and who are also the political, social and religious leaders, hold opinions different

---

[183] The world of truth, the next world

[184] Commandments, obligation combined with rabbinic laws and tradition

[185] Jewish law containing rituals and religious observances derived from the Torah

from yours. They say that the nephesh is not immortal and that there is no Olam HaEmet nor are there rewards or punishments after death. The Ṣĕdûqîm reject these concepts because they say that these are not explicitly mentioned in the Torah, whereas you Parushim say that they are implied in certain verses of the Torah. You say that my teaching is confusing but the teachings that come from the Beit HaMikdash are also contradictory and confusing to the people.

"Please do not burden the people with all the minute laws of the SAbath like how far one can walk, or to clean their hands before they eat, or what they can and cannot eat. All these are totally unnecessary except for health reasons. There are enough laws imposed on us by the Kittim. As human beings, we must focus on our task of doing good in this world. If we do that all other good practices will follow," I conclude.

"You disregard practically all the doctrine of our ancestors. What is there left to believe? What meaning has life?" asks Yôsēp̄.

"The answer is very simple. There would be no life without ruach. What we need is clean air to breathe, clean water to drink, and for plant and animal life to flourish. With healthy food to eat and with the help of toqeph from the sun, we must maintain a clean environment for a good and healthy life. With clean living, there will not be so much disease, sickness, and illness. Many of the diseases like tsara'ath and blindness can be avoided. When a person is struck with a disease you immediately put the blame on their sins and the work of the unclean satana. You ostracize that person and split the family and the community. Your law is constructed to oppress the poor, those with disabilities, the sinner, women and children. By doing that you bring illness to society. Reinstate the sick person into the community and you will bring healing to society.

"Your notion of clean and unclean is completely distorted. Nothing in Nature is unclean; only we bring blemish to Nature by our foul deeds. Those with power control and oppress the people. Go and tell them about love and goodness. That is all and nothing more," I say.

"Moreh Yeshua, you are a good man, and it is difficult to disagree with you and many of your views but to preserve the purity of Yahadut, your teaching cannot be accepted. We understand you, but you will face opposition from the authorities. You will be accused of being deviant. We advise you to leave this place and go somewhere else. Hordos Antipas wants to kill you. Shalom be with you," says Gamaliel.

"Shalom be with you, love be with you, tsedek be with you, and toqeph be with you," say I.

They leave somewhat disappointed, nevertheless, perplexed.

"Moreh, your teaching is turning Yahadut upside down. It is difficult to say if these men will be friends or enemies," comments Mariam.

"I believe these are good men. As scholars they are being honest even if they cannot accept what I say. They are part of the system and cannot think outside it," I observe.

In the morning my followers and I go into town and word gets around that I am back. Many people gather around me in the street itself. The owner of a house on the street welcomes me inside. The crowd follows. They bring a demoniac accused of being possessed by an unclean spirit, and others who were sick from different diseases. I speak to each one of them, touch them and suggest different kinds of herbs as remedies. My followers are closely observing me.

The people are asking about the coming of the kingdom which is the central theme in their expectation of salvation and liberation in Yahadut of the time.

I sit down and speak to the crowd.

"If you expect the kingdom to be somewhere in another world in the heavens, you will be disappointed. Even if you expect malke like Dawidh and Sh'lomoh to rise up and create a holy city like Yerushalayim of old, you will be disappointed.

"The kingdom is like a mustard seed. It's the smallest of all seeds, but when it falls on prepared soil, it produces a large plant, a big tree which becomes a shelter for birds of the sky. The seed, the soil, the tree, the birds and the sky – they are all connected. The material realities that we experience through our senses are the realities of the kingdom.

"The seed needs a prepared soil to nourish its growth. We are the farmers, and we must make sure the healthy plant becomes a huge protective tree. We are the builders of the kingdom. The kingdom is the world, and the world is the kingdom.

"However, not everything is perfect. There is no perfect kingdom. We have the sick, the crippled, lame, deaf and dumb – they are all part of the kingdom. It is for us to make it less painful for them. If we are the cause of these ailments, then we make society ill and destroy the kingdom. Not everyone is equal in the kingdom. You are worth more than the birds. You are more responsible. The bird builds the nest, you build the kingdom. The fundamental pillars of the kingdom are Tsedek, Love, Shalama and Freedom."

I believe I make some deep impressions on the people because, unlike the Soferim and the Perushim, I teach something totally different. It makes them think.

After lunch with Shemayon's family, we return to the base camp.

Scenario 30 - Death of Y'hochanan ha-mmatbil

Base Camp

When we reached camp Shemayon says, "I will take the boat out for a quick catch, so we will have some fresh fish for dinner.

"I'll come along," I offer.

Immediately Ya'aqov, Y'hochanan and Tauma said they want to go also. Arsinoe also joins us.

Shemayon steers the boat towards the rocks, and I say, "You will only catch small fries in the shallow water. Put out into the deep water and pay out your net."

"Moreh, this is not the right time for the big fish," corrects Shemayon.

"Go out anyway, you never know," I insist.

"Why do you cast doubt, cast the net instead," says Tauma.

"If you say so, Moreh, I will pay out the net," Shemayon calls the others to help him do it.

They haul in a decent load of big fish of all kinds.

"You should be a fisherman, Moreh," compliments Arsinoe.

We bring the catch ashore without separating them. Among the fish there are also two catfish and an eel and also some shrimps and crabs.

Shemayon asks the women, "Shall we cook what we have caught?"

"What have you caught?"

"Look!" said Shemayon showing them the bucket.

"Ooo ah!" exclaims Marta, and then, "and why not?"

"Moreh," says Y'hochanan, "we have gone against the Torah; we are going to eat fish that is considered unclean."

"Well, you have indeed changed," say I.

When the meal is ready, everyone is a little hesitant when I start on the catfish. The rest of them also eat and begin to enjoy it washing it down with some wine.

As we are finishing Shemayon's friend Addai comes along.

"Ah, Addai, have you come to join us in following Moreh Yeshua?" asks Shemayon.

"No, I actually came to take a loan of your boat for some time. We are going down south of the yam. But I also come bearing some bad news, which will be very disturbing for your Moreh."

We gather around.

"Yhochanan ha-mmatbil has been killed by Hordos Antipas. I believe he is your cousin, Moreh Yeshua."

"Yes, he is. Arresting him is one thing for which he had sufficient reason; but he must have had some other reason to have him killed."

"The news going around is that it was Hordos' birthday and during the celebration Shlomiŧ, his stepdaughter, the daughter of Herodias, did an erotic dance which aroused the drunken Hordos. He promised her, before his invited guests, that he would grant her anything she desired even if it be half his kingdom. When the daughter asked her mother what she should request, she was told to ask for the head of Y'hochanan ha-mmatbil on a platter. Although Hordos was appalled by the request, he could not go back on his word before his guests and reluctantly agreed and had Yhochanan executed in prison."

"That fox has never been a strong leader although he has to put up a pretense before his guests. He is fearful of Herodias," I say.

"There is also another rumour that he fears the great influence Yhochanan ha-mmatbil had over the people, and his followers who were getting more and more restless the longer he was held in prison. He feared they could raise a rebellion and the best way to put an end to that was to have him killed," adds Addai.

"Yhochanan's followers might have agitated but I doubt if Yhochanan himself would have called for a rebellion," say I.

"But what Antipas feared is coming true. There was already a large demonstration by his followers outside his palace demanding that Yhochanan ha-mmatbil's body and head be surrendered to them for a proper burial," says Addai.

"I knew Yhochanan well. When we were together studying the scriptures in Qumran, Yhochanan showed a particular interest in the Book of Malke which speaks about the prophets *Eliyahu*[186] and *Eliysha*[187]. He devoted much time in the research on the life and works of Eliysha. Eliyahu left his cave in *Har Chorev*[188] and found the young Eliysha ploughing on his father's farm with twelve-yoke of oxen before him. Eliysha left everything and followed Eliyahu who took him to the Nehar haYarden.

"Stories were told of Eliyahu performing a miracle of parting the waters and being taken up in a chariot of fire. Eliysha carried on the work of his master believing in his return. He is said to have cured a tsa'ra'at in the cleansing waters of the Nehar haYarden.

"Y'hochanan was so taken up by Eliysha that he too wanted to be like him. He could not do that in the enclosed community of Qumran.

---

[186] Elijah

[187] Elisha

[188] Mount Horeb

227

Although he was a very strict follower of the rule, he felt he had to bring about a change in the people from their sinful ways. He left Qumran and called people to the waters of the Nehar haYarden to repent and be cleansed and that is why he is called Yhochanan ha-mmatbil. He was angry at Hordos and denounced his sin of living with Herodias. He was a fearless preacher and became a threat to Hordos."

Addai adds, "Hordos Antipas has heard about you, Yeshua, and has expressed interest in meeting you. He is actually watching you and your followers. If he feels threatened, he will not hesitate to get rid of you too, Yeshua."

The next morning while we were having breakfast I say, "I have been thinking. With the death of Yhochanan ha-mmatbil and Antipas on the lookout for me it would be good for me to move out of his territory for a while. I plan to move north and west towards the Ha-yam Ha-Gadol to the coastal town of Tyre. You don't have to come with me, if you don't want to."

"Moreh, if it is dangerous for you here it will be the same for us too. We will go with you," declares Shemayon.

"We don't all have to go because the journey has to cut through mountainous regions and might be quite tiring especially for the women," I caution.

Mattithyahu says, "There are many routes that cut across the main trade route from Dimashqu and I used to collect taxes from the orechahs travelling the routes. I know some of the tax collectors there. We could ride on one of the orechahs."

"Yes, let's go without drawing too much attention, Let's make further plans." I say.

"First, let us go for a swim," invites Y'hochanan.

They all strip down to the barest minimum and go into the water. The women also follow them wading into the water.

"Let me show you how well I can float on the water," says Shemayon.

"Why don't you try walking on the water?" teases Natan'el.

After a refreshing swim, which is also their morning wash, they hang their brief linen to dry.

"We do not know how long we will be away, so it is best that we strike camp and put things away," I suggest.

"We just pitched out tents and now we have to take them down again," complains Mattithyahu.

"If we are going to travel to many places, we need to carry our camping equipment with us," observes Marta.

"Let's take all that we can carry," says Mariam.

"That is a good idea because we may not always travel with an orechah," adds Andreia.

We begin dismantling the tent and pack away some of the stuff at the usual place under the old, overturned boat.

We take the essential canvas, mats, utensils and provisions with different people carrying different items.

Shemayon told Addai, "You take the boat, but first take us to Kfar Nahum. We have a lot of things to carry.

Scenario 31 - Journey out of HaGalil

Kfar Nahum

Once we are in Kfar Nahum we unload the boat and Shemayon tells Addai, "You keep the boat and use it until we get back. Take good care of the nets and the boat."

On reaching Shemayon's house Rebecca is surprised, "You are back so soon!"

We settle down to make plans about the journey north.

"We can travel north in two ways. One is to follow the orechah route and go straight up following the river to lake Hulah, and then go west towards the sea or go northwest directly towards Tyre. This is a very difficult journey through the mountains and there are no orechah routes that way," says Mattithyahu.

"Getting off the routes into the mountains and out of HaGalil Ha'elion would be the quicker way to get out of the sight of Hordos Antipas and his territory," deduces Shemayon.

"We don't know much about the terrain that way, but I know someone who has travelled that way before and I could ask him to come and explain to us the best way to go. Otherwise, we could get lost there," says Andreia.

"When can we meet him?" asks Yehudah.

"I'll go and see him right away."

Mariam says, "If we are going to travel through the mountains, we need a good supply of provisions."

"Only yesterday we replenished our supplies," says Marta.

"That will not be sufficient for all of us. I suggest Yehudah and others go to the market again and buy more provisions like dried food that can keep," adds Arsinoe.

Yehudah says, "I do not have enough money to buy more."

"We have not brought enough money with us. I will go back home and get more money," says Mariam.

"I will go with you," says Shoshanna.

"I will follow, I have some money at home," adds Mattithyahu.

"I presume you will be taking a boat?" asks Joa'ana.

"Yes, that will be the fastest and we could be back before evening," says Mariam.

"In that case I too will go with you, continue to Tiberias and meet you back in Magdala. I am sure we will all come back with sufficient money for the journey," says Joa'ana.

"I will go and see if Addai is still at the waterfront and ask him to take you," says Shemayon.

That is settled.

Rebecca and the women prepare the meal after which Andrea returns with his friend.

"This is Barachiah, a merchant who has travelled widely within Hagalil and Yehuda and beyond. Please tell us the best way to travel," Andreia asks him.

We all gather around him under a tree.

"What is the best route to the coastal cities of Tyre and Sidon?" I ask.

"There is a long way and a short way. The long way is easier, the short way more difficult. If you take the short way you will have to

231

cut through the mountains and negotiate steep and rocky paths. The total distance to Tyre from here, as the bird flies, would be about 75 milin.

"On ordinary ground, good healthy people could cover about 20 milin by the sixth hour and after midday rest, if you continue travelling until the 12th hour, another 13 milin. That is if you are very fit. You will not be able to cover even half of that on the terrain if you took the short way. Not only is it rough, but you also must climb uphill most of the time and for short distances downhill. If you make 10 milin per day you will be doing good," says Barachiah.

"Are there any towns or villages along the way?" asks Pilip.

"Yes, there are scattered villages where you can stop and replenish your provisions. They are mostly small and poor villages. If you cannot make it to a village before sundown there are some places along small streams where you could camp and there are also several small caves, but you must be very vigilant. There may be wild animals," warns Barachiah.

"Are the people friendly?" enquires Mariam.

"Within Hagalil they would be friendly to you but once you cross into the land beyond, you have to be very careful. The older people will have historical ill-feelings toward the Yehudim," cautioned Barachiah.

"Let's decide which route to take and plan our itinerary," say I.

"If we want to get away from the watchful eye of Antipas, I suggest we take the short way," says Arsinoe.

"You will have to go prepared with food and camping gear," says Barachiah.

"Is the route passable with a cart?" asks Natan'el.

"No, that is not possible, at least for the first half of the way, but you can take a mule or a donkey," advises Barachiah.

"Alright, please help us to plot the short route," I say to Barachiah.

Barachiah smooths the ground and draws a small circle with a stick.

"This is Yam Chinneroth. We are on very low ground here," then he draws a straight line diagonally up in a north westerly direction away from the yam to a point. "This is the coastline of Ha-yam Ha-Gadol," placing a stone on another near vertical line, "This is Tyre," placing another stone further up the line, "and this is Sidon," he explains.

"If you take the long route, however, you have to go to the village of Tanchum near Beth-tsaida and follow the Nehar haYarden along the Hula valley to Yam Hulata. Keep following the Nehar haYarden towards Caesarea Pilippi, the territory of Pilip the Tetrarch. From there you can go west along the high valley of Lebanon to Tyre. You will be following the trade routes all the way."

To explain the short route, he draws a very heavy line cutting across the direct line to Tyre. "This is the mountain range that divides Hagalil and Syro-Phoenecia."

He then draws two strips of heavy parallel lines on the sand at right angles to the mountain range. "Between these lines runs the Beth ha-Kerem valley that separates Hagalil Ha'elion from HaGalil HaTahton. The shorter route is through this valley, but it is a steep climb. Go first to Khorazim. It is only four milin from here, but you will have to climb 600 *amot*[189]." Barachiah places a small stone there.

"You have to keep climbing another 450 amot to reach Acchabare which is another 13 milin. This part of the journey is the most difficult and dangerous."

"What is the danger?" asks Yehudah.

"You may come across a pack of wild dogs. Usually, if you are in a group your numbers will frighten them off. From there you can follow one of the less travelled trade routes to Sepph, only three and a half milin away but a very steep climb up 1,280 amot. Here if you

---

[189] plural of amah, cubit-measure of 19 inches (from elbow to tip of the middle finger)

are carrying valuable goods, you may confront some robbers."

Barrachiah continues, "This leads the way to *Har Meron*[190], the highest peak in Yisra'el. I am sure you do not want to go up there. You can, however go around it to the village of Meroth, which is on the slope of the hill, and you climb down this time about 550 amot and it is less than ten milin. It is a nice village."

"What is the climate there?" asks Y'hochanan.

"The air is fresh and cool, and at night it can get very cold. Take some warm clothing with you. It is grape country, and the villagers make their own wine. Next you can follow the route for another ten milin, but you must climb again another 450 amot to Gush Halav," elaborates Barachiah.

He indicates these places with stones. "Once you cross Gush Halav you leave HaGgalil and go into the land of Syro-Phoenecia. It is then all the way down to Tyre and before that you will come to the village of *Qana*[191] only 11 milin and 100 amot down. Another ten milin downhill and you are in Tyre," concludes Barachiah.

"We thank you very much Barachiah, you have given us a very comprehensive account of the journey and we know what to expect. We should start preparing," say I.

Shemayon, so well-known and respected in Kfar Nahum, easily secures a mule. They prepare the necessary things to take for the journey.

As they were busy doing this Mariam, Shoshanna, Mattithyahu and Joa'ana return.

I announce, "Much as I like us all to be together, the journey can be difficult, hazardous and dangerous. Are you women prepared to face it?"

---

[190] Mount Meron

[191] Cana

"It can also be dangerous for us here because we are known to be your followers. I will follow you," says Mariam.

"So, will we," chorus the women.

"I don't think that is a good idea," intervenes Shemayon.

"Why?" asks Mariam.

"First, the climb will be very strenuous; second the attack by wild animals, and third the robbers will go not only for our goods but also the women."

"If you are concerned for us, I appreciate that; but if you think we cannot defend ourselves or are a burden to you then you are wrong," responds Mariam.

"If we stay together as a group, we should have nothing to fear. I have no objection to the women coming with us, but we should all carry knives," says Yehudah.

"It is settled then. All you brave women, I respect your choice. Would you please help us to pack things?" I request.

"Yehudah, it is still early now, you can go to the market," says Shoshana.

"Please make a list," requests Yehudah.

"No need, we women will buy what we think is necessary," says Mariam.

"I will go with you, because we will have to buy some knives, and I know what kind to get," says Shimon.

They pack fruits and dried food, grain and water and wine. They help Rebecca to bake barley bread and make a good supply of taboon bread. Mariam makes sure they have some warm clothes. The men check the tent materials. Marta finds a special place for the basket of jars containing different herbs.

All are ready to make an early start in the morning.

As the men are settling on the mats for the night, Tauma says, "Antipas found Yhochanan ha-mmatbil a threat to his personal life, but Moreh is a threat not only to the malke but to all the religious powers and the Kittim. If his life is in danger, our lives too will be in danger. I am ready to stand up with him.

"If need be, we will defend him," says Yehudah.

"I don't think his plan is to raise an army and fight the authorities. He wants to change them as he has changed us," says Ya‹akov.

"We are not fighters or soldiers. His new ideas are our weapons, and we will learn to use them like he does," said Mattithyahu.

"We too will have to do our part in bringing the change in other people," says Andreia.

"I have been listening to what you are all talking about," observes Mariam, "nobody has opened our minds and hearts like he has. You talk about weapons. His words are powerful and challenging. In the whole history of our people, none of the prophets or the *malke* has brought this new vision to us. All of us must be born again. I am already reborn. I will follow him wherever he goes," asserts Mariam.

Part Four

Travels Beyond

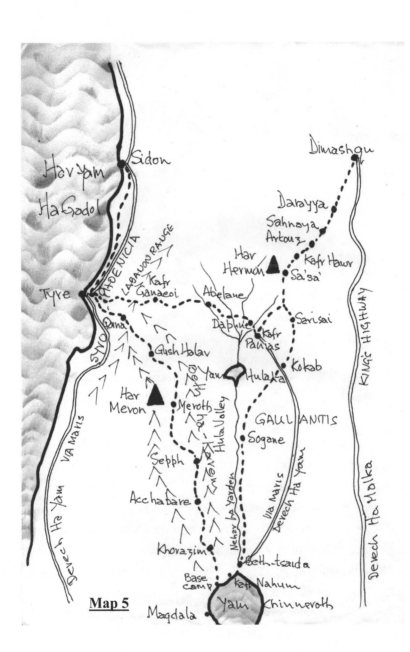

Map 5

239

Scenario 32 - ShAbat

Khorazim

Early in the morning we are ready, say our farewells and set off in the direction of Khorazim.

With most of the burden on the mule, we mount the stony track uphill, carrying only minimal personal belongings and staves. After an hour climbing, we rest. Looking back, we have a wonderful view of Yam Chinneroth. It is a serene stretch of water reflecting the blue sky with puffs and streaks of white clouds. There are hardly any boats on the water. It is the ShAbat. Some families are bathing in the water and children playing on the beach with seagulls sweeping the air. We continue climbing. As we go higher the vista of the yam opens up a breathtaking panoramic view.

Before dusk we reach Khorazim. People are sitting about and lazing around, and nobody pays much attention to us.

Someone then says, "This is the group that has been stirring up trouble around Yam Chinneroth."

Another man waves his hand saying, "Go away from here. We do not want any trouble in our village."

"We are on our way north and are just passing through," says Shemayon.

"Why are they so unfriendly?" wonders Andreia.

"I'll tell you why," says Tauma noticing a rabbi sitting among them, "it is the ShAbat and the rabbi is talking to them."

"Wait," says the rabbi, "have you just come from Yam Chinneroth?"

"Yes," admits Shemayon.

"When did you leave the yam?" questions the rabbi.

"About the sixth hour," says Shemayon who is the only one engaging in conversation with them.

"Let's move on, we may meet some other people," I say sensing some antagonism.

"No, no, wait a while. All of you have violated the ShAbat by walking this distance," accuses the rabbi.

Hearing this dialogue more people gather around.

I address the rabbi. "You, learned rabbi, have you not read in the Law that on the day of the ShAbat, the kohanim of the Beit HaMikdash break the ShAbat without being blamed for it? Why is that? Is the Law made only for ordinary people?"

The rabbi is silent.

One of the men turning to him asks, "Is that true, rabbi?"

He remains silent.

"Now, here is someone who knows more than a rabbi," someone whispers.

"This man is saying something we have not heard before. Let us listen to him. Adon, please tell us how they break the ShAbat," asks the first man. There is a small crowd now.

I speak to them about the crippling aspects of the Law and how it burdens the poor and allows the báyith authorities to live in luxury. "The ordinary people are forbidden to do manual work or even walk the distance we have walked today. On the ShAbat, the kohanim of the Beit HaMikdash do double the work they do on other days of the week. They make the fires, kill and flay the beasts, and dress the sacrifices. Isn't all that manual labour on the ShAbat?

The rabbi tries to defend the kohanim, "The kohanim do that in the service of the Beit HaMikdash."

"You say they do that in the service of the Beit HaMikdash. They make good money out of that work. Many poor people must walk and work hard every day to live. Why must the kohanim be dispensed from the law?" I question.

The rabbi remains in the background, embarrassed.

A woman comes forward with her son.

"I have heard of you, Yeshua, and what you do for the people. You heal the sick and make the blind man see."

"You mustn't believe whatever you hear, attha" say I.

"My son here has a withered hand. He is unable to find work because he cannot use his hand. Please do something," she pleads.

"Rabbi, I am going to do something now and let the people judge if I am breaking the ShAbat. Come," I say to the son, "what is your name? and how old are you?"

"My name is Yosiah. I am 26 years old."

Holding his right arm in both my hands I say, "How long has your hand been like this?"

"Since I fell from the tree about two years ago."

"Is it the same or is it getting worse?"

"I could use my fingers, but they are getting weaker."

"Is it painful?"

"It was very painful in the beginning, but now not so painful."

"You have not been using your hand because it is painful, and you use it less and less until you stopped using it, is that right?"

"Yes."

Pointing to a collapsed brick wall that has diminished in size with many bricks fallen off, I say, "That which is torn down must be rebuilt with like material. Your muscle is soft and weak because it is broken down like the wall. You must rebuild your muscle by using your hand."

"I cannot, because it is very difficult."

"Alright. Bend your fingers into a fist. Well, you can at least move your fingers and that is good. Now lift your arm."

I help him by lifting his arm and let go. The arm drops. "Lift your arm again." I offer some support. He was able to move it a few inches.

"Your arm is not dead, but it cannot become active at once. Go into the river and under water do the fist-clenching and upward movement of the arm every morning and evening. Use your good hand to move your bad hand. Your muscle is made of flesh and the nourishing material will come from the food you eat."

To his mother I say, "You must prepare food with meat and eggs, cheese and butter, and get him to drink plenty of goat's milk. Eat beans, seeds and nuts like pistachios and almonds. Each night rub down his arm with olive oil and massage it like this." I demonstrate this by squeezing Yosiah's upper arm with both my hands and working down his lower arm and finish by pulling his fingers. "If you do this every day without fail, even on the ShAbat, you will see strength come back to your hand, and you can do work again," I tell the young man.

They do not witness an immediate change in him, but they accept my advice.

The rabbi cannot hold himself. He comes forward again and says, "Yeshua, you have no respect for the Law. You have again broken the ShAbat by healing the man's hand."

"I have not healed his hand but only gave some good advice. Is it wrong to do good on the ShAbat? Is the ShAbat made for the people or are the people made for the ShAbat? Let me put it to you, if any of you here have only one sheep and it falls down a hole on the ShAbat day, would you not get hold of it and lift it out?

"Yes, I will," says one man plucking enough courage before the rabbi.

"I say to you that it is permitted to do good on the ShAbat day," I declare.

"The farming community is seeing sense in what Moreh is saying," whispers Marta to Arsinoe. The woman and her son invite us to her house and insists we stay the night with her. The house was too small, so we pitch the tent outside, and the women sleep in the house.

Shemayon makes sure that the mule is fed and watered.

The next day I want to meet more people, so we take a walk into the streets of the village. Seeing this group of strangers some of the local people join us. At the village square the people begin asking questions.

"We hear that you are a moreh who teaches Yahadut different from the Beit HaMikdash."

"I do not teach Yahadut. I only teach the way of tsedek. The worship they offer are worthless and the doctrines they teach are only human regulations which they claim to come from the dabar Elahh," I tell them.

"What is your teaching on tsedek?" asks one of them.

"Treat widows and orphans with mercy and kindness, and do not oppress the poor with heavy burdens of taxes for a start. Forgive your neighbours and love your enemies, live in peace," I sum up.

"We live in peace, but we don't love our neighbours," says someone on his left.

"Who are your neighbours?" I ask.

"There they are," says the same person pointing to some people on my right. They are gathered on two sides with a visible gap in between.

"They are the goyim, the unbelievers. We live together but we don't mix, we mind our own business, and they mind their own business," he says.

"And what is your business?"

"We are vegetable farmers, and we look after our sheep and goats."

"Don't you both bring your produce to the market to trade?"

"Yes, but that is strictly business, and we have no more dealings after that. We worship in our own way and they in their own way."

I turned to my right, "How do you worship?"

"We are the original people here descended from our ancestor Knaan, the grandson of Aba Noah. We worship our ancestral household gods and goddesses and offer sacrifice to Dagon, god of crop fertility, grain, flocks and humans."

"Both you people want the blessings from your god, and gods to bring prosperity to your crops and flocks. But both of you have missed what is most basic to good life. If there is a calamity it will hit your crops and flocks. The rain falls on your crops," I gesture to the right, "and on your crops," I gesture to the left. "The sun shines on all of you. Why are you quarrelling about gods? Whose god is going to save anyone of you?

"You will reap greater results if you can live in the shalama of brotherly love. You take your lamb and mint and dill and cumin to offer as sacrifice. Let me tell you that if you remember your neighbour has something against you or you against them, leave your offering there before the altar. Go and be reconciled with your neighbour first, and then come back and present your offering. All your offerings and worship to whatever god, gods or goddesses will be useless without tsedek. Let anyone believe whatever they want, all of you just believe in tsedek, embrace each other as brothers and sisters. If you say that Aba Noah is your ancestor, he is also the ancestor of all of us, and we are the same people. It is only religion that divides us. What good then is religion?"

I get the whole village thinking. The two factions of the village come to see me separately to ask more questions on issues of their belief and practice of religion. I guide them all in the path of tsedek.

The following day we decided to continue our journey, and people from both sides of the divide come to wish us well. There are already signs of people beginning to mingle.

We set out again on our journey northwest towards Tyre. It was again a climb, not as high this time, about 450 amot but much longer, 13 milin as Barachiah had said. It was a nice sunny morning and the Yam Chinneroth could still be seen in the distance. We went through untouched valleys and mountains hiking through thick foliage on a narrow rocky trail. I reach out giving Mariam an arm up, while Pilip guides Marta over the rocks. Shemayon is bringing up the rear leading the mule. As we climb higher, we are greeted with a vision of undulating hills stretching as far as the eye can see. We stop to rest and admire the scenery.

Ya'aqov leans back against a rock, "Look, eagles soaring way up high circling in the blue sky."

"There are also falcons among them," says Miriamne.

"They fly so high and so beautifully without falling because they are working together with the forces of nature. There are many forces of nature working together to keep them in the sky. The people we are going to meet have been observing these forces of nature and given them names, calling them gods. We can call them whatever we want but it is really the force of ruach and the work of toqeph that makes nature so beautiful and harmonious," say I.

We resume the hike and walk for a long time but cover little ground. By the sixth hour we stop by a small waterfall. The water was icy but clean enough to drink. We refresh ourselves, eat some bread and drink some wine and rest.

By late afternoon we are still climbing but cover just over three quarter of the distance to Acchabare. We are on the left cliff side of the Beth ha Kerem valley. Looking across the opposite side we see a few caves. There is one large cave, and it looks quite easily approachable. A shadow is beginning to fall across the valley.

Mattithyahu discerns, "I don't think we can make it to Acchabare before nightfall. Why don't we make our way across the valley to that cave? We can spend the night there."

"I think that is a good idea," agrees Shimon.

We climb down a steep slope and up a gentle slope. The cave looks very spacious, almost built like a tavern for travelers. Since the sun is setting the cave becomes alive with pigeons flapping in and out, and swallows coming in to roost and bats begin to fly. The sounds they made are like an orchestra tuning up instruments. Shemayon lifts the burden off the mule, and we settle inside the cave without having to pitch a tent.

Natan'el goes to look for a stream while Pilip, Tauma and Andreia collect wood to light a fire.

"I have heard of travelers who have stayed in these caves," says Mattithyahu.

Yehudah is surveying the place to ensure if it is safe from intruders or wild animals. The women unpack the food while Yhochanan and Ya'aqov prepare the bedding and while doing so, they find remains in some niches which appear to have been ancient burial places. Nothing much is left of them.

We settle for the night around the fire. As we eat Mariam asks me, "*Rabboni*, how did you discover all those remedies for the withered hand?"

"When I was with the Assayya in Mitzrayim I learnt a lot from them and the wise men from the East about wellness and illness, about caring and curing. They, of course, have developed healing as a religious art. The basic belief is that the earth is our mother and our birthplace. Many other living things absorb sunlight and store it in the form of toqeph, which has the power of healing, if we can learn how to use it. They have learnt to use common *owrah*[192] for natural remedies. It is an art because there are also many other owrah that can cause suffering and sickness. They have learnt to select the appropriate ones for specific illnesses. Most of them are commonly used as spices in food and therefore not poisonous. The art is in the way we can preserve a balance between the different toqephs."

Some of them are sitting and others reclining on mats.

I say, "We have had a long day's walk and I can see that you are all tired. Let us sleep."

We lay down and watch the full moon come up over the cliffs.

The next morning, we wash ourselves in the cold water of the stream, have a quick breakfast, pack and are on our way. We climb a hill that looks like the back of a single hump camel. As the sun rises, we are greeted by vast fields of greenery and colourful wildflowers.

I pick one of them and say, "This flower, resembling a Viper snake's head, is known as *achna'i*[193]; it changes colour from pink to blue after a day. A new flower replaces the previous flower each day."

Further up the hill I spot another species of wildflower. "This is called the *luf*[194] and it is poisonous, but some farmers know how to cook it safely."

"Ah! this beautiful purple flower is called *siah* Avraham or the balm of Avraham. The berries are used by men to control their sexual urges, and women use it to regulate their monthly blood flow."

"*Rabboni*, your knowledge of nature is astounding. You know so much about so many things," says Mariam in admiration.

---

[192] Herb/herbs

[193] Wild flower, *Echium Angustifolium*

[194] Local herb, *Arum Palestinum*

"Nature is the moreh of so many different powers of toqeph," I respond.

We walk past a small cave that contains an ancient shrine to some god. On a closer look we see a sketch on the wall of a figure that was mostly human but with goat's horns and goat's feet. The figure in the artwork is barely visible but it appears to be playing the flute. I explain, "This region of Hagalil Ha'elion is called the Hagalil of the goyim. From ancient times especially after the time of Tre-Qarnayia, this area has been home to a variety of different cultures of people such as the Kenaani and the different tribes of Yisra'el. They built shrines and temples here. This is the image of the Yavan god, Pan, who is associated with the countryside and is the guardian of shepherds and flocks. The Yavan have many gods and nymphs like this, very much part of the natural surroundings like caves, groves, springs, rivers and mountain tops, which are considered to be their dwelling places. They are harmless and often our teachers in the Beit HaMikdash call them satana and pagan worship.

Scenario 33 - Power of Shalama

Acchabare

It is getting hot and humid as we approach Acchabare. There is very little life left of what this village once was. Very few farmers eke out a simple subsistence living. They are not accustomed to seeing strangers, except for the occasional movements of the Kittim soldiers. Now confronted by a band of strangers, the women quickly take their children inside their homes and close the doors. The few men with their hands on their farm implements are staring at us.

I go forward, "Shalama, Shalom 'alekem."

They do not reply immediately. They very rarely have visitors. I repeat my greeting and move closer slowly.

Then one of them replies, "Alekem shalom. Who are you and what do you want? We are poor people, and we have nothing valuable for you to take."

They had evidently been harassed by robbers previously and were thus cautious.

"We are from Yam Chinneroth, we are not armed, and we come in shalama. We are on the way to the city of Tyre and would like to rest a while in your village," say I.

Mariam takes some bread from the pack on the mule and approaches them offering the bread. They feel safer and more relaxed. When the tension is dispelled, the women come out with their children. Mariam gives some bread to the children. One of the women then brings some water. We sit and begin to talk. Living so isolated they have many questions to ask about life in HaGalil HaTahton. They speak the older and purer form of Aramaic. They become more friendly and offer the group pistachios.

As we are talking, a young man comes up from the valley carrying a kid over his shoulder. He is happy but suddenly becomes wary of the large group of strangers. He is assured by one of the elders that it is safe.

"I have found the lost kid," he says, and the children run up to him and receive the bleating kid. They are all so happy that he found the kid that went missing the day before.

"Praised be Elahh!" says the elder.

I say, "We are happy to meet you. You are so isolated here by yourselves..."

Joa'ana looks up as they hear someone coughing inside the house. "Is someone sick?" she asks.

"Yes, she is my sister," said one of the women.

"We might be able to help. Can we see her?"

"Yes, you can come, but not the men."

Joa'ana, Mariam and Marta go inside. They come out after a short while.

"Our Moreh is a healer and if you let him look at her, he might be able to bring healing," says Marta.

The women hesitate, then the elder among them asks me, "Are you a magician?"

"No, I cannot do magic, but I have learned the methods of healing. If you are uneasy about it, it is alright."

"Moreh, the attha is with child and cannot come out. She cannot walk." Turning to them Mariam pleads, "Please let him inside."

They all look at the young man who had found the lost kid. He is the husband. He remains silent. The old man nods his head, and they lead me in together with Mariam, Marta and Joa'ana. The inside is dark with a little light coming in from above. I look at the woman but do not touch her. The sister lifts the woman's garment and reveals her legs which are both swollen, and the skin shinny and stretched. I touch her swollen shin with my index finger and pressed leaving a depression. I say nothing and leave.

When outside, I ask, "How long has she been with child?"

"Six full moons," says the woman's sister.

"The pregnant attha has dropsy. There is fluid in her legs. She is coughing because she has difficulty breathing. Open the door and let in fresh air. Put something under her legs to lift them up. Get some parsley leaves, wash them, and pound them to a paste and apply the paste on the legs and after one hour, wash it away. Do that every day. Take a handful of coriander seeds and boil it in water. Strain it and let it cool. Let her drink it two times a day. I am sure you have barley for making bread. Soak some barley in water with a piece of crushed ginger overnight, and in the morning strain it and let her drink the water. Don't let her take any salt. Do this without fail every day and the swelling in her legs will go down."

"Go on, start preparing it, "says Mariam to the women.

The young man comes to me and says thank you. We talk. The men speak of their farming on terraces.

Ya'aqov says, "On the way here we saw a small cave with a shrine. Are you Yehudim?"

"Yes," says the elder, "some of us are Yehudim and others among us are not. We have no problem here. We pray to Elahh and we also pray to Pan and the other gods to bless our crops and flocks."

"You are believers in Elahh, the one true God; how can you also worship the other pagan gods at the same time?" asks Shimon.

"Do you have a synagogue and do the kohanim from the Beit HaMikdash come and speak to you?" I ask.

"No, we have not seen one of them in ages. I read the Holy Book to the people," says the elder.

"You see, Shimon, these people live together in peace and have no problems; they have not been poisoned by the kohanim from Yerushalayim. We should stop labelling people according to religion. What does it matter what god or gods they worship? A life of peace and harmony is far more important than religion."

I address the elder, "Your gods are all so close to nature."

"Yes, nature is our mother who provides us with all good things," says one of the other men who was most probably not a Yehudi.

"That is wonderful, the ruach of mother nature blows through the hills and valleys bringing different kinds of toqeph to nourish life."

After sharing more stories, I say, "We must continue our journey. Please tell us how to go up to the town of Sepph."

"There is only one way to go there; follow the ancient route. It is not far, only three and a half milin, but it is a steep climb," says the young man who found the lost kid.

"You are happy because you found something that was lost. You have something good here – the shalama you enjoy among your-selves even with different beliefs. If two people make shalama with each other in a single house, they can say to that mountain over there to move and it will move. That is the power of shalama. Don't lose that treasure. Continue to live in shalama."

The others wish us well and we are on our way. It is indeed a steep climb, and the air is becoming cooler and the scenery becoming stunningly beautiful.

"Will these people who worship pagan gods be saved?" asked Tauma.

"Tauma, how long have we been together, and have you still not got the message I have been trying to get across? You talk of them being saved. Saved from what? From gehanna? Gehanna only exists in the mind of the Beit HaMikdash teachers. These people engage with nature and appreciate the environment in a way very different from the people around Yam Chinneroth and in Yehuda. They are already saved because they live in shalama. To live in shalama for the sake of shalama is itself salvation," I drive the point.

Scenario 34 - Mixed Marriage

Sepph

We approach Sepph, the highest town in Yisra'el, perched on a mountaintop. Sepph commands a panoramic view of the surrounding regions. Looking south we can still make out the hazy view of Yam Chinneroth, and to the west we see across the Amud valley the magnificent rise of Har Meron. Looking east we can make out the *Ramat ha-Golan*[195] and to the north is Har Hermon.

As we near the town the fields are empty. There is no sign of anybody working. When we enter the town, people gather around one house, well dressed in clean white garments and celebrating. They are standing around a white canopy supported by four poles called a *chuppa*. No one takes any notice of us. A wedding is taking place and the people think we are guests and welcome us in a friendly manner. We take our place among others and watch the wedding ceremony.

Under the chuppa, the *kallah*[196] circled the *chatan*[197] seven times

---

[195] Golan Heights

[196] bride

[197] groom

255

because the Holy Book says that the world was built in seven days. The elder then reads out the marriage contract in the original Aramaic text. He outlines the various responsibilities of the chatan to provide his wife with food, shelter and clothing, and to be attentive to her emotional needs. He is followed by another elder who calls upon the blessings of *Dagon*, the god of fertility and the Renewer of all toqeph, and *Kotharat*, the goddess of marriage and pregnancy, calling upon the swallow-like daughters of the crescent moon, those artful in the pleasures of the bed of conception.

The first elder then pronounces the seven blessings calling upon Elahh as the Creator of the world, Bestower of joy and love, and the ultimate redeemer of the people, reciting this over a cup of wine.

Also holding a cup of wine, the second elder calls upon *Dionysus* the god of fertility and wine to bring joy and divine ecstasy and curb the rage of drunkenness. The bride and groom drink the wine, and the celebration begins. As the string instruments start the music they dance around the bride and wine is served to everyone. Some of the village artists are juggling and doing acrobatics. It is a ceremony without elaborate rituals.

While I am thoroughly enjoying it, my followers are wondering what kind of marriage this is.

When we get talking with guests who are from the town, we are quickly noted as strangers. Because of the festive occasion, there is no hostility. But we are asked who we are, where we come from, and if we know the families of the married couple. When we are discovered to be from HaGalil HaTahton with a leader who looks like a rabbi, the other guests become cautious and fearful. I soon put them at ease.

"The wedding ceremony is one of the most beautiful I have ever seen," I say approving this particular mixed marriage between a Yehudi and a Kenaani. Mixed marriages are condemned by the Beit HaMikdash.

One of the women approaches Mariam, "Is your leader a rabbi from the Beit HaMikdash?"

"No, he is our Moreh ha Tsedek. Don't be afraid of him. He is not like the rabbim of the Beit HaMikdash. Why don't you take him to meet the chatan and the kallah?"

They invite me and the rest to first meet the parents of the newly married couple.

"We are very happy to have arrived in your town just in time for the happy occasion of the marriage. I can see that religion has not come in between your families. You are wise to give your approval to the marriage of your children."

The elders, one of them with a limp, then comes in and asks questions about the purpose of our visit, and who we represent. I again put them at ease and express the good intentions of our visit and congratulate them on the auspicious occasion. The parents call the young couple to come and meet the visitors who are a novelty because these people hardly have any visitors, especially people who come unannounced.

I speak briefly to the couple and the group gathers there.

"We come in shalama. Congratulations on your wedding. You have both made a covenant with each other to live together and raise a family. It is a lifelong commitment, remain faithful to it. We wish you love, happiness and shalama.

Shemayon asks one of them. "Why is no one working in the fields today?"

"When there is a marriage or if someone dies none of the people will go to work. Every family participates in the event of a marriage or funeral. This is how we remain united," he says.

Pilip says, "In the rest of the country, the kind of marriage we have seen today will never take place. It is condemned in Yahadut. There will be big fights and even killing. You seem to have no problems."

"We live a quiet, smooth and harmonious life here. We respect and share our religions. Mixed marriages like this only promote the sense of cooperation, mutual respect and love between the people. We have no problems," he explains.

The elders are keen to know more, so they sit and talk with us asking questions about life in HaGalil HaTahton and in Judea and Yerushalayim. They are not particularly interested in the Beit HaMikdash. I ask the Kenaani elder what was wrong with his leg. He says he has a pain in his knee and lifts his garment to reveal his knees. Noticing a swelling, I say, "You grow a lot of olive around here, so I am sure you brew your olives into oil. Take the purest of the olive oil and drink a spoonful before your meal in the morning and at night every day. You can also rub some of the oil on your knees. The swelling will go down and you will have less pain."

The elder promises to try out this treatment and says, "We would like to invite you and your group to stay the night in the village. A marriage in the village is like a festival and a time to announce it to the neighbouring villages. We do this by lighting a fire tonight on one of the five elevated spots in the village. The night will be cold, and the fire will keep you warm. There will be singing and dancing."

We join the villagers and have a very enjoyable time. The only big enough place to accommodate us all for the night is a barn. My followers have many questions to ask particularly about the marriage.

Yehudah, the zealot, was the first to ask, "The Yehudi idea of marriage is that it should be a covenant between two Yehudi. It is a sin against Yisra'el to enter into marriage with one who is not Yehudi. Today we have participated in that sin."

"My dear Yehudah, would that all of HaGalil, Yisra'el and Yehuda were like this village of Sepph. You see the shalama and harmony here. Religion or race is not an issue that divides them here, rather it is something that brings them together. Isn't that far more important than trying to preserve the purity of Yahadut?"

"If we let this practice go on then Yahadut and the Yehudi race will eventually disappear," says Shimon.

"Yehudah and Shimon, I know that as kana'im you are zealous about the preservation of Yahadut and the Yehudi race. We have been conditioned by history. When our people were exiled to Bavel, they were afraid of not being a nation again, so a core group of them rallied around the concept of the Chosen Race, the Beit HaMikdash and the Torah. When they were allowed to return, the leader, Nehemiah, the kohana, who was from the tribe of Yehuda and Ezra, began to organise the community to restore Yahadut and preserve the purity of the Yehudi race. You must remember that at that time there were many Yehudim who had foreign wives. These leaders declared that mixed marriages were an abomination and a betrayal of Elahh, and they ordered those marriages to be dissolved. Ezra spoke to them saying that they had committed treason by marrying foreign women, adding that to the sins of Yisra'el. This is the belief that has come down to us from the teaching of the Beit HaMikdash.

"They carried out an investigation to verify the foreign wives and listed the guilty ones. The women and children were sent away. This became the will of Elahh but there was nothing said by Elahh or men when Malka Sh'lomoh married hundreds of foreign women. Even Malka Dawidh married the foreign maid Maacha, a daughter of Talmai, the Malka of Geshur an independent northern mamlekhet. Bathsheba was married to Uriah from the tribe of the Hittite, and a soldier in Malka Dawidh's army. Esau married Judith the daughter of Beeri from the tribe of the *Hittim*[198]. It is written in the Book of Judges that the children of Yisra'el dwelt among the Kenaani, the Hittim, the 'Ĕmōrī, the Perazi, the Khiv'va and the Yebusi: and they

---

[198] Hittites

took their daughters to be their wives, gave their daughters to their sons, and served their gods.

"Previously, whenever the Yisra'el army made conquests, they brought the women and the virgins back for their use. Obviously, they were not concerned then with the purity of the race. Happy marriages were broken up and women were pushed out to places like Shomron to survive and take care of their children who were half Yehudi.

"We are in the land of the Kenaanim. Let us not forget that the Kenaani were the original people who lived in the whole of Peleshet and they spoke Aramaic. In early times the people of Yisra'el were practising the religious customs of the Kenaani and only later these same practices were declared foreign and against the worship of Yisra'el. Yes, if the teachers of the Beit HaMikdash from Yerushalayim were here today they would be asking for the blood of the young married couple. Would you like to destroy the happiness of these people? There is no commandment of Elahh concerning wedding ceremonies. There is a lot we can learn from these people on how to live in love and shalama and tsedek."

The next day more people come, mostly older people, to meet the visitors while the younger ones are already in the fields working. Once again, I congratulate them on the beautiful wedding ceremony.

"The Yehudi accuse the Kenaanim of offering human sacrifices to the gods. Do you still practise that here?" asks Ya'aqov.

"No, we don't. In the old days, in Knaan humans and particularly children, the first born, were burnt in the fire to please the gods and dispel adversity. Even Aba Avraham was prepared to sacrifice his son Yiṣḥāq. In the old days, our kohanim would have asked us to do that. We no longer do that. We offer animals and the product of our fields as sacrifice."

I fill in the background, "The religion of early Yisra'el was adapted from the religion of Knaan. The very fact that the scriptures condemn infant sacrifices proves that such practices existed. It is written in the Torah that El demanded the sacrifice of infants. I remember the text which says: 'You must give me the first-born of your sons; you must do the same with your flocks and herds.' In the Book of *Nebi Yirmiyahu*[199] it is written, 'They have filled this place with the blood of the innocent. They have built high places for Baal to burn their sons there.' There are many other passages in the scriptures that say we did practise human sacrifices. We should not be surprised. These people too have ceased such practices. Let us not be too quick to condemn them.

"In our old days also our kohanaim too would have asked the same thing, human sacrifice which now we condemn. I would condemn all sacrifice. Let's say, you have created a very beautiful object with your skillful hands, and you are very proud of it. I ask you to destroy it to please me. How would you feel? Would you rather destroy me than the work of your hands?

"We believe that Elahh, or whoever is the creator god, made everything that lives. Will destroying or killing one of his creatures as a blood sacrifice and offering it up to him make him happy? This idea is repugnant.

"The gods do not require sacrifices. When we do that, we are the losers, and the gods are not the gainers. The young people who were married yesterday will give you beautiful grandchildren. Will you put them in the fire and burn them? Of course, not. That would be something against nature and against tsedek.

"The aim of religion is to prepare you for the afterlife. I say to you prepare yourself to live well in this life. All people should enjoy the goods of the earth," I conclude.

---

[199] Jeremiah

"Yesterday," I turn to one of the elders, "you blessed the chatan and kallah calling upon the swallow-like daughters of the crescent moon, those artful in the pleasures of the bed of conception. So, the sexual act is for the marriage bed and not to be used as a ritual to be performed for the gods up on the hill. As long as all our customs and traditions are based on nature and the different ways the toqeph works in nature, all will be well. You recognise the different workings of toqeph in nature and refer to them as gods and give them names. The gods are not real but the toqeph in nature is real," I declare leaving them wondering and pondering.

Shemayon brings the mule loaded with our belongings, "We have to move on towards Tyre. Are we supposed to cross Har Meron?"

The elder says, "Har Meron is over 2,500 amot high but from here it is only 1,300 amot high. Do you plan to climb the mountain?"

"Oh, no. We want to go towards Tyre," says Andreia.

"We can go to the village of Meroth, can't we?" enquires Mattithyahu.

"That would be the way to go," says the elder.

The young man who got married yesterday says "You don't have to climb at all to reach Meroth. It is on the slope of the hill. It is less than ten milin and you climb down about 500 amot. You follow the old route, and it is not difficult."

"Thank you very much for your kindness and the breakfast," says Mariam.

"May shalama and tsedek be with you," I add.

"Alekem shalom," they reply.

Scenario 35 - Ha'Aretz HaMuvtahat

Meroth

On the way to Meroth, we are greeted once again by the majestic view of Har Meron. Although there are rocks and stones along the way, it is rather easy walking compared to the previous days. Lower down the valley we see a pool fed by a spring reflecting the blue of the sky. Pelicans are in the water and wagtails on the rocks. Wild donkeys graze on the side of the pool. We skirt the northeast side of Har Meron.

"Har Meron has the second highest peak in Yisra'el and the air is turning cooler," comments Shemayon.

"Look at that deep cave down there next to the pillar of stone," points Miriamne.

"That is the pillar I was told to look out for. It is supposed to be Nebi Eliyahu's Chair," adds Mattithyahu.

"Those valleys and mountains on the other side of Har Meron look wild and untouched. No wonder the people are so close to nature here," say I.

Cows are grazing on the hill slopes and some men and women tending grapevines. A woman is pounding something in a large mortar.

"What are you doing?" asks Shoshana.

"I am preparing hummus. I make it by crushing chickpeas," she responds.

A man who is pruning the vine asks, "Who are you people? What are you selling?"

"We are from Yam Chinneroth; we are not selling anything, we are on the way to Tyre," answers Y'hochanan.

We continue towards the village. At the entrance we are met by some old people and children.

"Shalom 'alekem," I say. Here too the response is slow in coming. Generally, the people here bare grudges against the Yehudim.

A very old man sitting on a stool beckons us to come forward, "What do you seek? You appear to be a group of preachers. If you have come to preach to us about your Elahh, then take your Elahh and move away from here. We do not want to hear about your Elahh. We have different Eloim here who provide us natural goodness."

I step forward, "Greetings, venerable *sib*[200], we come in shalama. We are Yehudim who come from HaGalil from around Yam Chinneroth. We are fisherfolk. We are not here to preach to you about the Elahh of Yahadut although we can discuss the idea of Elahh or Eloim. I understand your anger against Elahh."

"You are a young man. What do you know about your Elahh and the things he commanded your leaders to do against our people? We have lived on this land for centuries before *Yehoshua*[201] and your people came to claim it for themselves. Some people in Knaan fought against your Elahh's people and we were defeated while others among us chose not to raise the sword against Yisra'el. You call us sinners."

"Let him who is not a sinner raise the sword against the sinner."

---

[200] elder

[201] Joshua

"What is that you say? I do not hear too well. Can you repeat it?"

"I said let him who is not a sinner raise the sword against the sinner."

"Coming from you, you reinforce the idea that you people are not sinners?"

"On the contrary, my words should have been addressed to the Yehudi leaders who came to take your land." Shomron

"Ah, there was no one to tell them that, least of all your Elahh. As it is written, it was your Elahh who gave the command to Moshe, and he commanded Yehoshua to destroy all they found within Knaan civilisation. At that time, we were a more civilised people than the Yehudim."

"The Ha'Aretz HaMuvtahat belonged to Elahh even before you people came to live here, and you rebelled against the will and purposes of Elahh," enters Yehudah.

"So, you have come to pick a fight against us, have you? I will have you thrown out of here," says the elder who was becoming annoyed.

I intervene, "Yehudah, this is what our chief kohanim from the Beit HaMikdash have been teaching us. They say that to justify the Ha'Aretz HaMuvtahat. It is wrong to take land from the people who have lived there for a long time."

Then I address the elder and the others, "You, venerable sib, speak very old Aramaic, the language we speak. You are Aramaean and this west side of Hagalil Ha'elion is your home ground. We speak your language. Further north there are the Yavan-speaking *Iturians*[202] and the Phoenicians along the coastal cities of Tyre and Sidon. We hope to move into their territory.

"Over 100 years ago, Malka Aristobulus took control of this region and forcibly converted the people to Yahadut against our wishes. Af-

---

[202] Vagabond Aramaeans from Syria

ter that, the Kittim gave the Yehudi control of the place," pronounced the sib.

"I can understand your feelings. We, the Yehudi have been different tribes wandering in the desert, quite uncivilised. We wanted to be a mamlekhet with malke and used the name of Elahh to take lands that belonged to others. That is the truth of history. So, you see venerable *sib*, we have been misinformed and have been told that you are sinners who commit all kinds of bad acts particularly the sacrifice of children in fire. Your people did all that too in the past but when the Yehudi soldiers put the sword through your infants, did that make them any less guilty than throwing them into the fire? Our ancestors, both the Kenaani and the Yehudim have been guilty of sinning against each other. Now is the time to leave the past behind and learn to live in shalama," I say.

"You have spoken like a man of wisdom. Come and sit beside me," invites the elder. Some people began to gather around. As they were talking a young man approaches them.

"Moreh Yeshua, I have to come to thank you, I am Aqhat from Acchabare," says the young man.

"Ah, yes you were the one who found the lost kid. How is your wife?"

"That is why I have come. My wife can now stand up and walk. She has been healed by you. You are a miracle worker. Thank you, moreh."

"I am happy to hear that, but it was no miracle. She just took my advice seriously," say I.

However, the people pick up the word miracle and surge around me. There are many sick and disabled people in the village of Meroth. Word quickly gets around that a healer is in their midst. A woman comes to me and says, "Adon, my son is often troubled. Satana enters into him every now and then and he becomes uncontrollable.

I will bring him to you," she goes to fetch him. She brings the young man whose mouth is distorted and is not able to walk straight. He is suffering from some kind of palsy.

She says, "He is calm now, but it comes suddenly, and he becomes stiff and then his hands and legs begin to jerk. That is when satana enters into him. Sometimes he wets himself and bites his tongue and hurts himself."

I begin, "You must first believe…"

"Yes, Adon, whichever god you want me to believe, I will believe. Please drive satana out of him."

"Attha, you must first believe that there is no such thing as satana. Something inside his body is not right. Was he always like that since he was a child?"

"No. he was alright as a child. He is now sixteen and only one year ago, he became like that."

"This kind of problem comes suddenly but it will not go away suddenly. After some treatment, he may have these attacks less and less and eventually it might go away completely."

"What kind of treatment?"

"I see you have cows in the village feeding on luscious green grass on the hill slopes. You must get fresh cow's milk every day. Do you make qara[203]?"

The mother was not very sure, but an older woman says, "Yes, we do make qara but only sometimes because it takes a lot of work, and we use it for cooking special food."

"In Mitzrayim they call it *samna baladi.* The Assayya who live in the desert there and the wise men of Hodu in the East used qara for its medicinal value. Qara is the essence of milk. Make good pure qara from the grass-eating cow's milk, and every morning give a little bit,

---

[203] ghee

not too much, to the boy. The seizures will become less and less and could eventually disappear.

In the evening, the men return from the fields. Others bring their sick and disabled to me and as I advise them on what to do, I also invite my followers to attend to the others. We are invited to spend the night in the village. We spend the time discussing other matters. They are interested to know what is happening in the rest of the country. Shemayon explains to them that their king Hordos Antipas was busy putting up buildings and constructing cities like Tiberias on the western shore of Yam Chinneroth.

"He wants it to be his capital and named after his patron, the Emperor Tiberius. So, he needs plenty of gold and silver," says Tauma.

"Do his men come here?" I enquire.

"Yes, they do come to collect taxes. That is the only time we see them," says the elder.

"Do their religious teachers also come?" asked Pilip.

"They don't come anymore because we always chase them away."

The conversation invariably turned to religion.

"Although you reject the Elahh of the Yehudim you readily engage with the gods and deities with Yavan and Ugarit names worshipped in these regions," says Yehudah.

"Yes, because we find the culture of nature religions more accept-able and friendly. You look at the land around here with natural springs, caves, groves, rivers and mountain tops, which are suitable holy dwelling places of the ruach of the gods. They watch over the cultivation of our crops. They are not like your Elahh who is always commanding and punishing."

I follow by saying, "You say that the ruach of the gods dwells in these places. There is no distinct ruach of the gods. Ruach is everywhere and it blows through the natural springs and caves, groves, rivers and mountain tops. It is the same ruach that we breathe. It blows through our minds and hearts to make us realise and understand that this world is all that we have, and we are all that we have. There is no living ruach other than what is in nature. We cultivate the land, and it is the toqeph in the ruach that makes the plants grow. We have a good harvest and at other times the crop fails — that is not the doing of the gods, that is the working of nature. What I am saying is that there is no need to worship or placate any powers beyond nature. The toqeph in Nature is the only power in everything we see, hear, touch, smell and taste. This power shows itself differently and you give them different names and call them gods. If you want to call the world a mamlekhet, then toqeph is the makla. We must work to build this mamlekhet, to enjoy it and leave it a better mamlekhet than we found it.

During the night when we are together, I praise my followers on the way they treated the sick and disabled, "You are learning well, and I am proud of you. After spending a night with them we say we must move on to Tyre.

Mattithyahu, the informed navigator of the group says, "We have to go straight up north and there is a small road leading to Gush Halav. It is a climb of about 440 amot. I am told that it is about as high as Sepph and colder than there. The distance is about nine and a half milin.

We bid farewell to the people of Meroth and Shemayon leads the way with the mule. Once again, we are walking along the northeastern slopes of Har Meron into beautiful hill country so different from the barren landscape of HaGalil HaTahton, Shomron and Yehuda.

After two hours of climbing, we rest beside a rushing stream, and refresh ourselves although the water is very cold. A branch full of bright red bougainvillea hovers over the water. Along the water's edge are a few small animals called nutria, part of the beaver family, which are frightened to see us. We also startle some egrets in the water while a kingfisher is perched motionlessly, watching it all.

"We are now moving in the direction of the people whom we call the goyim, the unbelievers, the sinners. We took their land and call it our Ha'Aretz HaMuvtahat.

We continue walking along a path skirting the steep slopes of the mountain. Growing along the slopes are large olive trees with gnarled roots and twisted branches.

"These olive trees must be very old," remarks Shoshanna.

"I am told that olive trees are sometimes hundreds of years old and continue to bear fruit. We are in olive country. Merchants come here to buy olive oil. I have seen them brought in big jars. Gush Halav is known as the valley of the olive and it is also famous for grapes and wine," enlightens Mattithyahu.

Scenario 36 - Olam HaEmet

Gush Halav

As we reach the village of Gush Halav, the dogs bark, and the children stop playing and look at us. Some older people come out of the houses. Mariam and Marta go first to show them that we are not a hostile group of thieves and robbers. We identify ourselves first this time to offset any suspicion because of the experience in the village of Meroth. The people here are friendly after the women engage in conversation.

A funeral ritual is in progress. Mourners are gathered around a simple wooden coffin and are placing things inside it.

Mariam asks one of the bystanders what they are doing, and he explains, "They are placing dishes of the dead person's favorite food."

"Why?"

"To make sure he does not go hungry on the long journey to meet the ancestors. If he gets hungry, he will come back looking for food. He is also given other things like coins, ointment for the skin, bracelets, pins, necklaces and jars containing oil and wine. These are the grave goods, all of which he could make use of and ensure that he is not disturbed so that his soul can properly be sent to the afterlife."

"And what is he doing?"

"He is the father of the dead person. Watch."

The father takes a sharp knife and makes a small cut on his forearm and let the blood drip into the coffin. Then he makes a small incision on his face. After that he makes the same cuts on the corpse.

"What is the meaning of that?" asked Miriamne.

"That is an ancient custom, but we do it on a small scale, symbolically. When Baal died his father El came down from heaven and made cuts in his flesh and face. This is to assist in the passage to the realm of the dead. No one must interrupt this ritual."

Mariam turns and looks at me. "This is their concept of Olam HaEmet," I tell her.

After the funeral, the village elder by the name of Aharon then comes out and asks some questions and the purpose of our visit. I put them at ease.

"We are Yehudim travelling north, and we intend to cross the border of Hagalil Ha'elion into foreign land. You speak good Aramaic. Are you Yehudi?" I ask.

"Yes, I am Yehudi and my friends here," pointing to the other elderly men and women, "they are Kenaani."

One of them, by the name of Kilamawa, says, "You speak of foreign land beyond the border. We are very close to the border but actually we are not bothered about borders because over there they speak Ponnim which is another name for Kananim. We speak the same language, and we are the oldest people of this land until you people came to claim it. The Kenaani and the Yehudim live here happily now, and we have no problems."

"I understand the history and respect the fact that you live in harmony. But there are people in Yisra'el who will not agree with your view of the border. We are trying to get away from the Malka of Hagalil Ha'elion, Hordos Antipas," says Yeshua.

"Why? Are you criminals?" he asked.

"No, he is the criminal. He killed one of our leaders, Y'hochanan ha-mmatbil, who accused him of living with his brother's wife outside of marriage. Our moreh also speaks against wrongdoing and so that malka is after us too," adds Shemayon.

"We are only keeping out of his sight for a while until things calm down," say I.

"So, you are preachers of some kind, then," assumes Aharon.

"We talk about what people believe without forcing any doctrine on them," I explain.

"We live in developed towns, but we are an agricultural people. Our religion is based on the cycle of nature where life, be it in plant, animal, or human, keeps going around, renewing itself," says Kilamawa.

After talking for some time, we are allowed to pitch out tent and spend the night here.

While we eat Marta says, "Moreh, you were very silent during the funeral ritual earlier. What do you make of it?"

"I did not want to interrupt their ritual. It is very sacred to them just as our funeral rites are to us. In the early days, apart from grave goods, they were known to have offered human sacrifices of little children. Obviously, they no longer do that. We should not be surprised because we too did similar things in the past.

"As I said earlier the Yavan influence remains strong among the people. They too have their hierarchy of gods, and their lives are governed by the will of the gods. Their El is Zeus. Death comes when it is fated. So, the Yavan do not really fear death but embrace it because it is the gateway to the other world, the underworld which is ruled by the brother of Zeus called Hades. They also call gehanna, hades. Upon entering the underworld, the soul has to cross the river Styx on a ferry to enter the final resting place.

"The placing of coins in the coffin probably comes from the Yavan burial custom. They place coins in the dead person's mouth and tie a strap around the head and jaw to keep the mouth closed. These coins are to be used as the toll for the ferry across the river.

Gods are believed to live in another parallel world and the human soul can go to the place of the gods, a place of paradise — shamayin — where the ancestors are. So, the reason for placing all the grave goods in the coffin is to facilitate the passage of the soul to the other world.

Our concept of Olam HaMet is different. We are saying that these people will be denied the Olam HaEmet. We talk of the Olam HaEmet as though we know all about it. We know nothing about it. We claim to be holier than they are. This is self-tsedek. This path of religion only divides the people. My message is 'do not judge' them. Let us approach them with an open heart. There is sickness in their society too as there is in ours. My message is to bring healing to the whole of society, not only to the Yehudim. There are rich people in the structure of every society that deprive the poor of a fair share in the commonwealth. The poor cannot wait for the afterlife to have a share in that wealth. They need it here and now before they die.

"Death is, nevertheless, a fearful thing and always a sad reality. Every living creature has a beginning and an end, be it a plant, an animal or us. Because we can think and reflect, we become fearful of our death. Because it is difficult to accept it, we look for an answer.

"We look for an answer because we don't want our life to end with nothing. We want to continue to live on in some form in another world after we have left this one. We hunger for answers. If you can provide an answer that there is a spirit or a soul within you that cannot die and will live on, or if you can establish a resurrection to life, you can command a great following. If you can get people to believe it, you can become powerful.

"The teachers of religion are powerful because they have been able to create a space or place beyond this world where the soul can migrate to.

"Those who propose this doctrine place a condition that you must please the gods first before they can accept you into their domain. How do you please the gods? The conditions are laid out in the Law and Commandments just like in Yahadut, the Covenant of Elahh.

"The scribes of religion have very cleverly worked all this out in detail to make it easy for you but also to put fear into you that if you disobey the commandments, you will not be admitted into shamayin. So, they created another place called gehanna, a frightful place imaginable with the worst kind of suffering we can experience.

"You see, there is no great elaborations about shamayin, but there are detailed descriptions of gehanna. Apart from the pleasures of the flesh, we don't know what Elahh's domain is like, we don't even know what Elahh is like. We say that bliss is perfect happiness, what is that? On the other hand, we know all kinds of human suffering and the worst kind will be in gehanna.

"Religious leaders and prophets assume the authority they claim is entrusted to them by Elahh or the Elohim. People who accept this become followers of a religion and every religion claims to have the right path to shamayin.

"They also say that on the last day your soul will be reunited with your body which will be resurrected. The last day is to be the end of the world. What is the point of returning to life when there is no world left?"

"Are you saying that shamayin and gehanna do not exist at all?" asks Ya'aqov.

"Who knows if they exist? What evidence is there that they exist? It is just allaying our fear of death with a hope to make us feel good. As I said earlier, everything has a beginning and an end and there is no

275

more. The fear is real because parting is sad. We have no control over that. Why look for Olam HaEmet outside of our world? It is a creation in our imagination and so is shamayin and gehanna. Everything we need is here in this world."

"Yahadut, with its covenants, laws and rules, pretends to provide a secure basis for our belief. Follow the law and you will have Olam HaEmet. If we dare to venture out of these secure boundaries, we enter the area of unknown waters like what we are doing now, wandering without clearly knowing the path we are taking except that we are pursuing tsedek. The new areas we are walking into are nature, the environment and society with no ultimate purpose to existence other than what we have here.

"The world is indeed beautiful. We are all in this world together and therefore we are all responsible for our common fate, the fate of all life forms of adamah. The sickness, disease, illness or destruction of any part of the adamah affects all other parts because we are all connected. The quality of life here is more important than dreaming of Olam HaEmet.

"In these territories beyond Yisra'el all the gods are named after the different toqephs of Nature. So, the God of all gods can be summed up as the god of nature. If you want to give that God a name like Elahh, then Nature itself is Elahh. So, why is there a need for Olam HaEmet outside of our world?"

We will never rest secure in a comfortable interpretation of existence. We are overwhelmed by existence itself. The vastness of possibilities in nature makes us wonder knowing that we comprehend only a fraction of what might be known and realize that it is ongoing whether there is an end to it or not.

"Existence is always bubbling, it is a work in perpetual progress, and we are all part of it, connected to its dynamism. That makes us wonder in amazement. The knowledge that there is no other more grandiose world awaiting us in a life hereafter makes us all the more appreciative of the Adamah, and the paramount and urgent need to preserve it and all life in it. The security and serenity come not by knowing hidden mysteries from the past or the present but from watching nature's rhythms here and now. Let the ruach in you blow across the world through the hearts and minds of all people to wake up to the fact that this world is all that we have, and we are all that we have. For each of us life is a short time, far too short to live with enemies or in oppression. We have to contribute to building the adamah, to enjoy it and leave it better than we found it."

The tranquility of the place prompts me to say, "What paradise do our religious leaders talk about in the Olam HaEmet when we have this most beautiful place on earth. Here is something we can see, smell and breathe, hear and touch, and even taste. I tell you there is no Olam HaEmet, not even in the wildest of imagination. It is like dangling a carrot on a stick before the mule. The harder it tries; it can get no closer to it. We should live a life of fullness by becoming one with nature."

"If there is no Olam HaEmet then why do we have the Beit HaMikdash, the Holy Book and the covenants and the promise of Elahh and reward of a good life?" questions Y'hochanan.

"Y'hochanan, they have all been written and spoken so that the people may live rightly and honestly and not do wrong for fear of punishment. Must we do the right thing out of fear of punishment or even out of a desire for paradise? Reward and satisfaction are found in doing good for goodness' sake. The reward is living in peace and happiness. Let us use all the toqeph that is within us to make this happen and not waste our toqeph in building temples and creating gods and dividing people by saying that my god is better, higher and more powerful than yours. We should just stop talking about gods," I reiterate strongly.

"You see there is no need for us to be suspended between this world and Olam HaEmet. If we believe strongly that this world is all we have and will ever have, we can focus all our attention on doing good in this world and we will be liberated from the fear of eternal punishment and the anxiety of not measuring up to the merits of deserving a reward. As Yahudim we sometimes think that simply being the children of Avraham means we will inherit Olam HaEmet. Even these stones are worth more than the sons of Avraham for they belong to the earth," say I.

Scenatio 37 - Mother Goddess

Gush Halav

A woman sees the mule and says, "If you have come to buy oil you are early. We will start producing the oil after the harvest and it will take two to three months before the oil is ready."

"We are not merchants, we are just travellers," says Mariam. She looks at the basket almost full of olives in various shades of colour from purplish red to pink and blue and of various shades of green and even grey, and asks, "Are all these olives ripe?"

"No, they are in different stages of ripeness. The really ripe ones we eat and the others we use to make oil." She picks a ripe olive, wipes the thin white coating of natural yeast on it and offers it to Mariam. "Taste it," she says.

Maryam takes a bite of the juicy fruit. "Lovely," she says, and offered the rest to Shoshanna.

"You go on to the village and we will come later with the fruit, and I will show you the mill where we make the oil. We will sort out the fruit and start making the oil immediately because the fruit cannot keep long," says the woman.

"You have come at the right time. It is the olive harvest and tonight we will have a ritual. We would like to invite you all for it," says

Aharon.

My followers are beginning to feel uneasy because the customs and practices of the Kenaani are condemned and forbidden by the Mosaic Law.

Aware of their feelings I say, "We will be happy to attend."

The men and women from the fields bring in their baskets of freshly harvested olives. They are all unloaded on the floor and the women separate the ripe ones from the not so ripe ones.

One of the women says, "Once the fruit leaves the tree it begins to ripen very fast and can go bad quickly. That is why we have to start processing it before the sun goes down."

Mariam and the women join the women in separating the olives from the leaves, stems, twigs and grit while the men talk among themselves. The fruit are then put into a cistern filled with water. Everyone dips their hands washing the fruit.

The woman whom they met in the field whose name is Naomi points to a large circular granite stone flat on top with a routed recess. In the centre is a small pillar. In the recessed groove between the small pillar and the lip around the edge stands another round granite stone like a wheel with a hole in the centre. With a stick through the hole, this upright stone could be rolled in the groove around the pillar.

"This is *Gat Shemen*, the oil press or oil mill. Bring the fruit," she says.

Handfuls of olives are scattered along the groove and the stone is rolled. Both the fruit and its stone are crushed by the rolling stone. Arsinoe helps to roll the stone. When they are smashed to pulp, the paste is gathered in a container.

"Our parents used to tread the olives with their feet. It was a very painful process," says one of the women.

"That doesn't look like oil," remarks Joa'ana.

"Not yet," corrects Naomi, "the process has just begun. We keep doing this until we have a large quantity." She empties the contents into a big pot over a slow fire while other women tend the fire and slowly stir the paste with a wooden ladle. The men come to watch.

"You see, the fruit contains juice, which is water but there is also oil. As the paste gets warm you can see the tiny yellow drops. That is oil. These drops join together and become bigger drops. The next step is to separate the liquid from the paste. And this is how we do it," explains Naomi.

Some men have prepared strips of mat made with long grass. The men take over the job from the women. They spread the warm paste over the mats, roll and squeeze them until the liquid, both oil and water drip into another container. When allowed to settle the oil rises to the surface. This is *sheh-mehn zah-yeet*, oil of the olive.

"Now I smell the olive oil," says Mariam.

Aharon, the elder, leads the visitors to an old olive tree and beside it is a stout pole also made of olive wood. Kilamawa explains, "We will have a thanksgiving tonight," he said.

"We give thanks to our Mother Goddess for a plentiful harvest. We have had good olives this season."

"Who is Mother Goddess?" asks Arsinoe.

"She is *Asherah*, the Mother of Fertility. This pole represents her, and she nourishes the fruit of her womb with an abundance of milk from her breasts. Last winter we offered her a sacrifice by cooking a kid in the milk of its mother. Tonight, we dance with joy for a fruitful harvest. It is like a marriage ceremony when the Lord Baal mates with the Goddess Asherah. Baal is the son of El or Elahh, as you call him; he is the god who overcame the god of the sea, the god of storms, of rain, thunder and lightning, and the god of death. He has the power over rain, clouds and wind. He returns from the land of death bringing the rain to fertilise the earth, which is the Mother

Goddess Asherah. Together they revitalise the forces of nature as we cultivate the land," explained Kilamawa.

"Is it true that you or your priests actually perform the sexual act during the ceremony and offer children as sacrifice?" asks Yehudah.

"In the ancient days of our ancestors, I believe it was done, not here but in Bavel. We are concerned with the fertility of the crops, our flocks and humans, and the gods provide assurance of all these things. It was said that sacred sex was performed in the temples like sacred magic to ensure the fertility of the land and the womb. We no longer do that. What we do is symbolic to please the gods," responded Kilamawa.

Shimon turning to Aharon asked, "Do you as a Yehudi also participate in this ceremony?"

"Why, yes, we do, and we have no problem. It is the most natural thing to do."

I am listening quietly, then enter the conversation. "Please don't be offended by the questions my friends are asking. You see, we, the Yehudim in the south have been taught to condemn your religious practices. We are even told that Baal is Ba'al HaZvuv, one of the fallen angels of satana. I would like to remind my own followers and all of us here that the Lord Baal and the Mother Goddess Asherah are not strangers to Yisra'el. Our famous Malka Sh'lomoh loved many foreign women. He had 700 wives and 300 concubines. Malka Sh'lomoh became a follower of the Goddess Asherah whom he brought into the Mamlekhet Yisra'el.

"Manasseh, the malka of Yehuda, developed the olive oil trade by producing and exporting olive oil but he also built altars to the foreign gods and even installed the Asherah pole in the Beit HaMikdash.

"Jezebel, the wife of Malka Ahab of Yisra'el Ha'elion, was the daughter of Ethbaal, the Kenaani Malka of Tyre. She promoted the Asherah worship and entertained 400 prophets of Asherah paid by the royal palace. Of course, they were condemned by other prophets and kings. I think what sib Aharon said is very important, that this is the most natural thing to do. We should focus on that rather than on the hierarchy of gods and goddesses.

"We have almost forgotten that the gods and goddesses are only mere representations of the forces, the toqeph of nature. The Father God became more important than the Mother Goddess but tonight when you are going to dance to the Mother Goddess, you are honouring the earth. We should honour the earth with great respect. We should also honour the sun but not as the sun god. I know that you also consider Asherah as the moon goddess and the consort of Baal as the sun god. The moon reflects the light of the sun shedding light on the dark earth. We should rather see the toqeph of the sun that causes the productivity of the crops and the livestock and makes the earth fertile.

"You went through the meticulous process of extracting oil from the olives. Your process was like a ritual, but your purpose was to get the pure oil, the essence of the fruit. Religion has been built up with many rituals depicting battles in the heavens between the gods of thunder and rain and storms, but the essence of it all is Mother Earth with all the natural phenomena surrounding our life on earth. There is no life that we know beyond the earth. That is why I say we should focus on the words of sib Aharon that it is the natural thing to do. I will be happy to join you all in the singing and dancing to share the joy of the olive harvest, the olive oil, the food and other products of Mother Earth.

They prepare for the thanksgiving festival with special loaves called the Asherah bread, dancing robes, incense for burning and oil lamps using olive oil. They carry all these and climb the hill, the high place for the ceremony.

At the foot of an olive tree, they set up an altar on which they place a thurible of fire, the loaves and goblets of drink offerings together with bronze statuettes and nude clay figurines of goddesses, vessels of oil, wine, salt, cloth, incense, stones and metal. There is also cooked meat.

When the moon is full in the night sky the elders, both Kilamawa and Aharon start chanting while a woman puts incense into the thurible and other women light the votive lamps around the altar with olive oil. As the fragrant smoke fills the air, Kilamawa invokes the goddess in prayer saying that the flames are sacred sparks that only she could light. Aharon follows by saying, 'You light the flame every time you treat nature with care and respect'. Kilamawa adds, 'You light these flames when you honour the Goddess with your actions.' Aharon addresses the goddess as the true fertility goddess, the force of nature and life that she manifests in domestic herds and flocks, groves of trees and nurturing waters. Finally, Kilamawa invokes the goddess's power and presence not only for planting but also childbirth.

Then, amidst singing and dancing, they share the bread and meat and drinks.

We see with completely new eyes the beauty of this ceremony which is outrightly condemned by our religious teachers.

I speak and the people listen. "Neither I nor my friends would have thought, in our wildest dreams, that we would be sitting and eating with you people and witnessing this ritual to your Goddess. We have been taught by the teachers of the Beit HaMikdash that we are to be holy as our Elahh is holy according to the Torah. Holiness is something set apart from all that is unholy or unclean. What we have done tonight would be considered unclean and unholy deserving the punishment of Elahh. Will Elahh punish us for what we have done? I don't think so.

"God as a woman is unthinkable yet we all have the greatest respect for the mother. What you have done tonight is to honour the power of Nature and refer to Nature as Mother, as Goddess. All the gods and goddesses are nothing more than names given to toqeph, the forces of nature. The mother of all these forces is the Earth itself.

"In terms of nature, God was the source of the river. Water gives life to everything living, so God was called the creator of the creatures and the father of all people. God or goddess, father or mother, it is nature that we honour.

"Let us not be too concerned about gods and goddesses, they are not real. The goodness of the earth is what is real. We don't have to offer sacrifices to the gods to placate them. We cannot influence the actions of the gods. We cannot stop the lightning and thunder in the heavens. The gods are not going to come down to consume the sacrifice. See, they remain untouched, and we are feasting on them. Sacrifices are a waste of good things, things like meat, grains, vegetables and fruits, these are things for us to enjoy. You have captured the toqeph of nature in the olive oil. You use the olive oil for many things besides lighting up the night. It also has the power of healing, so let us focus on the essence that is the toqeph of nature."

"Moreh Yeshua, what you have said makes sense, but it is difficult for us to disregard generations of tradition and culture," says Aharon.

"I agree that it is not easy, but we have to be born again, learn again, see again, and listen more to the voice of nature. Goodness is in the earth, the mother of all goodness," I assert.

That night before sleeping, my followers ponder what this new revelation means to their traditional understanding of holiness — as separating clean from unclean, purity from defilement, sacred from profane, righteousness from sinfulness, friend from enemy, and Jew from gentile — using the Torah to define opposites based on the fear of divine judgement and punishment. I have not only dispelled the prejudices of the Jews but also made the gentiles aware that they are also misguided in personifying the forces of nature into gods and goddesses. Both Jew and gentile are now opened to a new world vision. It comes as a culture shock.

The next morning, we say farewell to our friends both Yehudim and Kenaani and make our way towards Tyre.

Kilamawa tells us, "It is a long way before you cross the so-called border. You will have to climb to the highest point and then go downhill before you reach the coast."

Aharon says, "Go in shalama."

I say, "Shalama, tsedek and toqeph be with you."

We are well rested and refreshed and walk briskly. The terrain becomes rocky as we start to climb. The air becomes cooler. It is midday by the time we reach the highest point. We have climbed for almost five milin.

"I am told that this point is 1804 amot above the level of the sea," says Mattithyahu.

We stop and have some lunch. The view is stunning. Looking back, we can see Har Meron. To the east we see the Kanaan Mountains. Observing the ground, I find a broken corner of a cistern. I know all about cisterns, "People had lived here before."

Pilip finds the broken head of an axe and other bronze implements buried in the sand. We also find ancient tombs. We rest and continue climbing downhill this time. It is much easier going than imagined, and we have covered about six and a half milin when we come to level ground with a mountain spring. We decide to camp there for the night. This area too had been an ancient settlement. We scout around and Yaʿakov says there could be wild dogs because he found dog faeces. We pitch the tent, light the fire, and prepare the meal.

As usual the perplexed followers are full of questions.

Marta confesses, "Moreh, we are no longer the same anymore. Your teaching has deviated so much from Yahadut and as your followers we will be rejected by the Yehudim. I don't know how we can face them when we go back."

"I'm glad to hear that you have changed. It took me a long time, thinking deeply upon the scriptures. There are many principles in the scriptures about doing good and not evil. However, the way they are interpreted and applied is wrong. We do not need a heavenly watchman to tell us what to do. To know something of our past will make us understand better the cultural and religious bind we are in.

I remind them of the history of the Yavan and Kittim culture imposed on us ....

"For the purpose of preserving our identity, our leaders have used religion and the idea of holiness to separate us from the others. That is not the way. We must break out of that structure to live in peace with other people. This is going to be the hardest thing for us to do."

"Moreh, can you tell us more about how all these stories of gods and goddesses began and why is it we, Yehudim, maintain Elahh as the one and only God?" asks Mariam.

"I have explained this but why do you still find it difficult to understand?

"This whole area beyond the border of HaGalil that we call Knaan was generally written as *Khna,* which was later called Phoenix, and the area we are going to visit is called Phoenicia in Yavan. The writing of symbols representing sounds began here in Knaan and our language, Aramaic, also has its source in this script. We can read the ancient scripts.

"What about our people?" asked Shemayon.

"Our people, the *Ivrim*[204], had no distinctive origin. In the Torah, the word Ivrim was '*Apiru*' referring to a 'people from across the river'. It also refers to the Hyksos slaves. They were a loose group of

---

[204] Hebrews

nomadic tribes wandering in the desert. Only after they encountered foreign influences and beginning with the Egyptian bondage, did they begin to aspire to acquire some identity of their own and to become a people. It became the task of writers then to create an origin and link it to the very beginning of creation. So, our people began to tell our story.

"Our people, the Yehudim, lived in small villages in this hill country of Knaan sharing the land and different cultures and even religions. We have seen that for ourselves. Tomorrow we will be moving into land that may not be friendly at all towards us.

"My friend, Barachiah has told us that after we cross the border, we will come to the village of Qana. Let us see what the people there are like before we hit Tyre," says Mattithyahu.

Scenario 38 - Yamm

Qana

Qana sits on the escarpment in the rolling hills of Phoenicia, which is a Yavan name but the people there are also Kanaani. We travel about 11 milin and cross the border where there is no clear demarcation. As we approach the village, we see several caves dug into huge rocks.

We are confirmed strangers when the dogs begin barking at us. We walk by some giant oaks among fig trees into an olive grove. Some people at a water spring pick up sticks and stand up prepared for any unfriendly encounter.

Again, the women, Mariam and Marta, go forward and greet them with shalama. The usual questions are asked and answered. When they relax, Mariam requests some water. The men hesitate but the women offer the water. "You can take the water."

The water is very cold. There is deep water at the foot of a waterfall and a fast-flowing stream. We fill our skins at the water's edge while Shemayon leads the mule downstream.

"This is very good spring water. Thank you," say I.

The women wash clothes while small children play about. They ask one of the young men to lead us into the village to meet the elders who come out to meet us.

Contrary to our expectations, the villagers are not hostile. One of the women asks them, "What are you selling?" Occasionally some merchants come up from the coastal towns to sell goods.

"We are not selling anything. We are on our way to the town of Tyre," responds Mattithyahu.

"Where do you come from?"

"We are from Hagalil, from Yam Chinneroth."

"You Yehudim are not welcome here especially those who come to preach to us," says an older man.

"We come in shalama; we are fisherfolk. We have not come to preach," I say.

"We will be grateful for your hospitality if we can spend the night here. We could pitch our tent outside the village," says Ya'aqov, and looking at me adds, "Is that alright, Moreh?"

"Moreh!" exclaims the older man, "you are a teacher, and you say you do not come to preach. Are you deceiving us?"

"I am a moreh, but we are not here to preach to you. In fact, we want to learn from you about your beliefs," I clarify.

"We know all about Yahadut. You are not tolerant people. You consider us as goyim and sinners. That and all the bad things you did to our people in the past is why you are not welcome here."

They are interrupted by a commotion at the spring. Some people are shouting and running towards to village gate while others are carrying a boy and rushing.

"What happened?" asks the elder.

"Yassib fell into the water. We pulled him out. He is not breathing," they say.

They bring the lifeless body of a nine-year-old boy and put him on the ground.

I take one look at the boy and say, "Quick, remove his clothes."

Without thinking or questioning they remove his wet clothes. I take off my outer garment and spread it on the ground, carry the boy, lay him down and wrap it around him. I immediately throw himself on the boy, my adult body putting pressure on the boy and at the same time warming him up.

The elder shouts, "Hey, what are you doing? Get away from the boy."

Mariam reassures, "Please, let him. Our moreh is a healer."

"But the boy is already dead," says the man.

The boy's mother comes, shouting the boy's name and wailing, "Yassib, please don't die."

I keep throwing himself on the boy saying to the others, "Rub his hands and legs. Salt, salt, bring some salt."

They bring salt and dipping my finger in the jar, I rub the salt into the boy's mouth. I put my own mouth on the boy's mouth and transfer some of my spittle. Not knowing what to do, everyone just watch. Once again, I push the whole weight of my body onto the boy and hold him tight. The boy coughs. I turn the boy over, hold him at the stomach and shake him. Some water comes out of his mouth and nostrils. Making him sit, I say, "Squeeze a lemon into some water and give it to him to drink." The boy is alive.

The mother embraces Yassib and cries. No one says anything. I gather my garment, dust it and put it on. The atmosphere has changed, and everyone looks at me with awe and respect.

"How long was he in the water?" I ask.

"Not long. We see him being carried away by the current. We jump in and pull him out," says one of the young men.

"It is good that you brought him quickly," I say.

"You people can camp outside the village," grants the elder.

"No," said the boy's mother. "You brought my dead Yassib to life. All of you will stay in my house."

"There are many of us," says Shemayon.

"There is room in my house," says another woman.

"And my house, you are welcome here," says yet another woman.

The boy feels better after drinking the lemon water. They take him home and ask us all to come. Different families are preparing food for us. After a simple meal of bread and olive oil with locally grown fruit and vegetable, we all gathered around talking while Yassib is asleep. The conversation centres around what happened that day.

"Are you a magician with power over life and death?" asks a man.

"No, I am not a magician. I have learnt some methods of healing. We can all learn such methods and know what to do."

One of them says, "We did not honour *Yamm* this year with flowers. That has made him angry. That is why he wanted to claim Yassib."

"Who is Yamm?" asks Y'hochanan.

"Yamm is the god of the rivers,"

"We call Chinneroth yam. Yam is water or sea or lake," says Natan'el.

"So, you have named your lake after our god Yamm."

"We know that our Yam Chinneroth or your yam the spring water exists, but we don't know of Yamm as a god who exists," says Miriamne.

"Maybe that is how Yam Chinneroth got its name after the god Yamm. Yamm is the name given to the power of the sea. That raging power or toqeph can bring storms and wreck disasters. It is indeed a fearful thing. That toqeph is real, whatever name we use to call it. Because we are afraid of its power, we pay homage to a god to keep us safe. If you drop something into the deep water, it is the nature of the water to swallow it up unless it is something that floats or if you are a strong swimmer. Yassib is a small boy and not a strong swimmer. The water does what it is supposed to do. Whether you had offered flowers or not to Yamm, the water would have acted the same way. There is no god who wants to claim him, and we cannot change nature from doing what it does. We must respect the power or the toqeph of the water. We need it for our life and respect its power," I explain.

Mariam and Marta spend the night in Yassib's home while the others sleep in different houses. The next morning, I sit with Yassib and speak to him. He is feeling alright after a good night's sleep.

We get ready to leave. The elder and the people of the village accompany us to the village gate. Just outside the gate is a cenotaph cut into the rock. Yehudah asks the elder about it. The elder explains, "This is a memorial dedicated to the Malka Hiram, the great malka of Tyre. That was the time when the people of that city enjoyed good relations with your malke. The people of Tyre will tell you more about that."

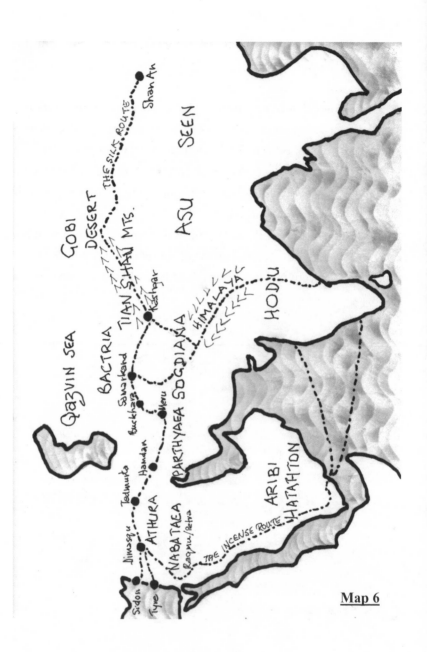

Map 6

Scenario 39 - Silk Route

Tyre

Descending the hill slope, we approach the coast. Tyre is less than 10 milin away and after walking for an hour we can see the sea in the distance. Soon the city comes into view.

From the knowledge I gained in Qumran I provide some introduction, "According to the Mikra, which is a collection of ancient Yehudi texts, Jezebel, was a princess and daughter of Ithobaaal, malka of Tyre and Sidon. She became the wife of Ahab, the malka of Yisra'el. She had incited the people to abandon the worship of Elahh in favour of the god Baal and the goddess Asherah. The Yehudim then attacked the people and punished Jezebel. This is the memory that some people could still have against us. But generally, the invasion of Aba Moshe and Yehoshua of Kenaan did not make an impact on the coastal cities.

"The people of this city of Tyre have lived through many civilisations and have a wide experience of culture, religion and language. We should be able to learn a lot from them."

We simple country folk, are overawed by the magnificence of this city. We walk through an ornate necropolis with huge tombs of the Kittim. Walking on paved roads we admire the monuments and aqueducts. Nobody takes any notice of us unlike the reception we got from the villages along the way.

We stop to rest at the huge hippodrome, a stadium for horse and chariot racing, the Kittim had built. This old Yavan city was destroyed and rebuilt by them. We continue walking along the colonnaded streets under a triumphal arch along the extended aqueduct, and after passing a public bathhouse we come to the marketplace.

People are busy buying and selling all sorts of goods. On display are merchandise from foreign lands like perfume, spices, incense, and local products like cloth of different colours. Seafood stalls are decked with all sorts of fish, crabs, prawns, lobsters that in Yisra'el would have been considered unclean. There are no religious authorities enforcing religious rules and regulations.

The money here is not very different from that in HaGalil — brass, bronze and silver coins. The *drachma*[205], *denarius*[206] and the *shekel*[207] are silver coins. The lower denominations are in bronze or copper. The most common is the shekel or the *stater*[208] minted in Tyre itself. We can buy goods with our own money.

We buy citrous fruits, mangoes, dried fish and bread. We wait while the flat rice bread is cooked on a large cast iron skillet on firewood. Yehudah counts the coins and pays for the food. We continue walking along the causeway towards what was once the island of Tyre.

The view from the harbour on the north side of the island is amazing. All of us, especially the fishermen, Shemayon, Andreias, Ya'aqov and Yhochanan are astounded by the size and number of boats in the harbour. Their boats on Yam Chinneroth are nothing in

[205] A Greek silver coin worth a denarius

[206] The Roman silver coin equal to a drachma

[207] Hebrew silver coin equal to about three drachma/denarius

[208] An ancient Greek weight unit

comparison to these huge, magnificent boats of superior technology.

Seeing their awestruck faces staring at the ships, one of the fishermen drying their nets on the rocks asks them, "You all are not from here, are you? Where do you come from?"

Shemayon answers, "We are from HaGalil. Do you go fishing in those ships?" pointing to the big ones.

"No, no. Those big, long ships are gallies. They are warships. Although they have sails, they are propelled by rowing. You see, they have two decks of oars on each side with 120 rowers. The hull is long and slender and can move very fast. These ships were invented by us. Our men build the ships, but the Kittim own and control them."

"Those other big ships?" asks Y'hochanan.

"They are merchant vessels. They are broad and round like tubs to carry a lot of goods. They are impelled by both oar and sails. There is only one mast and one sail in the middle of the ship. With strong winds the merchant captain uses the sail. When the winds die away or change direction, he drops the sail on the deck and gets his men to use the oars."

"What do you fishermen use?" asks Andreias.

"Our ships are almost like the merchant ships, but smaller. There they are," he points to some boats on the shore. "They have no beak, a small mast with a cross bar that carries the sail which we manage with ropes.

"How often do you go out to catch fish?" asks Shemayon.

"Almost every night except when Yamm is angry, and the weather is very bad."

"We are fishermen from yam Chinneroth in HaGalil. Can we go on a fishing trip with you? We can help with the net and manage the ship," asks Shemayon.

"You can ask the boss. We often hire extra hands," says the fisherman.

Shemayon turned to me and the others, "I want to go on a fishing trip with them."

Andreia, Ya'aqov and Yhochanan say they wanted to go too. The others are not keen. Shemayon asks the fisherman to take them to his boss.

"These are experienced fishermen from Yam Chinneroth. They want to go fishing," says the fisherman whose name is Alyun.

"Do you need extra hands?" asks the boss.

"Yes."

"How many?"

"I can take two on my boat and Matac can take two more."

"Alright, write their names in the register. One *denarius* for one trip," says the boss.

"Alright with you? Four of you be on the beach at the tenth hour. We have to load the nets and other things and be in the water before sunset. We will only return to land the next morning," says Alyun.

When the four of them meet the rest, they find us engaged in conversation with some local people who are explaining the huge gathering of people along the beachfront. They say, "The Silk Road Orechah has arrived. You can find traders from foreign lands. You find them haggling over goods that they barter. They exchange goods wholesale and what our local merchants can get they sell to the retailers who then take them to the bazaar for sale."

There are tents all along the beach and behind them is the orechah-serai consisting of lodging houses and open yards for the animals, mainly camels with hay and water provided.

"We should meet these people," say I.

"But first, we need to find a place to stay," says Mariam. Turning to one of the locals she asks, "Is there some place we can stay?"

"The lodging houses cater for many people, but they are somewhat rough and ragged. There are also several inns in the town and about this time most of them will be fully booked," says one of them.

Shemayon says, "Andreia, Ya'aqov, Y'hochanan and I are going fishing tonight. We do not need a place to stay, at least for tonight. We will be back in the morning."

"I know something about the orechah traders, and they can get rough and unruly especially when they have been drinking," says Mattithyahu.

"We don't mind staying in the lodge," says Yehudah.

"I don't think the women should stay there. Let us go and find a place in one of the inns run by a family," I suggest.

"I have a family friend who uses her house as an inn, come," invites one of the local women.

"The women and I will go and find the inn. You all go to the lodges," says Mariam.

"Let us meet back here in the same place," I say.

"We, four of us, will find something to eat before we go fishing," says Shemayon.

We parted company.

The women find the family and negotiate the price. Since they are not from the *orechah* traders but from HaGalil, the householder lowers the cost. They are given a large room to share without too much privacy. There are no doors, but mere drapes and children are running in and out. They have to sleep on the floor but feel safe here. Such an inn as this is called a *ksenia*, a Yavan name. One of the spoken languages in Tyre is Yavan or Hellenic.

We men go to the lodging houses. We come to a stretch of lodging quarters containing rooms of varying sizes. The men from the different regions group together remaining close to their goods and camels. There are women in some of the groups. We find a smaller place called a *kataluma*, also a Yavan word meaning 'to unharness' denoting a place to bed the animals for the night as well as a place for people to sleep. We unloose the mule and make ourselves comfortable after negotiating a price for the lodging.

I ask the innkeeper where the travellers come from.

The innkeeper, Baraket, who has been hosting travellers for a long time sits us down. He has stories to tell.

"We have seen all kinds of people come through here from far and near, from land and sea. Many land routes from different countries crisscross and meet at important cities where goods are exchanged. The path of the trade orechahs cross Seen, through the Gobi Desert, over the Tian Shan Mountains and across the grasslands of *Asu*[209].

They travel west and eventually reach Tyre. The route starts in the town of Shang An in Seen. They travel overland and harsh snow mountains to Seen's western border town of Kashgar. Goods from Hodu in the south also end up there. The road moves into central Asu at *Samarkand*[210] for more merchandise and then to Bukhara, Merv, and Hamadan. They are all ancient cities of the great Malka Koresh of Parthyaea. The route continues to Tedmurta and Dimashqu in Athura before reaching Tyre. The Seen people from Shang An are known as Han, and the Kashgar people are the Uyghur. Those from Samarkand are called Sogdians and the others are from Athura and Arabi.

"They bring merchandise from their native lands. The most precious and highly priced item is silk from Seen. It is worth its weight in gold. Not all the merchants travel the whole route although some do. The goods travel all the way in all directions. So, we have a mixture of all kinds of goods and people here. The exchange is not only of merchandise but also people with different cultures, ideas

---

[209] Asia (Phoenician for 'east'), land of the sunrise

[210] previously one of the greatest cities of Central Asia, now the third largest city in Uzbekistan

and knowledge of arts, craft and music. Merchants bring goods while missionaries bring religion."

"What are these people like? I would like to meet them," say I.

"Ah, but they may not like to meet you. They keep to themselves when they are not meeting to haggle over their goods. Often enough they fight over the price of goods and even kill. They are a rough and unruly lot. They are hardened by their travel over long distances through difficult terrain and harsh weather conditions. Of course, all for a good bargain. If they don't get what they want, they get angry and are prepared to kill. You be careful if you want to meet them."

"Can you point out to us the lodges where the different groups of people are staying? And what is the best time to approach them?" I ask.

"I would not advise you on meeting them. But if you insist the best time is before the evening meal. They would be back from trading and getting ready for the night. During the night, they gather at the tavern or by the open fire. They drink and play with the women and often fight. Don't go near them at that time."

"Thank you for the advice," says Shimon.

"By the way, another group has also arrived with them on the Silk Road. They are not merchants. They call themselves the followers of the 'Enlightened One'. They are on their way to Mitzrayim. They have come all the way from Seen."

"Oh, I know, they are the followers of the Buddha. I have met some of those people before. I would surely like to meet them," say I.

As we walked around the orechahserai, Baraket points out the lodges where the people from the different regions stay.

We all gather again at the meeting place. The women explain their lodging; we point to our lodge at the far eastern end of the orechahserai. The four fishermen, before they went off to the boats recommended a good place to eat along the harbour. We find the place selling food on the roadside. We choose a Levantine Arab food of hummus with tahini. Hummus is made from mashed chickpeas and blended with tahini — grounded sesame seeds — olive oil, lemon juice, salt and garlic. We supplement that with spicy meat in wraps. It is a different cuisine from what we are used to.

It was afternoon and I tell the others, "I would like to meet some of the foreigners at the lodge. It is no use going to the trading centres because they will be doing wholesale marketing. You can either go the bazaar or come with me."

"We can go to the bazaar tomorrow. We will go with you," says Mariam. The others are easy with that.

Scenario 40 - Incense Route

Tyre

Incense Route

We walk to the Arab quarter. Two-humped camels are drinking water from cisterns beside the stables while some men are sitting outside the lodge entrance talking. They are talking in Aramaic striking a common note.

I approach one of the men. He is bearded, dressed in an embroidered robe wearing a white turban.

"Shalama aleikhem," I greet. The man responds, "Aleikham shalama. What are you selling and what do you seek?"

"We are not merchants. We are travellers from HagGalil," I say.

"You bring women. Are they for service?" asks another man.

"No, No. We would like to meet you and get to know about the land you come from. We don't meet many travellers in HaGalil. We seem to be speaking the same language," observes Mattithyahu.

"We are a group from Aribi[211] and we bring frankincense and myrrh from Aribi HaTahton by camel orechah along the Incense Route. My friends and I here are not from Aribi Ha Tahton. We come from the

[211] Arabia

303

stone city of Raqmu where several trade routes cross. We are people of Athura and Aramaic is our cultural language. The Aribi name for Athura is Nabataea and Raqmu is the centre of the Mamlekhet Nabataean. So, we bring more than frankincense and myrrh. We bring goods that come to our ports from Hodu and Seen like spices, gold, ivory, pearls, precious stones and textiles. When we trade, they go to other parts of the world."

"You must be very rich," remarks Pilip.

"That depends on how much profit we make."

"We read in our Mikra that Yôsēp̄, son of Yisra'el, was sold by his brothers to orechah merchants who took him to Mitzrayim. Another time we read about orechah merchants is when the *mahl-Kah* [212] of Sheba came to visit our Malka Sh'lomoh with a camel orechah of spices, gold and precious stones like what you are carrying," I say.

"Yes, we trade merchants have a long history. We are survivors and have experienced knowledge of the desert."

"Tell us about your city of Raqmu," asks Tauma.

"We are not only merchants but also expert stone cutters. Our city is carved into the mountains with houses, monuments and structures cut in stone. We have our own water supply via aqueducts. It is the trade centre between the East and the West. We have a population of 20,000 people."

"Do you also have temples and gods?" asks Natan'el.

"Everything is stone, even our god is stone. Our expert stonecutters have carved a whole hill into stone block and pillars. They are our gods and our temple."

"Do they have names?" asked Yehudah.

"Oh, yes. The main god is Dushara, Lord of the Mountain. There are also other gods like Al Qaum, Al Kutbay, Allat and Al Uzza. We

---

[212] Queen

only honour Al Qaum and are not bothered with the others because Al Qaum is the warrior god who guards the orechahs. When the Yavan came they tried to equate our gods to theirs and then Dushara was called Zeus."

"How do you honour your god, Al Qaum?" asks Natan'el.

"We offer sacrifices before we set out on our orechah. That is all, otherwise we are not great believers in gods. Our only interest is trade and best profits from our trade."

"Who worships the other gods?" asks Shimon.

People go on pilgrims to the local shrines like those in Mecca and Yathrib[213] where the other gods and goddesses are worshipped. In Mecca there is a cubic stone structure called the Ka'ba. It is a very rare black stone. Aba Avraham laid the foundations of the Ka'ba. There are also stone idols of the gods and goddesses there in the shrine."

"Are you not disturbed by the historical fact that your people were once subdued by our people?" I ask.

"What do you mean?"

"About 50 years ago, our malka, the great Hordos, with the help of Cleopatra, the mahl-Kah of Mitzrayim, attacked your people and occupied your land for some time," I relate.

"We are friends with anyone who is prepared to trade with us and are not concerned with the past. If you have come here to establish your superiority, you get lost before we beat you up," says the trader.

"Please do not misunderstand. We are not proud of our malka or our history. If you have no ill feelings about the past then you are better than we," say I.

Others come out of the lodge and say, "Come on, let's go; we're hungry."

They all march out towards the tavern.

---

[213] Medina

As his entourage moves on, I say "You see these people are different from those we met inland. These people have no grudge against us."

"That is because their only interest is trade," remarks Yehudah.

"Yes, these people are very focused on trade and nothing else matters. It is not the malke and mahl-Kah, malkut or mamlekhet, the empires, or rabbim and religious leaders, but people whose business is trade – these are the people who will control the world," I declare.

We come to the lodge where the merchants from Central Asu stay. Baraket pointed out their place earlier and said they were from Samarkand, in the region of Sogdiana in the land of the sunrise. We are curious and approach cautiously.

We hear them talking in a strange language and yet we can pick out certain Aramaic and Yavan words. From the clothes they are wearing they appear to be prosperous. The outer robe or tunic - the *kaftan* - is decorated with dotted fabric, made of wool, cashmere, silk, or cotton. They are fastened on the upper part of the breast and reach to the ankles. The horizontal edge is stitched on pleated hem. The sleeves are long and narrow. Some wear belts decorated with metal plates. They wear triangular shaped pointed shoes that look like they are cut from one piece of leather and stitched. Their complete outfit includes cone-shaped headdresses, and some wear white and others red, with curved daggers lodged in their belts. They are a colourful, dignified people who would wear different clothing when they travel.

These Sogdians, the greatest traders of the day, were the first to travel the whole distance of the land route. Their main trade traffic was from Samarkand in Sogdiana to Seen. Most merchants did not travel the entire Silk Road but would trade goods through middlemen in oasis towns along the route. Their language became the common language of the Silk Route, and they played a role in the cultural movements of art, philosophies, religion and culture.

When we approach them, they immediately become alert. This

was unusual because the local people do not approach them. Some of them go for their swords because they have precious merchandise to safeguard.

One of the young men steps forward and asks in the Yavan language, "What do you want? Have you come to trade?"

I respond in the same language but use the Aramaic greeting, "Shalama! We come from HaGalil. We are interested to know about you and the country you come from."

"We are not interested to talk. You can go back to where you came from."

"Wait," says a much older man. "Are there rich people in HaGalil?"

"Yes, there are, but not too many," say I.

"Your HaGalil is not on the main trade route."

"Yes. We do not meet many foreigners," says Natan'el.

"We can send our merchandise there if there are people who have enough money to buy and sell."

"I know of some orechahs that pass through HaGalil. They come there to acquire common goods but not the very expensive items you have," says Mattithyahu.

"You tell them to come and see me. We can make arrangements," says the older man.

"Why are your items so very expensive?" asks Pilip.

"They are precious and very rare, and they can only be acquired from distant lands. We take enormous risks to bring them. We have not only the weather to brave and the long distances but also wild beasts and bandits who try to rob us. You understand why we were on guard when you approached us."

"That is understandable, and you are providing a great service. But your merchandise only benefits the wealthy people," says Tauma.

"You are correct. The wealthy people are our market. We do not care for those who cannot afford our prices."

"I understand that your goods pass through several trading posts and change hands. Each time, I am sure, the price goes up and up. You have no local competitors and so you can call your price," questions Mattithyahu.

"Correct again. As long as there are people willing to pay, we will deliver. We bargain for the best profits. We also bring other products that are less precious like spices," says the merchant.

"These too are very expensive for the ordinary people. They also need some of these spices because they have medicinal values," I add.

"We sell to other merchants who have their own retailers through whom they reach the markets."

"Perhaps if you choose to make lesser profits on these, the poor can afford to buy them,"

"Ah, I'm sorry. We negotiate for the best price. We are not almsgivers."

There are books and ledgers on the table with writings on the covers. They are in Aramaic alphabet. I read them aloud.

"You write in Aramaic, but you don't speak it," I observe.

"We speak Sogdiana. The language is similar to Parthyaea. Our writing is Aramaic. Sogdiana is and always has been the common language of the Silk Road although now everybody also speaks Yavan.

"Tell us about your country," asks Shimon.

"Our people are farmers and merchants. Our farmland is surrounded by Seen to the east, Hodu to the south, and the Steppes to the north. Samarkand is the oldest city in Sogdiana. Through our trade from the centre of Asu we have access to all the main regions and peoples. We are the people who have connected the East to the West.

"Besides your costly merchandise, you also bring new ideas and cultures and religions. What religion do you practise?" I ask.

"Please don't ask us to explain religion. We are businesspeople, we contribute to the religions, but we are not religious people. Usually, some religious people join our orechahs. There is a group of Buddhists who have come with us. They are from Seen. If you want to discuss religion, talk to them. They are at the far end of the orechahserai," says the merchant and they also get ready to leave for the tavern.

Scenario 41 - Followers of the Enlightened One

Tyre

"Shall we go and meet the Buddhists? I'm sure they will not be going to the tavern," I tell my followers.

We find them just finishing their evening prayers and getting ready for dinner in their quarters. I approach them with 'shalama'.

After the introductory exchange of identification details, the Buddhists graciously welcome and invited us to share their meal.

I decline saying that there are too many of us.

"Do not worry, there will be enough of our simple meal of soup and lentils to go around," says the man with a rather long beard. They also serve hummus with tahini prepared by a local cook. The women join in sitting at the back.

The Buddhists are of Seen origin dressed in loose fitting long pants. Some wore soutanes.

"We are very interested to know why you are travelling with the orechah of traders," I ask.

Huineng, the man with the long beard, apparently the leader of the group, instructs one of the young men to bring tea which is laid out with a pot and cups made of porcelain. He pours the tea into the cups before he speaks.

"We have been travelling on this road for three years now. We are on the way to Mitzrayim." He speaks in Yavan mixed with Sogdiana. "We are from Seen. We are followers of Buddha, the Enlightened One. Some of us are philosophers, others are monks. The rulers in our land worship their own ancestors in great temples, and the people also worship different gods of the earth from the four directions, the mountains and rivers, and many others. The Silk Road opens out communication to other lands and peoples. Together with goods, religion and knowledge also travel along these routes."

The others come and sit around in a circle.

"In the past, our people travelled on the Silk Road to Hodu and brought back sacred texts about the Enlightened One, which we have translated into our own language. Later Ashoka, the Indian emperor, who converted from Brahminism to Buddhism, sent missionaries who brought the Buddha's teaching to Seen almost 300 years ago. Another Hodu king Pandyan sent emissaries about 150 years ago. Now the Imperial Court has officially noted the arrival of Buddhism in Seen and Buddhism is now established with temples and monasteries. There are temples along the Silk Road too. We have been spending time there and have also been to Hodu, the birthplace of the Buddha. We are now making our way to Mitzrayim where a group of ascetics called the Assayya have been inspired by the teachings and practices of the Buddha."

"Yes, I know the Assayya well. I have lived among them and have heard the wise men from the East speak," say I.

"Oh, in that case you must tell us more about them," says one of the other men.

"Their early contacts were also from emissaries sent from emperor Ashoka," I say.

"Our Buddhist monks and philosophers have always travelled with the merchant orechahs. You asked me why we travel with them. They are experienced men who know the ways and how to endure the harsh climates. We have our own camels, and we find security in their numbers. Of course, we pay them for protection. These traders are very rough and ruthless men who will not hesitate to fight and kill for profit. We try to influence them with our belief system which is sanctity of life, compassion for others, rejection of violence and emphasis on charity and the practice of virtue. We try to show them the middle path of the Enlightened One which is between greed and asceticism."

"It is very enlightening for us to hear you speak like that," says Mattithyahu.

"What is your essential message?" I ask.

"It is very simple. Earthly life is impermanent and full of suffering but the cycle of birth, death and rebirth which is a painful process, can be ended through the Buddhist faith and practice."

"How do you accomplish that?" asks Tauma.

"By perseverance. It is contained in our thoughts, words and deeds, which as you well know, can be good or bad. All that we think, say and do is our *karma* and they have consequences."

The women too have many questions to ask but do not speak as women were considered inferior to men and incapable of thinking deeply. They are expected to remain silent.

Mariam takes courage to speak "Venerable Sib, what is karma?"

He pauses for a while before he speaks. "Just like the cycle of birth, death and rebirth, karma is the cycle of cause and effect. What happens to a person, happens because they cause it in their actions."

"Yahadut also teaches the same, that good deeds are rewarded, and bad deeds are punished, especially in the afterlife either with

Elahh in *d'bwashmaya*[214] or with satana in sheol," explains Pilip.

"We do not believe in the afterlife as some place of existence. When we die, we are reborn with the karma into another life. This goes on always depending on the karma until we reach a pure state of *nirvana*[215]."

"After we die our soul leaves the body and how can we be reborn?" asks Yehudah.

"Rebirth or reincarnation is all around us in the world where every material thing is recycled."

"Moreh," says Tauma turning to me, "you have spoken about being born again, how do you explain this?"

"You know what I told the Parush. Yahadut's teaching is that we are made of body and soul, and when we die the soul leaves the body and cannot be born again in another body.

"Sib Huineng, I understand how everything is recycled through life and death. In our *Tanakh*[216] we call the first man Adam because he is made of adamah, the earth. We know that everything springs from the earth and returns to the earth. However, a person is an individual and when the person dies their material body returns to the earth. The material body of a new- born baby may have a link to the material earth, but no way can the same individual be reborn in a different individual."

"This is how the Buddha, the Enlightened One, has described death. Life is a journey. Death is a return to earth. The universe is like an inn. The passing years are like dust. Regard this world as a star at dawn, a

---

[214] heaven

[215] A transcendent state in which there is neither suffering, desire nor sense of self. The subject is released from the effects of karma and the cycle of death and rebirth. It is the final goal of Buddhism.

[216] Refers to the three divisions of the Hebrew Bible, the Law, Prophets and Writings

bubble in a stream, a flash of lightning in a summer cloud, a flickering lamp — a phantom — and a dream. So, nothing is permanent, even the reincarnation will end in Nirvana. In the meantime, karma must be accounted for," responds Huineng.

"How will this be accounted for and who will account for it?" asks Mattithyahu.

"This will be accounted for by the practice of virtue to offset the bad karma with good karma."

Marta, taking the cue from Mariam braves the cultural stigma and asks, "It seems very unfair to me that when I am born, I should inherit the bad karma of some other person in the past."

Everyone turned to look at her, shocked to hear another woman's voice.

"How would you respond to that, Sib Huineng?" I ask.

"Let us look at it like this. What you call a soul is some form of toqeph which is within each one of us and it is passed on. The taking of a new body in the next life can be compared to lighting successive candles using the same flame of the preceding candle. Although each flame is causally connected to the one that came before it, it is not the same flame. Karma is passed through the connection."

I add, "Sib, I beg to differ. We consider toqeph as something natural and neutral. It cannot be connected to anything good or bad. The individual is responsible for the good or bad that they do, the karma, as you call it. That responsibility cannot be passed to someone else because the same flame belongs to the same individual. But then, you yourself said that it is not the same flame."

"Yes and no! What you have said is something for us to think about. But here lies the difference in our religious beliefs," says Huineng.

"Who then will attain Nirvana?" asked Mariam again.

"Nirvana is attained when this recurring flame is finally extinguished. It is the state of final liberation and an end of suffering.

There is no more thirst or grasping, no more greed and attachment to external things. Only the Buddha and those who have attained enlightenment will achieve Nirvana."

"Is Nirvana eternity and will Elahh be there in Nirvana?" asks Natan'el.

"We do not speak about Elahh, whether there is one or several. We do not consider Elahh as the creator of the world or One who will sit in judgement at the end of the world. We simply follow the path of goodness. As you can see the robes we wear and the bowls we carry are the only things we own. Just as a bird takes its wings with it wherever it flies, so we take our robes and bowl with us wherever we go until we find the nesting place in Nirvana."

"What is Nirvana like?"

"We will never know until we attain it."

There was silence and then Huineng asks, "You said you lived among the Assayya. Are our Buddhist brethren among them?"

"When I was there, there were a few of them who conducted sessions about Buddhism. The Assayya are mainly Yahudim who have settled in Mitzrayim near Alexandria by the Lake Mareotis. They are what we call Hassidim, the ascetics similar to the community in a place called Qumran in Yehuda. I was with them too. They are well known for their healing abilities. They develop healing as a religious art. Do you also practise healing?" I ask.

"Yes, we do, and we carry our medicinal owrah with us when we travel. Many men on the orechah fall sick and some die. They call on us to administer remedies."

He and I exchange many attributes about healing. It was getting late and Mattithyahu speaks on behalf of the group thanking them for the hospitality and dialogue, and we leave. The men accompany the women to their ksenia before retiring for the night. We have had had a long day.

Scenario 42 - Arrogance of the Yehudim

Tyre

The next morning the women get ready to rejoin the men. The innkeeper approaches them, "A woman who is a relative of mine has been asking about you and your group from HaGalil. She says she heard about your adon and what he did in HaGalil. Would you like to meet her?"

"Yes, certainly," says Mariam, wondering how the name of Yeshua has reached this far.

The woman comes with her little daughter who appears to be suffering from some impairments. "My name is Norana and I'm from Athura in Knaan. We are Kenaani and Knaan is our land. I have heard stories that your adon is a great healer and moreh. My daughter is 12 years old and is afflicted with convulsions and possessed by the unclean satana. Will you take me to your adon?"

"You can come with us, but don't expect a miracle," says Mariam. They meet the men at the marketplace and are soon joined by Shemayon, Andreia, Ya'aqov and Yhochanan, weary from a whole night of fishing. I am not among them.

"Where is *Rabboni*?" asks Mariam.

"He has gone back to the Buddhists for a final meeting," says

Tauma.

"Attha, what do you seek?" asks Mattithyahu.

"She has a sick child and wants to meet Moreh," says Marta.

"Our Moreh has come to Knaan for a quiet rest. I advise you to go home," says Natan'el.

"I will not leave until I have seen your moreh. I know he can cast the satana out of my daughter and I will not go until the healer has looked upon my daughter."

They all go to a street stall to have breakfast and the Kenaan woman follows them and sits down on the roadside with her daughter. As they are finishing breakfast, I appear carrying a bundle.

"Have you brought some food for us?" asks Shemayon.

"No, I talked to the Buddhists about their healing methods, and they gave me some of their medicinal owrah. Some of these owrah do not grow here. They also gave me some seeds which we can try growing here," say I. The Kenan woman immediately approaches me, "Adon, Moreh, please look at my daughter, she is possessed by satana. Please drive satana out of her."

"Attha, can you wait for a while?" asks Yehuda.

She persists, "Adon, I have heard of your great healing works in Hagalil. I have faith in you to heal my daughter."

"Your daughter has no satana in her," I say because the girl is quiet with eyes cast down.

"She is not always like that," she shouts. Just then the girl rolls up her eyes and is seized with a violent convulsion. She falls to the ground with her arms and legs violently jerking.

"See what I mean! My child is possessed by evil satana." A crowd gathers. This is a very different crowd, a metropolitan crowd. There are some Yehudim but mostly Kenaani who are very mixed themselves. I am well aware of the crowd, so I get them involved.

"The toqeph within this girl is out of control," I say and instruct

317

them to hold her arms and legs. I placed my palm on her forehead. When she had difficulty breathing, I put my other had on her chest applying gentle pressure. I close my eyes concentrating on the toqeph in me and within her. I maintain that until the seizure leaves her body. The child falls asleep. The crowd believes that I have worked magic.

I say, "She has a fever. Wet a cloth with cold water and apply it to her forehead."

"Has satana left her?" asks the mother.

"There is no satana. Tell me attha, has the child been sleeping well?"

"No, she keeps waking up very often."

"Has she been eating well?"

"No. Often she refuses to eat and vomits out what she has eaten."

"She looks exhausted. Does she complain of seeing flashes of light?"

"Yes, and when that happens, she closes her eyes and begins to cry."

"Why does she cry. Is she disturbed by something?"

"I think it is because her father left us. That is when all these things began to happen."

"Is her father going to come back?"

"No, he has abandoned us."

"Was she close to her father?"

"Yes."

"She is stressed by the absence of the father and her mind is disturbed. This will not go away immediately." Turning to my followers I said, "This is a similar case to the one we found in Meroth."

I turned to the mother, "Attha, you have to treat her very carefully. First, get rid of the idea that satana has possessed her. She is a very disturbed child. If you keep saying that she has satana inside her, you will only frighten her and make the illness worse. Do not scold her or beat her. She is your daughter and not satana. Be gentle with her. You must be both father and mother to her by showing love.

"She must eat well to gain her strength. Give her meat, like chicken, fruit and a lot of fat. Start with small portions and increase the food.

"Do you make qara? Samna baladi?"

"Yes, but it is expensive."

"You must make it out of fresh grass eating cows. Qara is the essence of milk. Give her a little bit each day. If you find that hard to get, give her plenty of butter and cream."

I dig into the small bundle I brought back from the Buddhists and pull out a tiny earthen jar. As I open it, there is a whiff of very strong odour.

"This is an extract from pegana, a small shrub with clusters of yellow flowers. If you look around, you will see it growing in these parts. You must boil it for a long time to get the extract. Can you get it here?" Some say, "Yes." To the woman I say, "Give her two drops with her food. I only have very little. I can give you some if you have a small container."

Someone produces a small cup and I pour a little into it.

"You know *ezob*, a common sweet-smelling plant of the mint family. You can also add some ezob oil in her food. Then use a lot of chives or garlic when you cook. Keep this up and she will have fewer seizures and get better," I assure.

"Why do you, a Kenaan attha, seek the help of a Yehudi? Asks Yehudah.

"I know you Yehudim look down on us like we are dogs. What do I care! All I want is to have my daughter cured," says the woman.

"Attha, the Yehudim are an arrogant people. Yehudah, you are a very zealous Yehudi. You hate the Kittim because they oppress us. They are powerful with arms and weapons and big armies and exert their superiority over the people. We, Yehudim, although we do not have the same might, think we are superior because we are the children of Aba Avraham, specially chosen by Ellah. We despise those who are not Yehudim. This is another kind of oppression. We are no better than the Kittim. Aba Avraham, if he really lived, had come to Knaan long before he arrived in Yisra'el. Attha, her daughter and all her people also call Avraham Aba. What makes them different from us or lower than us? We were never chosen. We just declared ourselves chosen. We are all adama, people of the earth," I assert.

Yehudah did not say anything but was not happy being taken to task in public.

I address the crowd, "You are people with different beliefs but that does not matter. You live together. What is important is that there is peace and respect for everyone. Traders from the Silk Road have made this place prosperous, but they also attracted powerful neighbours from Mitzrayim, Athura or Assyria or Aramea, Bavel, Parthyaea. Then came the Yehudim, the Yavan from Hellas, and finally the Kittim. All these people have had control over you politically, levying tribute, taxes and tariffs. Your own civilisation has been over-shadowed by the culture of the foreigners. The Yavan culture and beliefs have been the most powerful. Your city, temples, centres of learning were all built on the Yavan model. Even now you speak their language. There was much more freedom for the citizens then, before the Kittim took over.

"They invaded your land and split your society. You continue living your hard, simple lives, growing crops, herding sheep, working as potters and weavers. You are the working-class people. In the city, there are people without work. The Kittim and the large landowners make you pay more money. This is Kittim oppression. They do not respect you much.

"The attha of the little girl says that we Yehudim call them Kenaani dogs. That is very unfortunate. We forget that the culture of Yisra'el came from the culture of Kenaan. We are not superior to you people. It was the power our malke had in those days. Like us in Yehuda you also are now under the rule of the Kittim. Because they are powerful, they can oppress the weak. The rich among you have also learnt to oppress the poor. As I have said, we are no better than the Kittim in oppressing those who are not Yehudim.

"My message is for all people. We are not born to suffer or make people suffer. The illness of the little girl here is the result of many human factors, one of which is her father abandoning her. It is not caused by satana nor is it the punishment of the gods.

"Do not act out of fear. Do not fear punishment in a life hereafter. Do not fear the evil of satana. All these are ways of keeping the people ignorant and fearful of powerful gods and evil spirits. All gods are the imagination of powerful people.

"The suffering of the poor is the work of the rich and powerful who are greedy. We must not allow that to happen. We must stop being selfish and arrogant. Both good and evil exist in our world, but they only come out of the hearts of men and women.

Scenario 43 - Mazdayasana

Sidon

"Let's make our way up the coast to the city of Sidon," I say.

We check out of our lodgings, pack the mule and head to the marketplace to top up on provisions.

As we walk along the seafront towards the outskirts of the city, I pick up a seashell, wipe the algae off its spiky back, "This shellfish is called the murex snail which carries a gland that contains a dye which turns purple. They use that to dye cloth especially the silk brought in by the traders. This became the famous Tyrian purple worn by the royalty. The city is known for this. This dye was exported across the seas to other countries. The Yavan named this whole area we are visiting Phoenicia, which is a Yavan word for purple."

"What else is Tyre famous for?" asks Ya'aqov.

"It is written in the scriptures, in the Book of Shmuel, that Hiram I, the malka of Tyre, was an ally of our malke Dawidh and Sh'lomoh. They created a trade agreement. Tyre and also Sidon were famous for timber especially cedar. Timber was brought in from Tyre to build the palace and the Beit HaMikdash of Malka Sh'lomoh. Even after the destruction of the Beit HaMikdash, when our early Yehudim returned from exile, they started building the second Beit HaMikdash, again with cedars floated down along the coast and brought overland to Yerushalayim. So, there is a historical link between us and the people of Tyre and Sidon."

"What about Sidon?" asks Arsinoe.

"Sidon is also another prosperous Kittim city and, as far as I know, it is the oldest city of Knaan and known for the invention of glass. The purple dye from the murex shell that Moreh explained to us made Tyre famous, but I believe that it was first discovered in Sidon," says Mattithyahu.

"You know a lot and have been keeping quiet," chides Pilip.

"I hear stories told by the orechah merchants," says Mattithyahu.

As we kept walking along the coastal road I add, "There is also a relationship between Sidon and Yisra'el. I mentioned Jezebal the local princess. She married Ahab the malka of Yisra'el, to cement ties between the two states. Later Jezebal became the Mahl-Kah of Yisra'el."

We continue our journey. After about four hours we reach the town of Zarephath. It is quite late, and we find an inn run by a widow. In the morning we are on our way to Sidon.

About 500 years earlier, this city was under the Pares who had built a temple to their god *Eshmoub*[217] and maintained a royal park. A few lingering remnants of the garden are visible. Now under Roman domination, major monuments and a theatre have been constructed. Different segments of orechah traders are also in the city.

"This is a beautiful city on the waterfront. Moreh, tell us more about Sidon?" asked Andreia.

"From the scriptures I gather that Sidon is the name of the first-born son of Knaan, who was the grandson of Aba Noah. This was the first home of the Kenaani. In the beginning they were the oppressors

---

[217] Phoenician god of healing and the tutelary god of Sidon.

of the Yehudim. Tyre, the second city, overshadowed Sidon. I have told you earlier in Tyre about Jezebel and the conquest of these cities by our malke. It is the same story here now with the Kittim in control," say I.

"So, the Kittim who control us are in control of the whole of Peleshet?" wonders Shimon.

"Much more than Peleshet; Phoenicia, Syria and almost all the lands we know of. Your name Shimon, Shimon Qan'anaya, is closely connected. We must not forget that we were all like one people before the establishment of the malke and mamlekhet, and different systems of belief in elahh and elohim, which have divided the people.

"Although the Kittim are in control now, the major influence of the Yavan remains among the people and their beliefs. People will always believe in elahh and elohim. It is difficult to wean them away from such beliefs. Never mind, what is important is that they do not fight over their beliefs and live in peace. Despite their atrocities, the Kittim are able to maintain law and order because they are very systematic and efficient administrators. They will not get their tax money if there was chaos; that is why they allow different religious beliefs, philosophical teachings and traditional system of governance. However, they have the overall control," I explain.

On entering the city, the first thing we do is to look for somewhere to stay. There is an orechahserai here too. We eat the food we brought and rest before walking the streets. After visiting the market, we see a gathering of people outside a house. We mingle with the crowd to see what is happening.

We move on stopping by stalls along the street selling food and fruit. We buy some bread, fruit and wine and continue walking until we come to a shady tree on the waterfront. We sit on the ground to eat. There are also other people around sitting on the grass with children playing on the beach.

"I think I know why the people are gathered here now," I say. "It is the time of the full moon, which is called the *Sabattu*[218] and regarded as a day of mid-repose by the Kanaani. I know this because they follow the same liturgical calendar we use in Qumran. It is similar to our ShAbat."

We move on towards the orechahserai.

Mattithyahu says, "I have heard the merchants speak of the city of Dimashqu as the oldest city. It is where the different orechah routes meet from East and West, and the lands of Aribi and Africa. They say that the Kittim have built a huge temple to their god, *Mariah Elaha*[219], and a wall around the city. Perhaps we should visit Dimashqu."

"We have already travelled so far, and it will be good to visit Dimashqu, but how do we get there?" says Natan'el.

"Let us ask the travellers at the orechahserai," says Pilip.

At the orechahserai, we meet some merchants who are taking an afternoon rest. Shemayon speaks to one of them.

"Shalama aleikhem, we are travellers from HaGalil."

"Yes, and what is your merchandise?" asks the man with a bushy beard, and a turban.

"We are not merchants. We wish to go to Dimashqu and since you are experienced travellers, we would like to ask you for directions to get there."

"Are you prepared to travel hard, over mountains and valleys?"

"Please tell us and we will decide if we can do it or not," says Andreia.

"Alright, sit down and I will tell you."

Pilip tethers the mule to a nearby tree and they gather around the merchant who is seated before a brazier. There are other merchants

---

[218] A Babylonian, Akkadian word for the full moon

[219] Jupiter

too.

"The Kittim have built excellent roads and we use them whenever we can. There are major roads to Dimashqu and trunk roads to other places. We came here from Dimashqu using the major road and then the trunk road to Tyre and on to Sidon. There is no road directly from here to Dimashqu. As the eagle flies the distance from here to Dimashqu is more than 120 milin. The furthest you can go east is to Jessin 18 milin from here where there is a large cave. Even to get there is difficult, and beyond that are the snowy mountains of Lebanon. The valley beyond the mountain is watered by two rivers, the Abana and the Pharpar. Dimashqu is situated on the great plain, which is still on very high ground. It is a fertile oasis, an important orechah centre and junction of trade routes.

"There are major roads out of the city. One is called the *Derech HaYam or the Via Maris* as the Kittim call it. It goes down to Danos, then the western shore of Yam Chinneroth, and from there to the coast right down to Mitzrayim. The other major road is the *Derech HaMalka*, the King's Highway. This road starts from Mitzrayim, goes up through Har Sinay to Aqaba up along the east side of Ha-Yarden. It is joined part of the way by the spice and incense routes from Aribi coming into Dimashqu. Then, of course, the major Silk Route passes through Dimashqu.

I chip in, "When I went to visit the Assayya in Mitzrayim, I travelled part of the way on the Derek HaYam."

"If you are prepared to climb over the snow you might find a way to Dimashqu. There are no roads. Your best bet is to go back to Tyre and take the trade route to Danos and Caesaria Pilippi, and from there take the major road to Dimashqu. You can join one of the orechahs. They are always happy to have big numbers, but you have to pay them because they have to pay taxes to the Kittim for using their roads."

"Thank you for enlightening us. What is your name, sib, and where are you from?" asks Y'hochanan.

"My name is Chamrav. We are from the land of the sunrise, Sogdiana, from the city of Samarkand. If you stretch your hands, one points to Seen and the other to Dimashqu."

"In Tyre we met some of your people and through them we met some followers of Buddha who were travelling with the orechah," says Shemayon.

"Yes, usually there are a group of religious people who join the orechah. Some of our people are also followers of Buddha.

"We are the followers of Zarathustra, our Avestan. Our religion is *Mazdayasana*[220]. We were also attracted by other religions like Buddhism from Hodu. Many of our people became followers of the Buddha, became monks, and built temples. We are the people who spread Buddhism to Seen. Our ancestors had translated the Buddhist sutras into the Seen language."

"Very interesting, your brothers in Tyre said they were followers of Zarathustra, but they were not interested in talking about religion," I comment.

"Yes, we business people are not too taken up with religion. But I don't mind talking about it. You are Yehudim aren't you? If you are not traders, are you preachers of religion?"

"No, we are not preachers of religion, but we like to discuss religion and how it affects people," say I.

"Our religion, Mazdayasna, is very old and has influenced other religions and cultures. Like all religions, we too have a Supreme Being whom we call *Ahura Mazda*[221], the Lord of Wisdom. We also have our Holy Book called the *Avesta*[222]. In the Avesta we read about

---

[220] Zoroastrianism

[221] Lord of wisdom

[222] Collection of sacred texts of Zoroastrianism

YESHUA

Zarathustra who was a Magian priest and a prophet. The Mazdayasna priests are called the *Magi*[223], the men of wisdom."

"What are your beliefs?" asks Yehudah.

"We believe in a lot of things. We were taught all that when we were children, but I cannot remember everything. We traders are not really bothered with it. As children, we were told stories when Zarathustra's birth was foretold from the beginning of time. His mother, Dughdova, was a virgin and that the moment he was born, he burst out laughing and the whole universe rejoiced with him. As a child evil forces tried to destroy him, but Ahura Mazda protected him."

"Tell us about Zarathustra himself," asks Mariam.

"Zarathustra was a maker of footwear who lived by the riverside of Bactria, north of the snow-covered mountain range that divides Hodu from central Asu. You see the brazier in front of me? In our cold homeland it is the fire that keeps us warm. It is also something we carry with us in our travels. We venerate the fire. We believe in good fighting evil and reward and punishment after death."

"Do you really believe there is life after death?" I ask.

"I don't know, but we have been taught that there is life after death in heaven or hell. We have a choice in life that determines where we will go. We are responsible for the consequence of our choice in the battle of good over evil."

"What guarantee is there that good will win over evil? We see a lot of people who do evil winning all the time," says Yehudah.

"Zarathustra the prophet, predicted the coming of a mshikha sent by Ahura Mazda at the end of time. He will be known as the *Saushyant*[224]. He will begin the final battle between the forces of

---

[223] Priests in Zoroastrianism (like the magi who visited Jesus in Betheham)

[224] Saviour of the world

good and evil. Evil will be destroyed, and he will resurrect the dead and restore their bodies to perfection."

"What is your idea of perfection?" I probe.

"For me, perfection is prosperity."

"Mazdayasna appears to be very similar to Yahadut. True perfection is seen to be in the life hereafter and not necessarily in prosperity in this world," says Natan'el.

"In spite of what Yahadut teaches, we do not know if there is or can be life after death. We understand that prosperity is part of perfection, but all people should share in that perfection; not only the rich, don't you think?" ask I.

"Yes, but you have to work hard like we traders do, to become prosperous."

"But I am sure not all traders are good," says Andreia.

"Agreed. That is why like cause and effect, we make choices, and the effect follows. The purpose of life is to progress towards perfection. In Mazdayasna, we are taught three principles. *Humata* – good thoughts, *hukhta* – good words, and *huvarshta* – good deeds. There is only one path and that is the path of truth. Do the right thing because it is the right thing to do and then all beneficial rewards will come to you also."

"Well said sib Chamrav. If you live by those principles, you are a good man and you do not have to wait for Saushyant to come and fight for you. But then, why do you have to wait for the Saushyant to come and fight and destroy the evil in the world? Why don't we fight the evil now and make it the perfection of prosperity for all people?" say I.

"Yes, but I don't know how to do that."

"You said we are responsible for the choices we make and the consequences. Your notion of prosperity is to make as much profit as possible. If that is your primary concern, then you are not thinking of those people who cannot afford to buy your goods because the price is too high. Consequently, they cannot enjoy all the goods of the earth. I am not saying that your actions are bad but how is the Saushyant going to enable the poor to enjoy the goods of the earth? Doesn't he have to curtail your profit so they will have an equal share of everything?"

"Everyone cannot have an equal share of everything. Those who work hard deserve more."

"You are a wise sib, Chamrav. Perhaps a little less profit might give the poor an opportunity to enjoy the merchandise you bring and trade for local goods, which are produced by hardworking people who also deserve to enjoy the good things of the world."

"I have to compete with other merchants but what you have said is something for me to think about."

"The Kittim and religious leaders use their authority as power to control the people through taxation, rules and regulations, but you are the people whose business of trade influences the quality of life. You too have a strong controlling power and if you exercise that according to the principles of Mazdayasna as you have enumerated them, then you will be contributing towards the perfection of prosperity you described. You will be on the road of tsedek," I encouraged him.

"It has been interesting talking to you people. You do not talk like preachers of religion," comments Chamrav.

"Thank you, and now we have to make travel plans if we are to go to Dimashqu," says Shemayon.

We take leave and gather under a shady tree and share a meal.

"We have been on the road for quite a while now. If we take the trade road from Tyre to Danos then we can make it back home via the Derech HaYam," says Marta.

"Are you already longing for home?" asks Y'hochanan.

"We took the difficult way coming up here. If we take the roads described by Chamrav the travel will be easier. I would like to visit Dimashqu. The Hasidim with whom I lived in Qumran have communities in many different parts. They have found safe havens in wilderness centres away from the Perushim and Ṣĕdûqîm of the Beit HaMikdash. Like the Assayya in Mitzrayim, others have set up communities elsewhere and I believe there is one such community in Dimashqu. I read a document about them in Qumran. They could have easily travelled there on one of the major orechah routes. I would like to find and meet them," I say.

"You always show us the way. We will follow you," says Andreia.

"Is that alright with you, Marta?" I ask.

"Yes, Moreh, where you go, we follow," responds Marta.

We retrace our steps to Tyre. Mattithyahu contacts some merchants and finds a small orechah of Yehudi merchants moving east. Yehudah pays the fee for travelling with them, which covered the road tax as well as protection from bandits even though we are not carrying any merchandise of value.

Having travelled a day's journey going around rather than over the Lebanon range on the plain of Hazor in a southeasterly direction, we stop at the village of Kfar Ganaeoi about 31 milin from Tyre.

Mattithyahu asks the merchants about the people in Dimashqu. One replies, "There is a sizeable Yehudi community there and they are of two different types. One is the beit k'nesset-centred community, and the other a business community who mix freely with the local people and share their customs and practices."

Yeshua then asks, "Isn't there another community of Yehudi Hasidim?"

"Oh, yes," says the merchant, "but they are on the outskirts of the city and keep to themselves.

Scenario 44 - Nature of woman

Kfar Panias

The following day we travel east and stop at the village of Abelane, by the river, among other small villages with orechahsaries. We arrive at dusk only to sleep and continue the journey down along the river. Some merchants stop for a longer time to do business while others join the orechah that keeps moving on. On the third day, we pass through the village of Daphne, only stopping briefly and continuing in an easterly direction, crossing two more rivers until we reach the town of Kfar Panias.

Now we were in the territory of Pilip the Tetrarch. His tetrarchy extends from Har Hermon down to Ha Yarmuk, encompassing Gaulanitis, Batanea and Trachonitis. Out of the jurisdiction of Hordos Antipas, we feel safer. The orechah makes a stop here at Kfar Panias. Founded by Pilip, this town had become a city and was renamed Caesar in honour of the Roman Emperor Caesar Augustus, and it came to be known as Caesaria Paneas. Since Paneas was a Yavan name after the Greek god Pan, it was again renamed Caesaria Pilippi and he made it the administrative capital of his tetrarchy, which included the Golan and the Hauran.

We explore the magnificent city surrounded by lush greenery watered by the Panias river in contrast to the barren dry land we travelled through coming here. Because of the river people still call it Kfar Panias. The chilling waters come from the snowy Har Hermon and continue down the Nehar ha Yarden. The riverbanks are shaded by plane trees, willows and bramble. I point out a cluster of mint leaves, which I pick and crush in the palm of my hand and smell its fragrance. We hear the sweet song of a warbler in the thickets.

On entering the walls of the city, we are astounded by the massive stone.constructions. It was Hordos the Great, father of Pilip who had erected a temple of white marble dedicated to the emperor Augustus. Walking up stone steps we gaze at the niches carved into the face of the hill where kestrels build their nests and look down on the city buildings and the aqueduct bringing fresh water into the city. The HaGalil towns are nothing in comparison to this Yavan and Kittim architecture with temple and beit k'nesset side by side.

Near the beit k'nesset, the street is busy with the local people going about their business. One man on the street recognises us as Yehudim from the way we speak.

"Are you Yehudim from Yam Chineroth?" he asks.

"Yes," says Shemayon.

"I am from Kfar Nahum, and I have heard about the one who goes about healing people. Are you the healers?"

A woman sitting on the sidewalk overhears this conversation. She gets up with some effort and approaches us. She comes close to me and leans against me. Mariam immediately reacts, "Hey, you, what are you trying to do? Get away." She pushes her aside and she falls to the ground crying and trembling.

I address her, "Attha, why are you trembling? What are you afraid of?"

She remains silent, not daring to speak. People have gathered around this commotion. One of the men says, "She is unclean." It becomes clear to everyone that that means she is menstruating.

I bend down and pick her up.

"*Rabboni!*" protests Mariam.

"Attha, is this the time of the moon for you?"

She remains silent and after a while nods her head.

I looked upon the crowd with anger. Holding her close I say, "You stupid people, you do not understand the nature of a woman. Every woman goes through this period many times in her life. If not, none of us would be born into this world. Your religious teachers tell you to shun her because she is unclean. She is cut off from her friends because any contact with her will make you unclean until the evening of the day, and you are required to wash your clothes and bathe yourself in water. She is not allowed to participate in the public worship of Elahh. Your religious teachers tell you that this is written in the Torah. I tell you the Torah was written by learned men out of touch with life realities, who had no understanding of and no respect for women."

The man who declared her unclean speaks up again, "It is more than that. This woman has been struck by satana for her sins. Unlike other women, she has been like that continuously for 12 years."

"Attha, is that true?" I enquire.

She is afraid to speak. If this truth is known even this healer would reject her, she thinks.

"Attha, do not be afraid. If it is true, then there is something wrong with your body and satana has nothing to do with that. Has the bleeding become worse over the years?" ask I.

She speaks, "Yes. It has become worse. I have spent all my money seeing the local physicians."

I turn to the man who is judgmental and address all the people, "The attha is suffering from an ailment and it has become worse because of you. You have been judging and condemning her and denying her a place in your community. That is causing her a lot of stress and has made her condition worse. She is already weak, hardly able to walk from the loss of blood, and you increase her distress by condemning her.

"Attha, do you have a family?" I ask.

"No, my husband left me when I became ill and untouchable."

"She needs good food to nourish her back to health and she has spent all her money on physicians. Is there any among you who do not condemn her and believe that she is a sick woman who needs help?"

Two women come forward. They have lived among the local people long enough to dare go against the current of conservative Yahadut. I tell them, "If you who have food, share it with her and give her money to buy good food. She must eat well. I notice plenty of safflower growing here. If you have oil made from safflower, take a handful of cumin and some fenugreek, boil them and mix them in the safflower oil and let her drink it daily. In time she will experience a healing. Accept her as a member of your community and be a friend to her. All that will be of great help. Do not listen to the religious leaders," I advise.

Turning to the woman I say, "Attha, be not afraid. You are clean."

We spent the night in an orechahserai. During dinner I disclose a plan to make a detour.

Scenario 45 - Message on the Mount

Har Hermon

"I think it would be a good idea to go up to Har Hermon. It can't be much more than 20 milin from here although it would mean a climb," I propose.

"Sounds exciting, but it is going to be very cold up there," cautions Natan'el.

"Why do you want to go there?" asks Arsinoe.

I say, "People have always been fascinated with high places because they think that elahh or eloim are up in the sky and if they can go high enough, they can reach them. According to our books, after the Great Flood, the people in Bavel built a high tower to reach Elahh. Even in our own history Elahh is supposed to have revealed himself to Aba Avraham as El Shaddai, god of the mountains. Aba Avraham went up a mountain to sacrifice his son Yiṣḥāq. El Shadai was the name by which Elahh was known to Avraham, Yiṣḥāq and Yaʿakov. Aba Moshe received the Commandments on Har Sinay. Remember the Shomronim who have their own temple on Har Garizzim just as we have our Beit HaMikdash on Har haBáyith.

"Har Hermon is the highest mountain in Eretz Yisrael and is known as *charam*, meaning a holy place. Don't be surprised to find altars and temples up there. Different gods were worshipped in the high places not only by those we call goyim but by our own people including Malka Sh'lomoh. Har Hermon is also known as Ba'al Hermon, Sirion and Sion in the Tanakh. The words of Aba Moshe are also recorded in the Tanakh saying that the sons of God saw the daughters of men on Har Hermon that they were fair. They took them as wives and their children became mighty men. Our ancestors were good storytellers. Mountains have always played a significant role in everyone's lives. Let's go and see for ourselves."

The next morning, we ask some people about the way up to Har Hermon. We are told that the climb is quite steep but there is a more gradual slope coming down on the east side. Also, at the bottom of the hill there is an orechahserai meeting the Derech HaYam. We have a good breakfast at a stall that grills different meats — lamb, chicken, beef — and serves them in wraps called *shawarma*[225]. We don our warm clothing, replenish our skins with wine and set forth.

Higher on the rugged face of Har Hermon, mountain goats are grazing on whatever grass that grow between the rocks. Looking up we can see two high peaks toward the east and one lower. The snow on their heads sparkles like silver under the rays of the sun. Strong cold winds from the west blow against our faces. Then we see the stone pillars, altars and temples dedicated to the Greek and Roman deities. We explore the different shrines and meet some shepherds who were Yehudim.

One shepherd says, "It is often very quiet up here except during the festivals when there are plenty of people and the temples are full."

"Do you take part in the festivals?" asks Shemayon.

"Some of us do and that is when we sell our produce of meat, milk and cheese. Would you like some milk and cheese?"

---

[225] A Levantine Arab meat preparation

We buy some milk and cheese and sit in the temple grounds to have lunch with a magnificent view of the surroundings. Since it is too cold to spend the night up here, we start downhill along the eastern slopes. On this side the wind is shielded by the mountain and the land becomes greener. In the distance, cows graze on the plains of Bashan. Descending lower, we come to some villages with vineyards among the cluster of pine, oak and poplar trees.

After speaking to the villagers, we are surprised to learn that news about us has spread even to this place. Identifying me as the healer from Yam Chinneroth, the villagers come out to meet me bringing with them those who are ill with various diseases, fits, seizures, or paralysis, suffering pain or supposedly demon possessed.

I attend to them personally and invite my followers to help the others for there are so many. They follow what I usually do. They surprise themselves as they recognize symptoms and begin to advise and administer herbal remedies. All the people are impressed. Whether the healings are real or apparent did not matter, the sick and disabled are filled with positive toqeph that boosts their spirits. That in itself is a healing process.

More and more come from the neighbouring villages and there is quite a crowd. They ask many questions and finally I stand up on a rock on the slope of the mount to address them.

"Some of you have asked me what you must do to be good. I say avoid bad things. The Torah is full of rules and regulations telling you how to be good, but they are not all necessary. We are told that Elahh gave Aba Moshe the Aseret ha-d'varîm. We are told to obey them for fear of Elahh and his punishment if we fail. Only those that advise good relationships — like respecting the right of others to own property and not accusing others falsely or hurting others, honouring and respecting your parents, faithfulness in marriage through a partnership of love and by being truthful in everything —

should be obeyed.

Tsedek is born out of love. Do unto others what you would like them to do to you and naturally what you don't like others to do to you, don't do the same to them.

"The wise men from the East in the lands of Seen and Hodu spoke and wrote down these words 500 years ago. Alas! We have not learnt to live by them.

"You must have heard of the other wise men from the East like Zarathustra and their belief called Mazdayasna. They say that there are three things on the path of truth — good thoughts, good words and good deeds. That is generally enough without all the unnecessary rules and burdensome regulations imposed by the rabbim of the Beit HaMikdash.

"Blessed are you if there is peace in your heart.

"Blessed are you who are not bound by possessions for you shall be free.

"If you are poor, don't be envious of the rich unless you feel you deserve part of that wealth. If they are the direct cause of your poverty, get angry, then stand up and demand your rights. If you hunger and thirst for tsedek you will have the toqeph to fight for it. In a combined effort you will find comfort even if you are persecuted for the cause.

"Be gentle in your dealings with other people be they Yehudim or not, with children, with animals and plants, and the earth will be your heritage. Be merciful and don't inflict suffering on others even on your enemies except in self defence of course.

"Blessed are you if you are merciful for mercy will be your inheritance.

"Blessed are you if you show kindness, you will find comfort in kindness itself.

"You have learnt how it was said that you must love your neighbour and hate your enemy. We consider our relatives and Yehudi as our neighbour and all others as goyim and enemy. It is this hatred that has kept us from learning from others.

"Blessed are you if you are peacemakers, your barren land will be turned into a fruitful garden.

"Yahadut tells you that justice is achieved on the principle of an eye for an eye and a tooth for a tooth. If that is the case, we will all be blind and toothless. If anyone hits you on the right cheek, you do not have to offer him your other cheek unless you asked for it by an act of unkindness towards him. You may be angry, but you do not have to kill for it. The commandment says do not kill. But if you must kill, do it for a good reason but first control your anger. If you must kill another human being, do it only to save your own life.

Although it is always sad to take life, you do it for a good reason. You kill an animal to eat its flesh. You kill a dove, lamb or calf to offer it as a sacrifice to the gods. That is not a good reason. You may say you do it to atone for your sins. I say it is a sin to kill for a sacrifice. Has anyone ever seen Elahh or one of his angels come down and accept your offering and say, 'Thank you, your sins are forgiven'?

"If you have to fight back, fight to destroy the enemy in him. If you have been in the wrong, ask for forgiveness. If he has done you wrong, resist through forgiveness. It is easier to go up to one of those stone altars and make an offering than to forgive. It takes a lot of courage to be reconciled first.

Even the body of your enemy is a temple and his heart an altar. Sacrifice the enemy at that altar by turning him into a friend.

"Even when we do good there are always those who cheat, bully and will do evil and get away with it with power and might. We can try to stop them by not supporting them. In Yahadut we have numerous rules and regulations on ostracizing people, saying that they are unclean for stupid reasons. The dirtiest people are those who do bad things. Do not be punished by their bad deeds. Ostracize them. Don't give them a place in your community until and unless they stop their bad ways and change for the better.

"You yourselves be pure of heart, be the salt of the earth. That means being very balanced. Too much salt and people will spit you out; too little and you become insipid, tasteless. You are thrown out and trampled underfoot. Be the light of the world. No one lights a lamp to put it under a tub; they put it on a lamp stand where it shines for everyone in the house. If you light a big fire on top of Har Hermon everyone in this region will see it. A city built on a hilltop cannot be hidden.

In the same way, your light must shine in the sight of all people, so that they will be inspired to do the same. So be fair in your judgment of others. Own up to your own weakness before judging others. How can you say to your brother 'let me take the splinter out of your eye', when all the time there is a plank in your own? Don't be blind! Don't be a hypocrite! Take the plank out of your own eye first and then you will see clearly enough to take the splinter out of your brother's eye. Don't blindly believe everything that the Temple teaches. Be a judge of yourself first before judging others.

"We have been told that a murderer shall be put to the sword, a thief shall be crucified, and a harlot be stoned. If you mete out such a punishment, then you do not free yourself from the sin of the murderer, the thief, or the harlot. Rather, you shut off the light and bring darkness into yourself.

"If you have reason to mourn a loss or suffering, go ahead and mourn for it is natural but take comfort that it will pass with time and life will go on. We all must die. We do not know when nor how nor where. Leave behind a good memory of yourself when you are no more.

Blessed are you who hunger after truth and thirst for beauty. Your hunger will bring you bread, and your thirst will bring you to the cool spring water like that of Har Hermon.

"We are told that our good deeds will be rewarded in shamayin and our bad deeds punished in gehanna.

"Forget about shamayin and gehanna. Concentrate on doing good works here on earth and that is the best you can do. Be peacemakers and I assure you there will be peace and happiness on earth if all of us do just that. What more reward do you want? Surely, this is not too difficult to understand? You must have the determination to do that and not give in to the temptation of doing evil."

"In conclusion, this is my message to you on Har Hermon. Don't live in the expectation of someone — an adam, elahh or adam bar elahh — to come and save us from all evil and restore good. We must do that by ourselves. Do good in whatever you do. That is the way of tsedek.

I now finish what I wanted to say. I know I have made a deep impression on the people.

They all shouted, "Moreh ha Tsedek! Moreh ha Tsedek!"

Mariam exclaimed, "*Rabboni*, we have not seen such a response even in HaGalil or in Yehuda."

"Yes, a moreh is not always accepted in his own country," say I.

At the foothill we spend the night in an orechahserai.

We join a bigger orechah the next day. This takes the Derech HaYam to Dimashqu. Our first stop is the small village of Sa'sa' which has seen better days. There are broken down walls and cisterns. A few people are working olive presses extracting oil. Sa'sa' is about 37 milin from Kfar Panias but since we detoured through Har Hermon we have to travel only about 20 milin.

We carry on with the orechah to the next stop which is the town of Kfar Hawr only less than three milin away. The Derech HaYam skirts around Har Hermon and Kfar Hawr is built into the side of the hill.

In the valley below, we can see the river 'Arny. We spend the night here at an orechahserai, with dinner from our own provisions in the privacy of our cubicle.

"Moreh, your fame has really travelled beyond HaGalil," says Y'hochanan.

"It is not just me. We have become known as a group of travellers who teach a new way, the way of tsedek," say I.

"Moreh Yeshua, you are the way, the truth and the life," says Shemayon.

"No, no, Shemayon. It is wrong to say that. We together show people the way and the truth to a good life. All of you performed very well on Har Hermon when you dealt with the sick and disabled. The way you spoke to them brought them healing. You have learnt well. As we go along, I will teach you more about herbal healing. When I am no longer with you, you must carry on doing this work of healing not merely the broken bodies but the broken society. Change the way people have been made to think."

"You are right, Moreh, our life here on earth is what matters. All people should live in peace and enjoy the good things of the earth," says Pilip.

"But Moreh, you do agree that to bring about a better life for the people we have to fight the oppressors who are the Kittim?" insists Yehudah.

"Yehudah, I understand why you are obsessed with that idea, but we cannot match their might. They are good administrators, and they are clever enough not to deal with the people directly. The people we are directly up against are our own malke and religious leaders. Religious leaders can only threaten us with the fire of gehanna but the malke can do harm to us. We must make people see the game they are playing with the Kittim. One way is to get them to disobey the Kittim without violence. Sadly, there will be a price to pay even for that. Are you prepared for that? Think very carefully."

There is silence. Then both Yehudah of Kerioth and Shimon Qan'anaya say yes. The others concur. We retire for the night pondering how our future would develop.

The next day we do not join any orechah but travel the road by ourselves. There are others also on the road to Dimashqu. This is a picturesque part of the journey in contrast to the rugged terrain previously. On the left are the hill slopes and rock faces into which shrines to gods are cut. On the right is the great valley green with trees and the river Awaj fed by the waterfalls.

Joa'ana points to one of the shrines on the hill side, "Look there are some carvings on the rock. Let's take a closer look."

They turned to me, considered the source of all knowledge for them. Wiping away the dust on them I say, "I know what this is. Do you remember the sib in Sidon, we asked him for directions?"

"Yes," says Pilip, "Chamrav."

"That's right. He spoke to us about his religion, Mazdayasana, and their Elahh, Ahura Mazda. This mystery religion has a very strong influence among the Kittim. Ahura Mazda was supposed to have had a son, called the god Mithra, who is like the sun that appears in the sky at dawn and then crosses the firmament in a chariot drawn by four white horses. This image here shows the god Mithra slaying a bull in sacrifice. This cult of Mithra began in Parthyaea long ago and is now very popular throughout the Kittim empire especially in the north in the city of Tarsus in Cecelia. This shrine was probably carved out by Kittim soldiers.

We stop at a waterfall for lunch.

By the afternoon we enter the town of Artouz, just over 20 milin from Kfar Hawar. We cross a bridge over the river Awaj. Canals built by the Kittim branches out from here to irrigate the farms. In the distance we see the blue hills.

As we walk into the town hardly anyone takes notice of us until an old man seated outside a house says, "I know who those people are. They are the followers of Yeshua the Nazarene. There he is among them. He is a rebel leader and a healer. I have seen him and his followers in Kfar Nahum."

Then the people begin to pay attention and come to meet us.

"What brings you here from HaGalil?" asks one of them.

Shemayon quickly responds, "We are on the way to Dimashqu."

"Can you really heal the sick? We have magicians who try to heal the sick, and priests make rituals to the gods, but no one really gets better. We can bring our sick to you. Will you heal them?"

I respond, "I, or rather, we can help to bring a cure to some of the illnesses, but we cannot heal by miracles. It depends how ill a person is or how advanced the sickness has become."

"Come," they say and take us to a lame man under a tree.

"He is lame, cannot walk because he is cursed by the gods with tsara'ath.

I go down to him, examine him by touching his leg. This results in the crowd exclaiming, "He has touched the untouchable tsa'ra'at."

I address them, "You are victimising this man by calling him a tsa'ra'at. He is not cursed by any god. He has a very bad sore in his leg. It is swollen so he cannot walk. The wound is not healing because it is not taken care of. Bring me some water and a clean cloth."

I pour water over the open sore and wipe around it with a damp cloth. Mariam interrupts, "*Rabboni*, let me do it," and cleans the wound. Everybody watches.

"On our way here, we saw many owrah, plants and trees that have medicinal value. You see the *arabah*[226] with bright yellow flowers? Take the leaves and boil them. Let this man drink a little every day."

---

[226] Commonly known as wattles, a willow

Turning to the man I say, "Do you have relatives and a home to stay?"

"Yes, but nobody wants me. My daughter brings me food and leaves it under the tree. That's all."

"Who is your daughter?"

"Kalanit."

I look around, "Kalanit, are you here?"

Timidly she comes forward. "I have already said your father does not have tsara'ath and is not cursed by any god. He is just sick with a wound that is not healing. You are afraid because people have said that he is untouchable. I say all that is rubbish. Take your father home and care for him. Give him good food with meat, milk and eggs. Don't let him eat anything sweet and not too much bread. The wound will heal, and he will walk again."

Others bring more sick people. Just like on Har Hermon, my followers team up in pairs and administer to the sick with owrah and other remedies. They have watched and learnt from me.

The people welcome us with gratitude. There are some rabbis around, but they do not confront me or my followers. The Yehudim here, having lived in close proximity with other believers, are broadminded, unlike the Yehudim of the south.

That night Y'hochanan asks, "Moreh, you told the lame man not to eat sweet food or too much bread. Why, what is wrong with sugar and bread?"

"There is nothing wrong with sugar and bread. Just that they are not good for the man's illness. I only know what I have learnt from the Assayya in Mitzrayim and what they learnt from the wise men from Hodu and Seen. They have practised herbal medicine for centuries, studied and wrote down what works and what does not. I do not know why sugar and bread are bad for the man in his condition, but I know it works. There is so much for us to learn from nature. Even animals know what to eat and what not to eat, and how to heal themselves. When a dog has a bad stomach, it eats grass and vomits it out, clearing out its stomach and it works. You don't find many sick animals, but there are many sick people everywhere. With practice we can learn what works and what does not."

"We also want to learn more because sickness is everywhere, and our religion does not bother with healing. All they do is to condemn using the name of Elahh," says Joa'ana.

The next day we take leave of the people of Artouz and head for Dimashqu.

The region along the road is well populated. Within the hour we climb a hillside and come to a cave barely visible from the road. The entrance is partly hidden by shrubs and the interior is dark with a narrow tunnel. Shemayon goes in and quickly comes out. "It's quite scary in there," he says, "but it would make a good hideout for anyone who does not want to be found."

While we enjoy the view, I point out more medicinal owrah as we go along. Soon we come to the small town of Sahnaya nestled in a grove of very old olive trees. We do not stop here but go on to the next big city, which is only seven milin from Artouz.

Since it is almost lunchtime, we sit under an olive tree in the outskirts of this city and have bread, wine and some grapes we bought at the market. We continue our journey and in two and a half milin we reach the city of Darayya, one of the oldest in the region. Since it is still early, we travel the next eight milin to Dimashqu.

Scenario 46 - Hassidim challenged

Dimashqu

Dimashqu was named by the people of Athura or Aramea, people who spoke Aramaic.

Malka Dawidh fought against the Arameans who were then taken over by the Pares. Tre-Qarnayia conquered the city, which was later occupied by the Kittim General Pompey. He made Dimashqu one of the ten cities of the Decapolis. The Kittim improved the canals and waterways originally built by the Arameans to control the water flow of the river Barada for agricultural purposes. This resulted in Dimashqu becoming an economic and agricultural centre in this northern region now administered by Aretas, malka of the Nabataeans. Now we have gone beyond the territory of Pilip the Tetrarch into Syria.

There are about 10,000 Yehudim in Dimashqu mostly engaged in agriculture and commerce. They are middle persons for the orechah traders and have become wealthy and influential. Most of them are traditional loyalists to the Beit HaMikdash in Yerushalayim and sendlavish offerings to the Temple and strictly observe Yehudi laws. They have financed the building of a synagogue. There are also temples to the different gods.

Yavan culture and religion maintains a strong presence and there are some Yehudim who have intermarried with the locals. They are liberal in their religious practices. In contrast to Yahadut, Hellenism is humanistic. It glorifies human beings and looks upon the human body as the ultimate in physical beauty after the horse. The Kittim now maintain the theatre, gymnasium, games in the arena, and centres of education. Yahadut sublimates the spirit over the body. Hellenism excels not only in the knowledge of the mind but also pleasures of the body sometimes to excess. This leads to condemnation by the Yehudim.

Removing themselves from all these beliefs and practices are the Hasya or Hasidim. This was the first group of the original Hasidim from Qumran to branch out in search of a wilderness refuge in Dimashqu. These are the people whom I am interested in meeting. We go to the marketplace to enquire about their whereabouts.

A vegetable and fruit seller tells us where to find the Hasidim.

"They supply the fruit and vegetable I sell. They are known as 'the Way' and live in their communities in the *Ghouta*[227], an oasis along the Barada river. They have farms growing cereals, vegetables and fruits. You follow the road down south and then turn east. You cannot miss them."

We buy some fruits from the vendor before setting out.

"This is the way we came, admiring the river and the canals," says Miriamne.

Going east along the river, we arrive at the settlement built after the design and structure of the Qumran complex. The farm is fenced off with a gate that is not locked. Men are working in the fields and women are milling the grain. We approach the first building.

I make the introduction, "We are from HaGalil and we have come

---

[227] Fields in Arabic, an agricultural region supplying food and furniture to Damascus

to visit you."

"What is your purpose?" asks the Hasya who greets them.

"We come in peace to get to know you and understand your 'Way',"
say I.

"Please wait outside, I will call our chief," he says.

While waiting, we watch the members of the community working
in silence. Shemayon let the mule graze on the grass.

The chief comes out, "If you have come to visit us, you have come
a long way."

"We have been travelling to the west coast to Tyre and Sidon and
come to visit you before returning to HaGalil," I explain.

"How do you know about us and what do you seek?"

"My name is Yeshua. I am from Qumran, and these are my
companions."

"Oh, come inside and sit down. You are welcome here. We can
show you around the place and how we live and work here, but it is
nearly dinner time."

Just then another person walks in. "Hello, we have visitors?
Visitors who come in shalama are always welcome in our community.
My name is Hadassah. I am an elder here."

"I am Yeshua bar Yôsēp̄."

The chief who welcomed us in says, "Sib, Yeshua says he is from
Qumran."

"Wait. Are you really Yeshua bar Yôsēp̄, the Moreh ha-Tsedek?"

"Yes, indeed."

The elder bowed to Yeshua, "It is an honour to have you here. I
know you are no longer with our Qumran community, but you are
still famous as a moreh. We have a lot to talk about, but it is dinner
time. May I invite you all to join us at dinner."

"But we are too many and have come unannounced," say I.

"Not to worry, Moreh Yeshua, there is always enough food to go around in our community. You should know how our community operates. I am sure you all need a place to stay. We have many rooms and you all can stay with us."

The elder instructs the chief to show us where we can stay and says, "Before dinner we will assemble for prayer. You can clean yourselves and rest. When the bell rings one of us will call you to come and join us for dinner."

"Sib, thank you for your hospitality," say I who have been the only spokesperson thus far.

We are shown a place with rooms, but the women must stay elsewhere meant for women and married couples. The community members retire to the baths to purify themselves through ritual immersion. We wash off the travel dust and change into clean clothes. We can hear the members of the community chanting their prayers.

At the sound of the bell two members, a man and a woman, come to fetch us. We are ushered into the refectory where the community has assembled. The elder, Hadassah, tinkles a small bell to catch everyone's attention. He introduces the guests.

"We have some visitors from HaGalil and I am privileged to welcome the former Moreh ha- Tsedek of Qumran. After dinner we will have a dialogue with the moreh and his companions. Those of you who wish to participate can remain here."

We join the members who sit on mats in parallel rows while the food is served. This comprises lamb, barley bread, dates, honey and new wine, which is more like fermented grape juice. We all eat in silence.

After the meal, the members get up and take their dishes with them to wash. We follow suit.

Many of them come back into the refectory, which also serves as the assembly hall. Usually, the time after the evening meal is spent in spiritual pursuits like community prayer, study of the law or in discussion with some wise people who may be visiting. This was an opportunity for the latter.

Sib Hadassah addresses the group, "Although we have not met, Moreh Yeshua was once the Moreh ha-Tsedek of Qumran. You know of Y'hochanan ha-mmatbil who also left the community to preach repentance in the wilderness. Sadly, he was beheaded by the cruel Malka Antipas. Yeshua too has been travelling, preaching and healing with his followers, and Antipas is also after him. This is all I know. Now that he is among us, he can tell you what his mission is."

A member quite high up in the hierarchy asks, "Moreh Yeshua, before you tell us of your mission, can you tell us why you left Qumran?"

I respond, "Qumran, just like what you have here, is a beautiful and peaceful place. I was very happy there in the community. They elected me as the Moreh ha-Tsedek, although that was not my wish. With so much time to meditate and contemplate I began to think what a blissful life that was, set apart in the name of holiness, away from not only the Beit HaMikdash, the Perushim, the Şĕdûqîm and the Soferim but also separated from the people. People, especially poor country people, are suffering at the hands of the malke and the Kittim and oppressed by the Beit HaMikdash religious leaders while we enjoy the peace and tranquility of our secluded oasis. I couldn't be at peace thinking of their sufferings, heavily burdened by taxes, numerous rules and regulations of religion, and ostracized due to illnesses.

"I began to realise that there is a sickness, a disease in our society, which needs healing. I could not do anything for the people had I sat contemplating in the desert wilderness. I had to be among them. That is why I left although I was sad to leave the brethren."

"How do you intend to accomplish this?" asks sib Hadassah.

"This is something that I cannot accomplish on my own. I have followers and together we intend to change the minds of people by showing them the way of love based on justice and equality, the way of tsedek. To bring an end to oppression, the people will have to overcome ignorance, false notions, and wrong interpretations of the scriptures, stand up and demand their rights.

"As Moreh ha-Tsedek I travelled to Mitzrayim to visit the Assayya. I'm sure you have heard of them. They developed healing as a religious art, and I also learnt a lot about herbal healing from the wise men who came from the east. I learnt about owrah from them. There is a lot of suffering among our people from illnesses and diseases and they do not know how to treat them. Sickness takes away the joy of life and we put the blame on satana. There is so much healing properties in plant life that we can learn and discover. The more we learn the better we can cure illnesses.

"All people should enjoy the goods of the earth living good, clean and healthy lives and we should be more concerned with life here on earth than the life hereafter of which we know nothing. The message we bring is not only for the Yehudim but for all people. We have travelled to Tyre and Sidon and seen how people live there.

"The basic principles of life like kindness, not hurting others and doing unto others what we would like done to us apply to everyone. No one person is superior to another. We claim that Elahh chose us through Aba Avraham and consider ourselves greater. This is a completely false notion."

"Are you teaching a new religion?"

"No. You are known as a people of the Way. You have your way of life. We are showing a new way of life in pursuit of love and peace among all people. It is not a religion because religion is focused on the afterlife. It is a movement towards achieving the fullness of life on earth."

"Moreh Yeshua, what you are doing is indeed praiseworthy, but as you know we too condemn the way the Beit HaMikdash teaches religion. We are committed to a separatist ideology and live in the expectation of the coming of the Mshikha. Our ultimate goal is to return to Yerushalayim and restore divine worship in a future, purified Báyith.

"When Yhochanan ha-mmatbil went out to preach repentance we were wondering if he was the expected Mshikha, and now there is talk whether you are the one."

I respond, "The disciples of Yhochanan ha-mmatbil also came to me asking the same question. Please rest easy. I am definitely not the Mshikha. When I was in Qumran, we all believed in the coming of the Mshikha. As you know we in Qumran have been studying the fragments of the Tanakh and know that they have been rewritten and redacted several times over by different people.

"Forgive me if I appear to dash your hopes. The Tanakh is not the dabar Elahh. All the books were written by men. I no longer believe in the Mshikha. The belief in his coming will only end in frustration. There is no such thing as an everlasting dominion or an indestructible mamlekhet. No one coming from the clouds will solve our problems. We, the people, will have to seek and find a solution to our problems. To seek justice and equality we will have to confront the authorities, both civil and religious. When we go against powerful people we must be prepared to get hurt. Our mission is to get the people to believe in their own strength."

"Moreh Yeshua, again your way is admirable, but it goes against our own belief. You are putting yourselves at great risk. People who have believed for generations in a particular way of life will not be easy to change."

"But you have changed. You have denounced the practice of the Beit HaMikdash as unclean and have broken away to live differently. If you can change, the people also can change. Sib Hadassah, thank you for your warning. If people do not change, they will continue to be oppressed and live miserable lives, existing on a false hope.

"Initially, I was so impressed with the Qumran community. I was convinced we did the right thing by dissociating ourselves from the Beit HaMikdash. Later I realised that what we did was to escape from confrontation, waiting in the wilderness for the Mshikha to come. Until now he has not come, and the Beit HaMikdash is as strong as ever. We chose to change ourselves without trying to change them."

Unexpectedly one of the members stood up and said, "What Moreh Yeshua has said makes good sense to me."

Sib Hadassah was taken aback by that comment and decided to bring the meeting to a close in a civil manner. "We would like to thank Moreh Yeshua and his followers for sharing their belief with us. We respect his views, but we are committed to our own. We wish him and his followers well."

That night the dialogue with the sib is the topic of discussion among my followers.

"I think sib Hadassah got a little worried that you might have sown the seeds of conversion among the members, and quickly brought the discussion to an end," says Shimon.

"Well, they too cannot live this life of isolation and dream of the coming of the Mshikha. They too will have to change," say I.

The next day some of the community members took us on a tour of the place, showing us the living quarters, library and farms growing barley, fruits and vegetables.

"This is where we package our products and send them to the market. We are self-sufficient here. Moreh Yeshua, what you said last night made me think beyond this place. Although we have our way and belief, I see that you are addressing real issues while we have separated ourselves from the people. We want to be your friends and some of us may even leave this place to follow you and your way," says one of them.

"I am happy to hear that but think very carefully of the risks involved. Once you dig into the earth and set the plough moving there can be no turning back," say I.

We take leave of sib Hadassah and the community in a cordial manner. The community gives us dates and grain to take on our journey. The sib also tells us that the best way back is to go south towards Gaulanitis. "The road will descend and lead you to Yam Chinneroth."

Mariam turns to me, "The seed you planted is taking root."

"Yes. I hate to break up the Hassidim community, but the members will have to wake up to the fact that locking themselves in a cloistered life when people outside are suffering in poverty, is rather selfish," I point out.

Mattithyahu says, "We have only about half a day left and if we set out now and retrace our steps through Darayya and Sahnaya we could reach Artouz before nightfall."

We pass through Darayya on to Sahnaya, the way we came. Here we stop by a stream next to the scary cave. We continue to Artouz.

The people there immediately recognise us from before, and once again bring out their sick. After administering them with some remedies, we met Kalanit. She takes us to her house to see her father who had been accused of being a tsa'ra'at. He looks well and his leg is much better. Kalanit implored us to stay the night with her family.

The next morning, we set out early retracing our steps to Kfar Hawr, reaching it by midday. After lunch, which we buy from some roadside stalls for we are running low on rations, we continue to Sa'sa. From here we detour from our original route and go south. Ten milin away we come to the town of Sarisai a popular stopover on the Dimashqu road. We stay at an inn for travellers, not quite an orechahserai. During the night, we are reviewing our trip over the foreign lands and encounters with the people.

In the morning we take the road going south. We pass through the small village of Kokab. The people, assuming that we are merchants, come to see what we are selling. Seeing us as mere travellers they lose interest. We enter the region of Gaulanitis. By midday we reach the village of Sogane located on a ridge with a deep valley on its south side. We are in Upper Gaulanitis. The village is a wooded area with big trees and date palms and the villagers live in stone houses built on both sides of the road along the edge of a cliff overlooking a deep valley. The stones are held together with a mixture of mud, hay and fragments of ceramics with wooden roofs. There is a synagogue with stone pillars and arches. This is a Jewish village.

Scenario 47 - Experiences shared

Beth-tsaida/Kfar Nahum

We settle down beside a fountain under one of the big trees and have lunch, watched by the grazing sheep and cattle. The fresh water of the fountain is clean enough to drink. The fountain feeds the marshland covered with rushes and eventually supplies water to the Little Nehar ha Yarden which becomes a big river flowing into Yam Chinneroth.

The villagers are busy in the fields, so we continue our way back. We follow along the bank of the Nehar haYarden until we reach Beth-tsaida, the home of Ya'aqov and Yhochanan.

Ya'aqov and Yhochanan's parents, Zebadyah and Shlomiṯ are surprised and delighted to see us all.

"You have all been away for a long time," she says as her sons greet her and then pay respects to their father.

We unload our travel baggage and one of Zebadyah's men takes care of the mule.

"All of you wash up and rest. Give me some time to prepare dinner."

"We can help," says Mariam and the women.

"No, no you also rest with the others. I have enough helpers to get dinner ready," says Shlomiṯ.

After a much-missed splendid home-cooked dinner of fish and

lamb we sit down to talk.

"Tell us about the great cities of Tyre and Sidon," says Zebadyah.

"When we went fishing in Tyre with the fishermen, we learnt so much about how they fish and how big and efficient their boats are. We are so stuck in Chinneroth and know so little about others. We think we are the greatest people on earth chosen by Elahh and better than the others. It made us humble to see and learn from other people," says Andreia.

Ya'aqov, Yhochanan and the others also share their travel experiences and talk into the night.

The next day we move to Kfar Naum. Rebecca welcomes us. I pay my respects to Abigail, Shemayon's mother-in-law, "Attha, how have you been? You are looking well."

"After taking your remedies I have never been sick again," she says.

Shemayon's family are eager to hear all about the travels.

"Before we talk about our travels, tell us what has been happening here. Is the fox still hunting for us?" I enquire.

Hordos Antipas has heard about the things that are happening. He is confused because some people say that Y'hochanan ha-mmatbil had risen from death. Others say that Eliyahu has come to life. It is also believed that one of the prophets from long ago has been resurrected.

"After the beheading of Yhochanan ha-mmatbil, the Yehudim keep their distance from Hordos Antipas. In his usual way, as he was educated in Roma, he spends his time mostly in his new capital, Tiberias, dining in his ornate palace, having his hot baths and watching sport in his stadium. He behaves more like the Kittim than a Yehudi. The lives of ordinary people have not changed much," says Rebecca.

"There has not been a lot of talk about you, Yeshua. They probably think that you have faded away out of fear for your life," says Abigail.

"Hordos is known to have said that he had cut off Yhochanan's head and still keeps hearing about Yeshua. He has expressed the wish to meet you personally," adds Rebecca.

"I have no desire to meet that fox," say I.

After sharing our adventure stories, we gather again at our lakeside rendezvous to plan our next course of action.

Scenario 48 - Mshikha

Base Camp

Then next morning we stock up on supplies at the Kfar Nahum market and walk the short distance of three milin to our Chinneroth reserve. The place is much the same as we left it but for the overturned boat, now almost hidden by the undergrowth. We get the place habitable again clearing the area and pitching the tent. The Zebadyah brothers join Shemayon and Andreia to go fishing, and upon returning go through the usual chores of cleaning the fish and preparing the fire. Under the tent, we talk over the meal.

"Soon word will get to Antipas. His wish to meet me is not an invitation. That fox will start his hunt again, for me and for all of us. But let's not worry ourselves over that. Let's reflect on the experience of our travel beyond HaGalil," say I.

Pilip says, "Moreh, in the dialogue with the Hasidim in Dimashqu, They raised the question of the coming of the Mshikha wondering if it is you. We also have raised this question several times but never got a definite answer from you. People living a life of hopelessness against oppression find strength in the belief that Elahh will send someone to save us."

"Our people live in the hope of peace and freedom in a perfect mamlekhet that can only be in the Mamlekhet Elahh in Olam HaEmet," says Shoshanna.

"I am more interested in a mamlekhet here, free from oppression by the Kittim and our own malke. You have destroyed our belief in the Mamlekhet Elahh, but you have no plan of action to bring about a liberation from the Kittim," questions Yehudah.

"Yehudah, do you expect this Mshikha to raise an army to liberate us from the Kittim? I am not a malka or a military general. I am only a tekton, a naggara. My aim is not to build an army to overthrow the Kittim or to start a new religion against the Beit HaMikdash. As I said before, people do evil because of selfishness and greed. There will always be such people and we can never have a perfect society. All we can do is influence as many as we can in the way of tsedek. This will of course, mean challenging those who are powerful and do evil. They will not like that and will use their power against us. We must be prepared to pay that price.

"The authorities are also well aware that it is almost impossible to get rid of the Kittim yoke, so they use the scriptures to boost hopes of the people by projecting the coming of a liberator, a great political leader, the Mshikha. He will come as a Yehudi malka from the line of Dawidh. He will unify the tribes in Eretz Yisra'el and rebuild the Beit HaMikdash. He will be the malka in the Mamlekhet Elahh. They say his coming is imminent. With the way our malke are conducting themselves, they are not going to tolerate another malka.

"Their notion of the Mshikha is for the triumph and glory of Yisra'el in the Mamlekhet Elahh. They place their belief in the words of the Nebi Daniel who looking into the night visions said, 'Behold, I saw One like a Son of Man coming with the cloud of heaven; and to Him was given dominion, glory and a kingdom, that all the nations and people of every language might serve Him. His dominion is an everlasting dominion which will not pass away; and His kingdom is one which will not be destroyed....'. Ever since, we have been waiting for him to appear.

"Does this not sound very much like the doctrine of Mazdyasana when Zarathustra predicted the coming of the Saushyant who will begin the final battle between the forces of good and evil. Evil will be destroyed, and he will resurrect the dead and restore their bodies to perfection? Zoroaster and Daniel both lived at the same place and time over 500 years ago."

During the Exile in Bavel, Nebi Daniel was appointed by Malka Nebuchadnezzar as the chief of the Magi. Bavel was in Mesopotamia, a part of Parthyaea. Parthyaea was not only the original place of Aba Avraham it was the home of Zarathustra, the founder of Mazdayasana whose priests are the Magi. If Daniel was the chief of the Magi, he must have known of the coming of the Saushyant and was speaking about the Saushyant. Or else he was speaking of the anointed one like Koresh, the malka of Parthyaea who later freed our people from Bavel. What are we to expect?

"If we continue to believe that some mysterious saviour will come one day to solve our problems, we will never make the effort to use our own resources of knowledge and strength to liberate ourselves. The rich and powerful will continue to oppress us, and we, our children and our children's children will be condemned to live in misery. Hopefully, the efforts we make will bring some change in the people for the better."

"When people begin to choose the path of tsedek they will enjoy peace of conscience and their example will inspire their children. That, I'm afraid, is all we can hope for. As a Moreh ha Tsedek that is the purpose of my life. If you think that way of life is worth following, we can go on together. If you expect more than that from me, you will be disappointed. People must be free of ailment and pain and enjoy peace and happiness in a free and comfortable life. What more is there to life?

"*Rabboni*, before we left for our journey you met and discussed matters with the Parushim from Yerushalayim, Nikodemus, Yôsēp̄ of Harimathea and Gamaliel. That night we reflected among ourselves on that conversation and wondered about following you. We wondered how far you would go to defend the people. Together we decided we would follow you no matter what. You spoke to Nikodemus about being born again. I can say, if I can also speak for the others, that through that journey with you, meeting and interacting with different people, we too have been born again," says Mariam.

"Shimon and I had doubts about how far you would go to heal the society if it meant using violence against the authorities and the Kittim. You have reorientated the motivation of our zeal for race and religion," says Yehudah of Kerioth.

Pilip said, "I too had doubts until you said in Acchabare not to label people by religion. Moreh, the people in those lands are generally different from us in HaGalil and Eretz Yisrael. We have condemned them as goyim, unbelievers, and sinful people. Even though historically they have grievances against us, none of them have been hostile towards us. Even the Yehudim there are different. They are more tolerant, and the synagogue people are not so assertive. They have learnt to live with each other."

"The way we participated in the wedding ritual in Sepph gave me a completely different outlook on people we had condemned and looked down upon as goyim. After what you told us about Malka Sh'lomoh and his wives, who are we to judge others?" says Y'hochanan.

"Your teaching deviated so much from Yahadut that I was afraid I would be rejected by the Yehudim when I get back. I understand better now how we are bound by our culture and religion to the extent of being blind. You not only dispelled our prejudices, but you also have a message for other people. I won't use the word goyim anymore. They were also misguided by personifying the forces of nature into gods and goddesses," says Marta.

"You have showed us that religion and Elahh are used to distract us from the real issues of suffering and injustice. I have joined this group to follow you, Moreh, because you inspire hope in us to stand up and challenge the oppressors. I have vowed to fight them. So, we will fight the Kittim and our religious leaders not to save our religion but the people," says Yehudah.

"Well spoken, Yehudah. If we must take up the sword it must be to save the people," says Marta.

Meeting the merchants of the Silk Road and learning about the beliefs of Mazdayasana and the Budddhist idea of rebirth all make me want to visit them in their lands to learn more," says Tauma.

"The meeting of sib Hadassah and the Hassidim in Dimashqu shows how highly they respected you, Moreh. You even cast a doubt in their belief, made them think of a new way of life, and left a seed of change in them," says Ya'akov.

"When we met Norana, the attha from Athura in Knaan with a sick daughter, you taught us about using owrah for healing. You also told the woman that the illness of the little girl was the result of many human factors, not satana, nor was it punishment of the gods. I realize how much religion misleads the people," says Natan'el.

"We met a lot of people with different kinds of illnesses, and you taught us how to use owrah to bring about healing," says Shemayon.

"We can also see the big picture of sickness in the society that requires healing," adds Mattithyahu.

Up until now my sixteen followers have primarily been observers and hearers. I have spoken to the crowds in their presence, day after day, week after week, and month after month. I have also molded their thinking through intimate discourses and answered all their questions. They have witnessed all these and have changed to think like me. Now it is time to act like me.

"In Dimashqu we had a very good reflection and discussion and I think you understand me better now. I do not claim to be anything but a plain ordinary man. My experience with the Hasidim in Qumran, the Assayya in Mitzrayim and our travel beyond Ha Galil has convinced me that our new way of looking at reality is totally alien to our people. Yet it is a different way, a way that will change people and bring meaning to life in this world.

"I see that the journey out has been beneficial. We all have changed, and it is your task to change other people. This is what I propose to do. We will spend some time here. I will teach you more about owrah and their usage, and also teach you how to read and write or to improve what you already know. After that I would like to send you on missions to the people without me," say I.

"This will be a new experience for us. What we are doing is like the sower sowing seeds on the earth. These must take root, grow, and bear fruit. Change will come with a plentiful harvest. We cannot rest and waste time. We must continue this work. We are with you all the way, *Rabboni*," assures Mariam.

Y'hochanan says, "Shimon and Yehudah, you are both kana'im, and Mattithyahu, you worked as a tax collector for the Kittim government. You are enemies and instead of fighting and killing each other, you have chosen to follow our Moreh. That is because you have chosen to follow the way of tsedek. The rest of us, fisherfolk, farmers and women have also made the same choice. Moreh, lead the way and we will follow."

Scenario 49 - Owrah

Base Camp

"Tomorrow morning let us spread out into the countryside and collect owrah. We will sort them out and I will explain how they can be prepared and used," I propose.

After the evening meal Shoshanna, Arsinoe and Miriamne start the preparations for breakfast. They use the wheat and legumes they bought already milled into flour. Miriamne combines some flour with water and adds some pomegranate juice, kneads it in an earthen trough, adds a dash of fennel and cumin and sets it aside. Shoshanna selects handfuls of lentils, broad beans, chickpeas, field peas, and soaks them in water, while Arsinoe attends to the fire on the pit that they keep burning all the time.

The next morning the same three women get up early and prepare breakfast. Arsinoe kindles the fire and restarts it. Over the hot ambers she places pottery in the shape of a convex dome. Miriamne flattens dough between the palms of her hands and places this on top of the hot dome called the *machabat*[228]. This process is known as pit-oven

---

[228] Pit-oven or griddle for baking flatbread

baking. The resulting thin unleavened flatbread is called *ugah*[229].

Shoshana rinses out the soaked beans, adds fresh water, cuts up onions, garlic and leek, puts them all together in a pot over the fire to stew.

When everybody is up, we all sit down, and I give thanks to the three women for providing breakfast. We pass the bread around, tear and dip it in the stew, eat and drink water, finishing breakfast with dried figs.

I then tell them to break into small groups and spread out in search of owrah.

"Pick whatever looks like owrah, also pick the flowers, fruit or seeds. Let's go."

We spontaneously form into four groups. Shemayon, Ya'aqov, Tauma and Joa'ana, are in one group; Marta, Andreia, Pilip and Y'hochanan in another; Shoshanna, Shimon, Yehudah and Natan'el in a third; while I join Mariam, Arsinoe, Mattithyahu and Miriamne to form the final group.

We branch out into the countryside moving inland from the shores of the lake into the plain of Gennesaret. We fan out walking among the tall grass, shrubs and rocks towards the foothills. The plain is sparsely dotted with trees. Among them are oak, pine, cedar, juniper and elder. On the hill slopes are plane trees, sycamore and palms, and willows alongside streams. We have to wade through rough thistle, crocus, ivy, hawthorn and honeysuckle. Among them also there are wild roses, lily, tulip, anemone, poppy, hyacinth and cyclamen and balls of bright yellow wattles or acacias. It is a beautiful, coloured landscape with an air of fragrance from aromatic shrubs.

We find owrah among the arbutus, pistachio, carob, or locust trees, styrax, bay and wild olive and mulberry bushes. We pick whatever

---

[229] Thin unleavened flatbread

looks like owrah. As we pick, we also engage in conversation.

Shemayon says, "All we fishermen know is fish. We know nothing about owrah."

"If we are going to use them to heal people we might as well learn about them" says Joa'ana.

"Shemayon, our Moreh wants us to cast a broad net over the people and bring them to understand a new way of life in pursuit of love and peace," says Ya'aqov.

"After being with our Moreh for so long and seeing all the good work he has done, it appears to me that the people have not really changed," observes Tauma.

"I think the change will take a long time in coming. We are merely planting the seeds. Once the mind has changed the rest will follow. It took us more than two years before we began to change, and yet some of us have not really changed," says Joa'ana looking at Shemayon.

"Why are you all looking at me?" asks Shemayon.

"Shemayon, you have not changed your attitude towards women. You want them all to be like men. We don't want to be like men and that is why you don't treat us as equals," says Joa'ana touching a shittâh plant whose leaves immediately fold.

"I too was like you, Shemayon. I have changed. Your reluctance to change your attitude towards women may be because you are jealous of the closeness of Mariam and Yeshua," reasons Tauma.

"Look, Yeshua has known Mariam long before he knew us. He surely has a special love for her," says Ya'aqov.

"Yes, they are attracted to each other. We all have special feelings for people, and we should be able to understand that," adds Joa'ana.

"We are picking owrah to heal people. There is no owrah to heal your prejudice against women. You have to heal yourself, Shemayon, otherwise you belong to the Beit HaMikdash and not to us," surmises Ya'aqov.

"You have to close the old ways and be open to the new way of Moreh Yeshua," says Tauma.

"If we bring about healing with the owrah, people will only expect more of the same. As long as they attribute their sickness because of their sins and the work of satana, there can be no cure," says Marta in the other group that has moved closer to the foothills.

"That is the teaching of religion, but I think what our Moreh is trying to tell us is that religion has become a sickness among our people," says Andreia.

"So, is our Moreh trying to replace that religion with another kind of religion?" asks Pilip.

"No, he himself ruled that out. Our Moreh is the Moreh ha-Tsedek. I believe that he is creating a way and a movement, not a religion," explains Y'hochanan.

The third group has wandered down a valley to a stream. Yehudah sits under a willow, "I am getting impatient with all this healing with owrah. It meets the needs of the people, but it does not liberate the people from oppression. We must have a plan to fight the Kittim."

"He has told us repeatedly that we do not have the means to fight the Kittim. We can challenge our own leaders," says Shoshanna.

"That would be futile because they have the support of the Kittim," rebuts Shimon.

"I think that our Moreh hopes to undermine the teachings of the Beit HaMikdash to such an extent that the people will rise and question their teachings. The laws of religion also justify heavy taxation and other burdens imposed by the malka. Our Moreh's way of tsedek means fighting for justice and equality. We surely cannot match the military might of the Kittim, so the fight is within the people in their numbers," Natan'el assesses the situation.

"That sounds like an impossible task," says the skeptical Yehudah.

"It is up to us to make that possible. We have to get more and more people thinking like we do," says Shoshanna.

The remaining group has picked quite a lot of owrah and is turning back to the camp when Miriamne says, "A good and clean life is a necessity for all of us. Sickness takes away the joy of life and we put the blame on satana. Very few people know the healing properties of owrah."

"We are going to teach them," responds the optimistic Mariam.

"There are some sicknesses we cannot cure because we do not know enough about owrah or all about the human body. People are mute, blind and deaf from birth. Something must have gone awry when the baby was growing inside its mother's stomach. We have no knowledge on how to cure them. We see this as something bad, and because of our inability and ignorance, we blame some power beyond us like satana. Our religion makes us believe that this is true not only because of evil satana but also because the parents have sinned against Elahh. It is Elahh's punishment. Is Elahh then using satana to do his work for him? People become sicker because of such religious nonsense," say I.

"We must do whatever we can to liberate people from their sick body and sick mind," says Arsinoe.

"People want to see magic and miracles before they will believe what we have to say," adds Mattithyahu.

"This will not be an easy task. You must make the people believe in you. They must believe that your love and concern for them is genuine even when there are limitations in using healing owrah," I assure.

The other groups also retrace their steps back to the camp. There we lay out all the different owrah on the ground and begin to sort similar looking ones together. After the midday meal I start identifying and naming them.

"When a person is sick or inflicted by a wound that does not heal, you immediately put the blame on sin and satana. Alright, there may be some truth in that. The sick person's body is possessed by something that is alien to that body. It works against the body. If the body is not strong enough to fight it, the possession gets stronger, and the body gets weaker. This something is in nature with a toqeph of its own. They are not possessed by satana, by some spirit outside of this world. We study the nature of that affliction and read the signs. When the body is too weak to fight it, we help the body with appropriate owrah to fight that possession. When the body becomes stronger, healing takes place, and the possession is expelled. There is no miracle."

I take a bunch of green leaves with silver stems and greyish green leaves with whitish undersides.

Among the shrubs I point to a spiky plant, "This is *ahalot*[230], good for reducing swelling and healing of wounds, like the wound we saw in the man's leg." I snap off a frond and point to the yellow juice beneath the skin of the leaf. I tear the thick frond and expose the gel beneath, "This can be used to rub on the swelling of arms and legs."

"This is *la'anah*[231] sometimes called wormwood. It is so bitter you want to spit it out. It is poisonous."

I pick twigs with small, pointed leaves and spikes with purple flowers still attached to them. "This owrah is ezob, mentioned many times in the Tanakh as a symbol of cleansing and inner healing used in rituals.

"Ezob, called *owrah qadosh*[232], is more than ceremonial. It has healing properties. It alleviates stomach pains, eliminates coughing, and is good for those with difficulty breathing. It can also be used to

---

[230] Aoe-vera

[231] Wormwood, regarded as poisonous

[232] Holy herb

heal cuts, wounds and insect bites. We should gather more of them and dry them in the sun. When the leaves and flowers are dried, they can be chopped up finely and used for making ezob tea, which has a minty taste. That is good for people with swelling and pain in their joints.

It is one of the common owrah found in Peleshet and Kenaan. It is a sweet-smelling plant of the mint family. It is often mentioned in the scriptures. It has several uses. You remember I told the attha in Tyre to give her daughter a little of the oil of ezob.

"Very often on the streets and at the temple gates we find beggars who are lame and blind. People are repeatedly told that they have been struck by satana for their sins. We must look closely and study what really causes this. Very few of them are born lame or blind and that is very difficult to explain. Nature is not all that perfect. Most cases of those who are lame are due to injury they have had. Most injuries will heal by themselves with good exercise. Those that do not may be due to the kind of food eaten. Those who take a lot of sweet food may find that the leg or foot does not heal. This is when we can advise them to avoid sweet things and add the oil of ezob to their meal. There is never an immediate magic cure. Most of the time the body heals itself. This will take time with proper cleaning and care of the wound."

"The religious leaders speak so much of cleaning the hands before praying but they never advise the poor and sick people to keep themselves clean," said Marta.

"You can also extract oil from these. You put some of it in a mortar, crush and grind it, and slowly you will see oil coming out of it. This is *mish'cha t'china, owrah*[233] ground into oil,"

"Remember, in Gush Halav we saw the women making olive oil. It

---

[233] Herbs ground into oil

is a slow process," says Miriammne.

"We should collect the oil and carry them with us. You only need to mix a few drops of it with olive oil to use it," I explain.

"We should start working on that," says Mariam.

Next, I pick up the owrah with the green leaves with a cluster of small yellow flowers.

"*Shittâh*[234], this is quite a rare plant here. The Yavan call it *mimos*. It is a very sensitive plant, watch," say I and touch the leaves which immediately fold up and close.

"This owrah too can be dried and grounded, and the powder used in the healing of wounds. It is also known as acacia. After these bright flowers die the pods contain seeds. They too should be made into powder.

"When an animal senses harm or is threatened, it runs away. Plants cannot run away, but they can sense danger in the environment. When we walk past and touch them or when we pick a flower or step on them, they cannot complain or escape. But they can feel and respond. For this plant, closing its leaves is a form of defence. Even when a drop of rainwater falls on them, they will react like this. We must respect life in plants and trees and study how they react and learn what they can give to us by way of healing. The defence system in some plants is so strong that they can harm us, so we must study them closely.

I pull out a small jar from the bundle that the Buddhists gave me. "Remember I gave a bit of this to the attha's daughter? It is the extract from the common shrub called pagana. The Yavan call it *paganon*. Healers have found that a few drops of this calms down a person with seizures. They cannot explain why it works, but it does.

We have seen many cases of seizures and all the time they are

---

[234] Acacia, commonly known as wattles and *mimos* in Greek

attributed to sin and the work of satana. This can happen for many reasons like when a person sleeps too much or does not have enough sleep, when he eats too much or drinks too much wine or fasts for too long. The body is stressed by these extremes. We should make pegana oil and carry it with us. Because it is effective, people would say that you have worked a miracle. Don't be taken in by that."

I then explain those owrah used for healing and separate them from those owrah used as condiments like thyme, basil, oregano, sesame seed, caraway seed, cumin, coriander, sumac berries, cinnamon, cloves and fennel. Grouped together like this, they are called za'atar[235]. I also explain that some of them, apart from adding taste to food, also have medicinal value for good health. I particularly mentioned chives which belong to the onion family including garlic, shallot and leeks. I say, "These don't directly heal but after you have administered a healing owrah encourage them to eat plenty of these to help the healing process. Keep an eye out for plants, shrubs and owrah. Many of the common vegetables we consume have medicinal value."

I select one with bright green leaves and white flowers in a cone-shaped bunch. I say, "Remember we saw this on the way to Darayya. This is basil, holy basil and the wise men from Hodu call it *thulasi*[236]. It is a remedy for many illnesses like people with difficulty breathing, are stressed or if they are sick due to something harmful entering their body causing sores inside the stomach, and others." I squash the leaves which give off an aromatic smell. "The juice extracted from the leaves should be drunk every day until the illness disappears. Can you remember all these things?"

"People should follow our way not because we heal their sick as

---

[235] A generic name for a family of herbs used as condiments for culinary purposes

[236] Sacred basil plant (Tamil)

though we work miracles and possess divine powers. We must make them see the disease plaguing our society, and that the power of healing is within each of us," I reiterate.

It is not enough merely to heal the sick but there must be a way to heal the disease in the society," says Yehudah.

"Moreh, we are learning so much from you," says Natan'el.

"Moreh, you know so much about using owrah as healing remedies. We too should teach people to understand owrah and how to use them," says Miriamne.

"Yes, I am only passing on to you what I have learnt. The Assayya have discovered and applied marvelous physical remedies.

"Let us start preparing the necessary medicines," suggests Mariam.

"We should put the medicine into small containers and identify them with a mark," says Mattithyahu.

"It is alright for you because you can read and write but some of us cannot do that," says Shemayon.

"While we are preparing the medicines, I will teach you how to read and write. Those of you who already know something about letters can help the others. We can then read not only some of the writings of the Assayya and the wise men from the East, but also our scriptures," say I.

"We are only learning to use herbs for pain relief and healing. The healers in Seen are really specialized in different methods of healing. About 100 years ago the healers of Seen were using sharp needles to pierce different parts of the body to relief pain as a healing remedy. We have so much to learn from the wisdom of the East.

The Healing Touch

"We need to know more about healing because some of the cases are so complicated that we are not sure what remedy to apply," says Mariam.

I respond, "Be realistic. Question the person on details of the ailment, how long it has lasted and what they have done about it. Try and discern the natural causes. There is no such thing as an instant cure. Dismiss any notion they may have that you are miracle workers.

"Physical healing is not the main purpose of going to the people. We are concerned about making them see the truth against the falsehood of the religious authorities. However, since they also have physical needs in the face of sickness and disabilities — these are a priority for them — attend to these and then lead them on to see the sickness within society itself. In many cases their conditioned thinking also becomes the cause of the illness. The mind and the body are connected. The mind feels the pain in the body. The wrong thinking that causes the sickness can also make it worse. When the people bring someone sick to you, make a quick assessment of the person and their surrounding conditions. Don't look merely at the sickness itself but look at the whole person. Ask questions about the illness. Look for more than physical causes. The owrah and oils are only remedies. The problem could be in the mind."

"We know that agents of disease that attack the body are less of an enemy than the fear, worry and stress that are caused by negative concerns. So, we must look at healing from the point of view of the attitude to life. The Assayya find that changing the mind from hopelessness and desperation to joy is the secret of healing power. The important factors to healing are love, peace, laughter, rest and relaxation with music and art.

"Compassion and love are also integral to healing. Apply these to the sick, touch them and the healing that passes through you to them will also be healing power for yourself, for your own body and mind.

"Help the person to enter into the self to see if they harbour anger, hatred, animosity, fear — all of which cause tension and misery, which disturbs the mind and burns the body. Calm them down and try to change these feelings and thoughts to love, compassion and forgiveness. Nature will take over from there and begin the healing process with the help of medicinal herbs, of course.

"How are we to know what the sick person thinks?" asks Joan'na.

"If the sick person, man, woman, or child can speak, question them. Most often though, the people who bring the sick would speak for them. The first thing they will say is that satana has taken hold of the person and what they have done to control that. The sick person also begins to believe the same thing, that satana has control of their body and that they can do nothing against satana who does things to them, like turning them aggressive, hurting others or hurting themselves. You have to find ways to calm the mind of a sick person."

"Owrah can alleviate the pain, but the real cure is in the mind of the sick person and of the people around them. We have to try and correct that thinking."

"We need to know more about herbal cures," says Shoshanna.

"You have to be careful when using owrah to cure and heal. Some can be poisonous and harmful. Some may not work. In most cases they do, and healing takes place. Why it works we do not know, but it does. Perhaps they believe you have healing powers. For many generations people have studied the effects of medicinal owrah and wrote them down. The Assayya of Mitzrayim, from whom I learnt the art, are continually studying *owrah* and learning new remedies.

"Always use only the tried and tested herbs. Tell them to be patient and try another similar herb or oil. Be wary of the reaction of the skeptics. When things do not work, and people feel helpless, the easiest thing to do is blame it on some evil power out of this world like satana. They will also blame you as being fake healers. The biggest culprits in this area are our own religious leaders. It only reveals their learned ignorance of human nature. Even if it works some may accuse you, as they did me, that you work with the power of satana. You just tell them that good cannot come out of evil.

"We cannot rest and waste time. We must continue this work. We are with you all the way, *Rabboni*," says Mariam.

Part Five

Mission

Scenario 50 - Disturbing factors

Base Camp

In the weeks that follow we are busy preparing owrah essence and learning the alphabet.

Letters

"We travelled north beyond HaGalil into the land of the Kenaani, considered as inferior and separated them from us. Yet we found that those people are not all that different from us, and we are the ones who have adopted their culture. We saw their ships and found how superior they are to ours. They sail to distant lands. To communicate with different people, they developed a language and an alphabet with 22 square letters, like this," clearing the stones, I level the sand and draw those letters on the ground.

"They look almost like our *Ivri*[237]," says Mattithyahu.

"Yes, it is called *ktav Ashuri*[238]. We borrowed their script and called

---

[237] Hebrew

[238] Assyrian lettering

it *ktav Ivri*[239], the original spoken language in Mamlekhet Yisra'el and Mamlekhet Yehuda. The language we speak now is not the same. We speak the language of Athura, the same as the written *ktav* Ashuri. We forget that we are all from the same original people who broke out into different tribes like the Emori, the Perizi, the Khiv'va, the Heth, the Yebusi, the Girgasi and others. All these people, including us, are considered the descendants of Aba Noah or his first-born son, Shem.

"According to the Tanakh, Aba Noah had three sons, Shem, Ham and Japheth. The Kenaani take their name from Knaan, son of Shem and grandson of Noah. Further down the line of Noah was Iver from whom the Ivri take their name.

The fifth son of Shem was Aram who lived in the valley of Beth Nahreem, also known as Athura or Aramea. We speak *Ărammì*[240]. All the lands from Mitzrayim to Bavel spoke *Ărammì*. So, you see, we are all connected."

"If originally, we spoke Ivri, why have we now changed to speaking *Ărammì*?" asks Pilip.

"About six hundred years ago, the Mamlekhet Yehuda was conquered by the Baval emperor who destroyed Yerushalayim and the Beit HaMikdash and took our people in captivity to Bavel. For 70 years they lived among the people there and began to speak their language, *Ărammì*. When Malka Koresh of Parthyaea conquered Bavel, the Yehudi were allowed to return to their homeland. They rebuilt Yerushalayim and the Beit HaMikdash, and *Ărammì* became the common spoken language in Yisra'el.

"The manuscripts we were looking at in Qumran were those before the destruction of the Beit HaMikdash and were in Ivrit. Both Ivrit

---

[239] Hebrew lettering

[240] Aramean/ Aramaic

and Ărammì are similar."

"Write something for us," asks Andrea.

I erase everything on the sand and write my name Yeshua from right to left and read it out. Then I write the first four letters, ׳ י ו ה א and sound them, *aleph*, *bet*, *gimel* and *dalet*, and then the rest of the 22 letters. I explain that the whole alphabet is called *abjad* after the first four letters. I get the group to start writing and reading. This was the beginning of my lessons.

When they go to get provisions, they also buy wax tablets with stylus for writing and small earthen jars for herb mixtures and oils.

They are busy in the weeks that follow collecting herbs and processing them while learning to read and write. They scratch the appropriate labels on the earthen jars. All the time I keep reminding them what they should do and how to conduct themselves.

Disturbing Factors

"Our society is like the body of a very sick person. The illness is in many parts of the body. Some parts are malnourished, some are neglected like the withered arm, others malfunction like the blind and the deaf, yet others suffer the feverish pain of injustice and oppression. Society sees the sick person as the sinner and condemns them. Our religious leaders preach a salvation based on repentance from sin to gain the favour of Elahh, to save the nephesh from hellfire in gehanna and to reap the reward of healthy and pleasurable living forever in the Olam HaEmet. This privilege, claim the rabbim, the Perushim and the kohanaim of the Beit HaMikdash, is reserved only for the believers of Yahadut. Have we not missed the whole point here?

"Sickness, illness and pain reflect the disturbing factors in our society. To bring about healing we have to address these factors."

"What are they, these disturbing factors?" asks Mariam.

"Moreh, before you answer that; why are you allowing only the women to ask all the questions? Tell them to stop asking so that we can also have a chance," says Shemayon.

"Shemayon, you are disturbed because you have not got over your prejudice against women. That is a disturbing factor. You have an illness there that needs to be cured. You have not been paying attention to what I have been saying. If you had been thinking you would have questions to ask. Have I stopped any of you from asking questions? This is also a reflection of the disturbing social factors."

"Shemayon, you are a good leader of fishermen, but you are not quick enough to ask questions. The women have put us all to shame," says Natan'el.

"Alright, *Rabboni*, please tell us about the disturbing social factors," says Mariam who is annoyed at Shemayon and does not want to engage him in an argument.

"There, you see, why is it that you alone call the Moreh, *Rabboni?*" asks the irritated Shemayon.

"It may be that she loves me more than the others."

"As I always thought," murmurs Shemayon.

"Are you jealous, Shemayon?" asks Yehudah.

"Moreh, you said everyone is equal. Yet you say she loves more than the rest," says Y'hochanan.

"Loving more does not make you less equal. Let us get back to the disturbing social factors," say I.

"Tell us," asks Mattithyahu.

"We are people, we are all children of adamah. We find ourselves disconnected, separated, divided and classified. We have no choice as to where we are born and into which community of people. We identify ourselves with that community. We also find other communities in other parts as we discovered in our travels.

"The old scriptures speak about the Kenites, the Kenizzites, the Hittites, the Perizzites, the Rephaim, the Amorites, the Canaanites, the Girgashites, the Jeubsi and others. We were all one people until we began to occupy different territories and adopted different languages. People chose to live in different places and the different communities developed different characteristics conditioned by the climate, land and their work. Through their breeding, their skin and eyes took on different hues and they too created their own gods. We categorise them as different peoples and, of course, each thinks they are the best and superior to others. They fight to dominate one another. So, this different grouping of peoples is a disturbing factor that disconnects us."

"We witnessed something when we travelled north that we do not see here," says Mattithyahu.

Marta took the cue. "We saw that some of them, even though they were different people with different religion and language, are able to live together accepting their differences."

"This is something that the Yehudim are unable to do. Even within our land we cannot live in peace with the Shomronim," say I.

"What are the other factors, Moreh," asks Soshanna.

"They are closely linked. We disconnect ourselves from the Shomronim even though we are the same people. The thing that separates us is religion, and it is because we think that our Elahh is the only Most High God."

"The Beit HaMikdash wants us to believe that that is the truth," adds Arsinoe.

"People who are rich have become powerful and control the poor. People are then placed on different levels of society. This is the other factor that we see all around us. This difference is carried into the way we are governed by powerful people. We have our malka and we also have the Kittim. They all exercise their authority over the people and restrict their freedom."

"*Rabboni*, I see all these factors are connected. The superiority of the Kittim over our people, rich landowners over poor farmers, learned leaders of the Beit HaMikdash who use religious laws to burden the people, and the overall dominance of the Kittim. All the powerful people at the top are connected to each other and they use all these factors to oppress the people and disconnect them" says Mariam.

"Mariam, you have summed it all up. I am going to send you into such a society. You now seem to understand how it operates, and how it is very sick and in need of healing.

"I may not be with you for long and you must carry on the work that I set out to do. We have all seen how the poor are treated by the rich and powerful, helped by years of religious indoctrination about sin, fear of eternal punishment or distant hopes of a reward in the afterlife. Ordinary people are bullied and burdened by the authorities claiming to be the mouthpiece of Elahh. The people need first to be liberated from these misconceptions. To change their thinking will invite the wrath of the authorities. You will be accused of being criminals. You must be prepared for that.

After brief contemplation I continue, "You are in fact ready to go out on a mission. However, you will need to be like sheep among wolves. Be smart like snakes but also, be like doves and don't hurt anyone. Be careful! There are people who will arrest you and take you to be judged. They will whip you in their synagogues. You will be taken to stand before governors and kings. People will do this to you because you follow me.

"Apart from the clothes and sandals take also a walking stick. If you have a purse, take it along with some copper or silver. Arm yourself with a knife, but keep it hidden. For food and shelter depend on the people as we have always done. Take with you some essential owrah

SCENARIO 50 - DISTURBING FACTORS

and oil. We will prepare small kits with what is necessary.

"When you enter a city or town, find some worthy person there and stay in their home until you leave. When you enter that home, say, 'Shalama aleikhem.' If the people in that home welcome you, they are worthy of your peace. May they have the peace you wish for them. But if they don't welcome you, they are not worthy of your peace. If those in a home or a town refuse to welcome or listen to you, then leave that place and shake the dust off your feet.

"Don't be afraid of those people. Everything that is hidden will be revealed. Everything that is secret will be made known. Focus on the truth. The truth conforms to real issues of life here on earth. The truth will make you free. I tell you all this privately, but I want you to tell it publicly, shout for everyone to hear."

"The people may expect too much from you. They have heard of wandering wonder workers and magicians who use charms, omens and incantations to drive out the evil and bring healing. They would have heard of Apollonius, the Yavan man who was also a god who performed miracles, claiming to preach a mystery religion full of mythological stories. None of his work has lasted. People also want immediate results. Don't promise them anything. Do only what can alleviate their sufferings. Bring them down to nature and change their thinking to real human values like love, compassion, forgiveness and peace. This is the way of tsedek. Denounce the evil teaching of the Beit HaMikdash."

"Where shall we go?" asks Shemayon.

"You should go home first and spend some time with your families. Then move out into the neighbouring districts. Stay first within the areas that we have already covered. Cover the areas surrounding Yam Chinneroth. You shall travel in twos for mutual support and encouragement."

"Let us decide which areas we will cover," says Mariam.

Ya'akov says, "From our home in Beth-tsaida, Yhochanan and I will cover the northern shores of the yam."

"I am also from Beth-tsaida and I can cover the northeastern shore of the yam, the place we went to, called Gergesa or Kursi. Who will come with me?" asks Miriamne.

Mattithyahu volunteers, "Too many people here know me as a publican. I will go with you to the area outside the jurisdiction of Hordos Antipas."

"Andreia and I will canvas the northwestern shores of the yam," says Shemayon from Kfar Nahum.

"Since I am from Kfar Kanna, I could cover the western region," said Natan'el.

"I could join you and we could cover the central west coast of the yam including Tiberias. I can access most of the city of the Malka. If we go further down from Tiberias along the coast, we will come to the city of Chinneroth after which the yam is named. We never went there. If we have enough time, we will go there," says Joa'ana.

"Maybe I could go there. Who would like to come with me?" asked Marta.

"I will," says Arsinoe, "and can we take a boat from Tiberias?"

"Sure, you come with me to Tiberias first," says Joa'ana.

"Shimon and I will go south to Yehuda and even to Yerushalayim. We would like to contact the kana'im and also find out what the situation is like there," says Yehudah.

"I would like to venture south to the town of Sychar in Shomron. Tauma and I followed you there and I said I would like to revisit that place sometime. Now is the opportunity. Shall we go together, Tauma?" asks Pilip.

"Yes, I would like that," replies Tauma.

"Shoshanna and I are from Magdala so that is the obvious place for us to go," says Mariam.

"Can you two women manage on your own?" asks Shemayon.

"Yes, have faith in us women Shemayon.," replies Shoshanna.

Hearing their plans I say, "I will go to Naṣrath and spend time with the family. Before long, it will be time again for the orechah and the journey to Yerushalayim."

The soon-to-be missionaries take medical kits with them but go home first. Those in their homes were already busy preparing to join the Orechah to Yerushalayim for the Paskha. The group then spreads out in pairs to establish Yeshua's Tsedek Way.

Scenario 51 - Challenging the law

Magdala

One morning Mariam tells Shoshanna, "Everybody is busy preparing to dry the fish. Let's take a walk downtown and meet the people."

They both walk down the narrow alley between the parallel walls of the houses and come to the three underground pools, the miqva'ot. Stone steps from two sides lead to the pool below and there is some activity. A kohan is supervising the procedure of tvilah, a ritual bath. The men walk down one side of the steps and are immersed into water, then come up the steps on the other side.

Mariam asks one of them, "Why do you do this?

"We hunted some birds and were carrying them home. We are considered unclean because we did not slaughter them according to shechita. We are made to do ritual cleansing in the miqva'ot as punishment," says one of them.

"Shechita does not make any difference to the meat you eat. We catch and kill hundreds of fish every day and everyone eats them. You are subjected to unnecessary laws," says Mariam.

The kohan overhears the conversation and come up the steps towards them. "You speak about fish. The law does not apply to fish. They killed birds. Besides, who are you to question the law?"

"These unnecessary laws are made to control the people and make their life difficult," says Shoshanna.

"You attha, what business of yours is this? Go away and don't interfere," remonstrates the kohan.

"You are a blind man leading the blind. You follow a law that serves no purpose," responds Mariam.

"Where did you learn to speak up like this, you attha?" challenges the kohan.

"Do you think you are all that clean to declare this man unclean?" retorted Mariam.

"I will take you to the synagogue and you answer to the authorities there," threatens the kohan.

"Well, take us," says Shoshanna.

The synagogue is next to the miqva'ot. The women are asked to cover their heads on entering the hall that serves also as study room. It is very spacious with stone benches against the walls, which are decorated with elaborate coloured frescos. The floor is made of mosaic. The women are told to sit on the stone bench while waiting for the Sopherim and Perushim to arrive. Women seldom enter the synagogue, and they sit admiring the solid piece of stone with engravings in the middle of the synagogue.

The relief carving on the stone depicts the *menorah*, the candlestick with seven branches with a pair of two-handled jugs on either side enclosed by two columns.

The women stand up when two Sopherim and a Parush enter.

The kohan says, "These women have challenged the mitzvot and criticised the tvilah in the miqva'ot."

"What concern is that of yours? The tvilah is only performed by men. You attha are not allowed to even comment on it. Now that you have done so, you have spoken against the commandment of Elahh. By challenging his law, you have profaned the name of Elahh," says

393

the Parush.

"We did not even mention the name of Elahh, so how could we have profaned his name?" asks Mariam.

"The punishment for taking the name of Elahh in vain is, as you know, death by stoning. However, because you did not speak directly against Elahh or swear by his character, you will be excused from that punishment. But you are not guiltless," says one of the Sopherim.

"Your punishment will be to observe the family purity laws by lighting a candle on the ShAbat," decrees the Parush.

"So be it," says Mariam and the two women walk out of the synagogue.

"Nobody is going to check on us lighting any candles," remarks Shoshanna.

Scenario 52 - Path of Tsedek

Beth-tsaida

When Ya'akov and Y'hochanan reach home they find that their city of Beth-tsaida, which had been entrusted to Herod Pilip has been fortified by him and renamed Julias, in honour of Caesar's daughter.

Ya'akov and Y'hochanan are fussed over by their mother, Shlomit. The two brothers then get their fish and other preserved food ready for the trip to Yerushalayim. They join the band of fishermen and go fishing. In the boat with them is Ananias who recognizes them as they came with Yeshua.

"I am the one that your Moreh Yeshua cured. He cleaned out my eyes. I followed his instruction and now I can see clearly. He cured my blindness. I am a fisherman like the others. There is also a girl in the village who has problems hearing. I will bring her to you when we get back," says Ananias.

They haul in the net with a big catch of fish. While they are sorting the fish, Ananias takes off to bring the hearing-impaired girl. Ya'akov and Yhochanan leave the beach and walk up the hill slope on the east side of the Ha-Yarden. Below them stretches the fertile delta. From their vantage point they can look across Yam Chinneroth and see Har Tavor, and towards the north, the rising Har

Hermon. When they enter the city, Ananias brings the girl.

Ya'akov asks the girl, "*Almah*[241], what is your name? "Imma," she replies.

"How long have you been hard of hearing?"

The girl draws closer to him to catch the words. Obviously, she is not totally deaf nor deaf from birth. Ya'akov repeats his question loudly and she says, "Only in the last few months."

"Y'hochanan, could you please fetch our medical kit," asks Ya'akov.

"Have you had any head injury?"

"I fell down once, and I feel pain when sleeping on the side of the bad ear."

Ya'akov makes her lie down on her side with the bad ear exposed to the bright sun. He looks into the ear and blows into it. "Can you feel me blowing?" "Yes, only on the outside,"

"You are not deaf. I think your ear is badly blocked with wax. From the oils in the kit, he selects eucalyptus oil and pours some of it into her ear. "Stay like that and don't move for a while," says Ya'akov while Y'hochanan tears a strip of clean cloth and rolls it onto small sticks. Ya'akov turns her head side to side and massages around the ear to loosen the wax. Yhochanan then gently dips the cloth stick into the ear to soak up the oil and wax several times to make sure most of the earwax is removed.

Ya'akov then uses the olive oil to massage in front and behind the ear to increase the blood circulation. Meanwhile Y'hochanan asks, "Do you have hawthorn berries growing here?"

Someone in the crowd watching the two healers at work says, "Yes, we often pick them."

"You should use the berries to make tea and give her to drink twice

---

[241] maiden

a day, but avoid fatty meat, milk and sweet foods," he tells the girl.

"How do you feel, now?" Ya'akov asks.

She sits up and tilts her head from side to side and says, "Better. I can hear better."

The women in the crowd whistle tapping their lips with their fingers. They all praise them.

Ya'akov addresses the crowd, "Ananias here had difficulties seeing and Moreh Yeshua helped him to see clearly. Imma here, has had difficulty hearing and we have helped her with what we had learned from Moreh Yeshua. She can hear better now. All of you who have good eyes and ears may see but not perceive, hear and not understand. That is because we are taught by our leaders to see and hear what they want us to see and hear. To perceive and understand, we must learn not to believe everything we are told. Using our mind to think and judge, we must look for the truth in practical terms. We naturally know what is right and what is wrong, like not to kill, not to steal, not to be unfaithful to your spouse, not to tell lies and so on. We do not need Elahh from heaven to tell us that and threaten us with punishment if we fail. We do not need all the numerous minute laws and rules on what we should eat or wear or walk or work. Tsedek and common sense will tell us how to behave."

One of the men says, "But we find people who do wrong and hurt people. Should they not be punished?"

"Yes, we need good laws to maintain good order and just punishments. We must be able to see and understand that there are far too many rules, many which are unnecessary, and we should not be compelled to obey them," adds Y'hochanan.

One of the curious religious authorities prowling in the growing crowd speaks up, "Who are you and on what authority do you speak against our customary rules and regulations, which we have observed for generations?"

"It is these observances that have kept our people blind and deaf for generations. We follow our leader, Moreh Yeshua who teaches us the path of tsedek," says Ya'akov.

Seeing that the crowd was in favour of the two, the religious men choose not to pursue the matter further but say, "We will report you to our elders."

Scenario 53 - Hypocrisy

Kfar Nahum

When Shemayon and Andreia walk into the house after washing their feet they are met in the courtyard by Rebecca and Abigail.

"Where is Moreh Yeshua and the others?" asks Rebecca.

"Yeshua broke us up into pairs and sent us on missions to different places," says Andreia.

"We are to do his work by talking to people about tsedek and healing the sick," says Shemayon.

"The people are asking to see Moreh Yeshua," says Abigail.

"He says he may not be with us for long and wants us to carry on his work," says Shemayon.

"Oh, why would he say that! Never mind, you two men wash up and we will get the meal ready," says Rebecca.

After a simple meal of fish and bread the two brothers take a skin of wine and climb the stone steps to the roof. They can feel the breeze blowing from the yam with several fishing boats.

They sit discussing what to do on this mission. Then they come down from the roof and walk into the streets of Kfar Nahum.

They walk down the narrow street hemmed in by the walls of buildings made with coarse basalt blocks reinforced with stone and mud. At the end of the street is the synagogue. Standing on the steps between the pillars were a few Parushim decked in purple robes with tassels. One of them beckons to a beggar on the street. As the beggar approaches the Parush says, "No, no, that's far enough." That catches the attention of the people on the street.

"Elahh says to help the poor." He spoke loudly for all to hear and then to the beggar, "Here you are," tossing a coin in his direction.

The crowd reacts with awe, one of them saying, "Praised be Elahh!"

Shemayon also speaks, "If Elahh wants this poor man to be helped, why doesn't he do it himself. Why does he need your help? Has your coin really helped him to stop being a beggar? The more coins you throw at him the more he will beg. The more glorified you will be."

"Who are you to talk? Bring him to me," orders the Parush.

"They are the sons of Jona, respected member of our Kfar," says someone.

"Shemayon is the leader of our fisherfolk," says another.

"We have not seen you both here for some time," observes the other Parush.

"Where have you learnt to disrespect your leaders?" questions the first Parush.

"We are followers of Yeshua, the Moreh ha Tsedek, who has been here in your midst," says Andreia.

"Yeshua, would say that almsgiving is best done in secret, and it is hypocrisy to make a show of it. The important thing is that the poor should not have to beg. The wealth of the land should be enjoyed by all and not by the rich alone. It is your rules and the Law that make this man poor," asserts Shemayon.

"Who are you to question the Law? You will be made to answer for it in the Sanhedrin.

The Parushim underestimated the popularity of Shemayon and Andreia among the fisherfolk of Kfar Nahum. They rallied around the two saying, "Yes, the poor should not have to suffer at the mercy of the rich."

The Parushim are not ready to confront the people. They move into the synagogue, but the two brothers know they have become marked men. However, they are reassured and strengthened by the support of the people. Their message gets through.

Scenario 54 - Asclepius

Kursi

Mattithyahu and Miriamne take a boat across the yam to the lakeside village of Kursi, also known as Gergesa, on the eastern shore. This is the country of the Decapolis, the Ten Cities. Kursi is one of them. It belonged to Tre-Qarnayia whose vision and mission were to bring the whole world under the influence of Yavan culture. This was also a region where the HaGalileans were also Greeks, Romans, Phoenicians, Arabs and others. The *Khashmona'im*[242] had encouraged Hellenistic culture, and at this time it is a mixture of both Yavan and Kittim.

Since Greek complemented Aramaic as a language of daily use in HaGalil, Mattithyahu says, "They speak Yavan more than Ărammì or Ivrit, so we must try to converse in Yavan."

"We also have to be careful because this is the country of the goyim," he adds.

"I thought we decided not to use that name to describe people," reminds Miriamne.

Kursi itself is a small fishing village but the hub of this region is the

---

[242] Hasmon /Khashmona'im - Hasmonean dynasty

city of Hippos, a very old Yavan-Kittim fortressed city only two milin from Kursi and situated on a hill overlooking the Yam Chinneroth. Also, one of the Decapolis, it is strategically situated with control over the surrounding countryside. The main traffic of people is to and from this city.

"Let us go to Hippos where we can meet more people," says Miriamne.

Mattithyahu and Miriamne fall in step with those walking towards the hilltop. They walk a zigzagging road up the hill. When they reach the city the first things that catch their attention are the stone cisterns for collecting rainwater. They enter a gateway and walk on a path paved with rectangular slabs of stone leading to the huge Yavan temple with numerous pillars whose tops and bottoms are enlarged with elaborate engravings.

On the walls, there are depictions of animals and humans, and bronze figurines of deities like Pan and Prometheus. These are things one would not see on the other side of Yam Chinneroth. People here seem to enjoy a lifestyle different from the bulk of Galileans – a laissez-faire attitude towards religion. The constant vigilance of the Perushim is also absent here.

People gather at the front of the temple where some ritual is taking place. Animals like sheep, goats and even pigs are being sacrificed.

Miriamne asks one of the women there, "What is happening?"

She says, "People have come here seeking healing from Asclepius, the god of medicine. They offer sacrifices to obtain healing."

As a goat is about to be killed a young girl sprinkles some seeds on the animal's head.

"Why is she doing that?" asks Mattithyahu.

"The seeds signify life and regeneration at the moment of the animal's death, so that life will continue," she explains.

"Tell us about Asclepius," asks Mattithyahu.

"You see the statue against the wall? That's him. He is a kindly, bearded man holding a staff with a snake entwined on it. He is the son of Apollo, the god of healing. Asclepius is the god of medicine, and he has five daughters: Hygieia, goddess of health and cleanliness; Laso, goddess of recuperation from illness; Aseso, goddess of the healing process; Aglaea, goddess of beauty; and Panacea, goddess of universal remedy. The attendants who serve this god are also physicians."

"Wow!" exclaims Miriamne, "they are a family of healers."

"Do the physicians heal the people?" asks Miriamne.

"They do it by the offering of sacrifice and laying of hands."

Some of the people who cannot afford an animal, leave offerings of incense, flowers and food in hopeful prayer or in gratitude of some remedy. Some of the sick appear to be physically better.

"This seems to be some kind of faith healing. They don't use any healing herbs," remarks Mattithyahu to Miriamne.

"Let us talk to them," says Miriamne.

Thay approach some people leaving the temple. A couple have just left some flowers at the temple and are taking their young daughter home.

Miriamne asks, "What were you seeking at the temple?"

"We came for a cure for my daughter. We have been coming every season, but her condition has not improved. We dare not take her to the front for everyone to see because anyone who has tsara'ath is condemned."

"Can we look at her?"

"Are you healers?"

"We might be able to help," says Mattithyahu.

"What is your name?" Miriamne asks the girl.

"Sapphira," says the girl not daring to look up. Her face neck and chest were covered with pimples of different sizes either black or red in colour with some of them inflamed. She covers her breasts with her hands, very conscious and feeling ashamed.

"How long has she had this?" asks Miriamne.

"Since she came of age," says the mother.

Mattithyahu and Miriamne look closely, then at each other. "We don't think it is tsara'ath," says Mattithyahu. Don't be frightened of it. Is it itchy and makes you feel like scratching it?"

"Yes," says Sapphira.

"Well, try not to do that or break the pimples. Do you know the leaf called the silver lace fern? It is green, spreads out and is pointed, sometimes silver in colour. Rub that gently over your face and other parts with pimples. That will help ease the itch. You can also boil the fern and drink the juice. Eat one or two eggs every day. I am sure you use argan oil with your bread and salad. Rub pure argan oil on your skin all over the pimples twice every day. The lumps will go down and your pimples will subside," says Mattithyahu.

"The story of the god Asclepius is very interesting. His five daughters, Hygieia, Laso, Aseso, Aglaea and Panacea are goddesses who symbolise cleanliness as the basis for remedy in the healing process from illness and restoration to beauty, are an excellent teaching of good healthy living. It is not the offering of sacrifices that will bring healing but applying remedies and following the symbols of the goddesses. You try what we have suggested, and you will see a difference. Believe that you will once again be a beautiful girl," says Miriamne.

The couple thank them and Mattithyahu and Miriamne continue to explore the magnificent city of Hippos.

Scenario 55 - Taxes reduced

Kfar Kanna

Natan'el together with Joa'ana meet his father Tôlmay. They discuss the development of the winegrowers' dispute with the tax collectors.

Tôlmay says, "We have made good progress. The winegrowers from the other villages joined forces with us and we sent representatives to meet the landlords. We held several meetings bargaining with them. At last, they saw both parties stood to gain by the proposal that would bring a better yield. Taxes have been reduced, we have better yield and more wine for ourselves. This, of course, depends on the weather of the season. If there is bad weather and poor yield it is back to the original deal. So far, we are doing alright."

"You have told us a success story. We have gone to different places in twos without Moreh Yeshua to spread the good news of tsedek and to bring healing to the sick," says Natan'el.

"Yes, we have sick people here too, I will take you to them," says Tôlmay.

The following day Natan'el and Joa'ana go with Tôlmay to the homes of the winegrowers and attend to common ailments. News quickly gets around that the healers are there. Soon people from neighbouring places and even from Tiberias come over bringing their sick with them. Natan'el and Joa'ana attend to all of them. At night, they gather with those who have finished working on the vineyards and discuss matters over good wine. The discussions reveal many different views and perspectives on the person of Yeshua.

"Yeshua is a miracle worker who heals by the power of Elahh. My daughter was dead, and he brought her back to life," says the woman from the kfar.

"He is a hasid of HaGalil with power to drive out satana and establish the Mamlekhet Elahh," says another.

"He is the Mshikha we have been waiting for," says a man.

"We see too much in him. Yeshua is just an ordinary Yehudi who works and travels, sits and eats with both the ordinary Yehudim and sinners like the tax collectors," says one more person.

"He is not an ordinary Yehudi, he is a kuvikoi, like those dirty, free-ranging fellows who teach uncivilised behaviour. Although he is not completely like them, he teaches almost the same things. He considers himself the friend of freedom. He is courageously outspoken and stands up for individual freedom. He is different, and everybody likes to listen to him," a woman says.

"Yeshua is a great thinker with deep knowledge and a good moreh," observes another.

"Yeshua is your moreh, but he does not teach much about Yahadut and does not speak much about the Torah or quote from the Tanakh like our Parushim. He even speaks against the teachings of the Beit HaMikdash. He is more like one of the Yavan gods like Osiris or Dionysius," says one man who appears to be an atypical Yehudi.

"Yeshua is not a religious person, he is more of a mystic. He speaks about ruach and toqeph through which he does his healing," explains another.

"No, he uses the medicine of owrah and spices to heal. He seems to know a lot about those things."

YESHUA

"He is a magician who uses magical formulas like '*talitha kum*' and '*ephphatha*'. Whether he uses the power of Elahh or satana we are not so sure."

Listening to all these descriptions of Yeshua, a woman from Tiberias said, "Malka Antipas has heard about all this and is curious to meet Yeshua. He will either give him a job in the palace or have him killed as a threat to him, like what he did to Y'hochanan ha-mmatbil."

"Moreh Yeshua is different from the local leaders. I think he is a nebi who will restore our land, people and the Báyith, and bring together the 12 tribes of Yisra'el," says one of them.

They went on and on describing Yeshua from different perspectives and experiences.

Natan'el says, "I don't think he is that kind of nebi. He is a nebi like nebi Amos because he denounces corruption in high places. He has spoken of illness as a disease in the society to which he brings healing. He understands working people like us because he is one of us. He understands how taxes have made the rich richer and the poor poorer.

Yeshua is the Moreh ha-Tsedek. If you listen to him carefully, he teaches a new way, the good way of tsedek through which all problems will be solved."

"We would like to visit Tiberias after here," says Joa'ana.

Scenario 56 - Tenants on own land

Tiberias

Natan'el and Joa'ana bid farewell to the people of Kfar Kanna who besiege them to bring Yeshua along when they next visit.

After approaching Tiberias from the south and walking through the village of Hammat, they find Marta and Arsinoe.

"Ah, Joa'ana, we have been looking for you. Can you guide us to a boat that goes to Chinneroth?" asks Marta.

"Come, you can catch a boat from this village itself." Joa'ana arranges for them to get the boat.

As Natan'el and Joa'ana walk on, they meet some farmers at work in the fields. They discover that when their crops had failed, they were forced to mortgage their land, and through further failures had ended up as tenant farmers working on their own land that has been mortgaged.

They say, "If our crops fail, we become servants to pay off our debts by mortgaging the land. We need to hire day labourers to till the fields, pick the crops, and tend to the flocks and herds. Then the tax collectors come and take whatever is left. It is a never-ending cycle."

Natan'el tells them, "We faced the same situation in Kfar Kanna, but we got all the farmers together, made a deal with the tax collectors and came to an agreement that the farmers would work harder for a better yield if taxes are reduced. It is an agreement where both sides stand to gain. You should try it here too."

"But what can we do when the crops fail?" asks the farmer.

"That becomes difficult. Try to save some grain as we all do for times of failure. Try to save a little extra. You can only plead with the landlords and tax collectors," says Natan'el.

"Talk reason to the tax collectors. Try it any way," said Natan'el.

"They are so close to the Malka. He is not a reasonable man," whispers one of the farmers.

"I know the steward at the palace. I will speak to him. He holds the position of manager of the malka's income and expenditure. I will ask him to contact the landowners and tax collectors to be more reasonable," says Joa'ana.

"You must have a meeting among the farmers first and discuss this," advises Natan'el.

As they approached the palace Joa'ana tells Natan'el to wait outside while she approaches the guards. She speaks to them and then waves to Natan'el to come. They walk into the foyer and some of the servants recognise and greet her. She asks to see Chuza, the steward, her husband.

As they are led to his chambers Natan'el asks Joa'ana, "Do you have children?"

"No, we don't but we agreed to live apart."

Chuza greets his wife formally, "You should not come here. It is known in the palace that you have become a follower of Yeshua. The Malka is not in residence now, but he will come to hear of your visit. What do you want?"

"We don't want anything. We came to tell you that the farmers are unhappy with the heavy taxes. They want to meet the tax collectors and talk about tax reduction with the promise of greater output. Now with crop failure, they are desperate. The matter will be brought to you, and we would like you to grant the farmers a favorable hearing and mediate with the tax collectors and the malka," says Joa'ana.

"This issue keeps coming up again and again. I cannot guarantee anything, but I will do what I can. The malka is keeping track of your Moreh Yeshua. People tell him that he is Eliyahu or one of the nebi or Y'hochanan ha-mmatbil has risen from the dead. His own people tell him, 'How can that be, you saw the head of Y'hochanan ha-mmatbil on a dish.' He remains doubtful and curious and wants to meet Yeshua for his own reasons. My advice is to stay clear of the palace," cautions Chuza.

After some small talk Joa'ana and Natan'el leave Tiberias and go north along the coast.

"I take it that Chuza has given us a warning that Antipas is planning to snare Yeshua."

"Tiberias has become so famous that now they call the yam, Yam ha-Tiberias instead of Yam Chinneroth."

"But elsewhere from Tiberias the Yehudim still call it Yam Chinneroth because of the town of Chinneroth where Marta and Arsinoe have gone," says Natan'el.

Scenario 57 - Son snatched away

Chinneroth

Chinneroth, near the southern tip of Yam Chinneroth does not have a proper harbour but a wooden jetty. The boat pulls in and is secured to it. It is a small town, a sizeable village quite isolated from others.

Marta and Arsinoe disembark and walk through a fence to enter the town. The whole place is fenced in, fortifying itself from outsiders and wild animals. However, there is no restrictions on merchants and people who come to visit.

They meet some fisherfolk mending their nets. One of them looks up at them and says, "I have seen you both at Kfar Nahum following that man Yeshua. I used to work with Shemayon and the fisherfolk there. He, his brother and some others joined Yeshua's group. Have you left them?"

"Oh, no. We are now going to different towns and villages to carry on the work of Moreh Yeshua," said Marta.

"Are you going to work miracles, then?" asks the fisherman.

"We don't work miracles, we try to heal the sick," says Arsinoe.

One old woman hears the conversation and comes over. She is coughing very badly.

"Your cough does not sound good," says Marta.

"You don't worry about my coughing; I can look after myself. You say you are followers of that evil man Yeshua? He takes people away from their families to follow him and his magical ways. Have you also cut yourselves away from your families to follow that man?"

"What do you know about Yeshua?" asks Arsinoe.

"He pulls away people from their families. He is a heartless man. I am an old sick woman and a widow. He has drawn my son away from me. My son left me alone and found it more important and worthy to follow that madman than to care for his mother.

"What is the name of your son?" asks Marta.

"I had two sons. They were twins. One died, the other abandoned me. His name is Yehudah," she says punctuated by heavy coughing.

"Do you mean Yehudah the *kanai*[243] from Kerioth?" asks Arsinoe.

"No, no. He is the double. The Yavan call him Didymos, he is the other *teom*[244]. We call him Yehudah, others call him Tauma," she says still coughing badly.

"Attha, we know who he is. We are sorry that he abandoned you. He follows Yeshua willingly. Yeshua never asks anyone to follow him. We will talk to him about your situation. Where are you from?" asks Marta.

"I am from Tarichea. I came here to buy vegetable. He used to do the shopping for me, but now I must do it myself. He is a useless son. That Yeshua has set the son against his mother."

"He would not do such a thing. Our Moreh is gentle and humble of heart. You should meet him sometime."

"Why should I want to meet him when has snatched my son away?"

Seeing that she was coughing ceaselessly, Arsinoe held her by the shoulder and patted her back. "Are you taking any medicine for your

---

[243] zealot

[244] twin

cough?”

“Who is going to give me medicine? Nobody cares,” she mourns.

“Attha, listen. Buy some onions in the market. Do you have honey at home? This is what you must do. Peel and wash the onion, slice it thinly and place a layer in a clean container. Pour some honey over it. Place another layer of onion and cover it with more honey. Do this a few times with the honey on top of the last layer. Cover it and let it stand overnight. Make sure ants and insects don't get at it. The next day you will see a clear liquid. Drink one small spoonful of it every three hours. You will find that your cough will slowly disappear,” says Marta.

“Where did you learn this cure?” asks Tauma's mother.

“Our leader, the Moreh ha-Tsedek, taught us how to treat ailments like this,” says Arsinoe.

Some who are listening ask the two women for help with injuries and others bring some sick people to them. Both Arsinoe and Marta separately attend to all of them prescribing herbal remedies.

“Will you tell my son to come and see me?” asks Tauma's mother.

“Yes, we will,” say Arsinoe and Marta together.

Marta and Arsinoe walk through the small sleepy village and nobody bothers with them.

Scenario 58 - Sha'ul, a kanai, a Parush and a Moreh

Yerushalayim

Yehudah and Shimon in Yerushalayim approach the tomb of their hero Malka Dawidh within the walls of the city. There is a room on the upper floor above the tomb. This is the place where the kana'im often gather to plan their operations. There are some in the room and they exchange greetings.

Yonatan, a kanai leader, says, "Shimon, Yehudah, welcome back. We have not seen you since you went to join your Moreh ha Tsedek. We have started planning our protest during the Paskha. Would you join forces with us?"

"Yonatan, we have the same objective as you, but our Moreh is proposing a different approach. Instead of a violent overthrow in which many will perish, we work towards shalom and *ratson*[245], in the path of tsedek," says Shimon.

"That will never work with the Kittim, my brother," says Yonatan.

"We must try to make it work; but if all fails, we will join you," says Yehudah.

---

[245] goodwill

"The immediate problem among most of our people is sickness and poverty. We must bring relief to the sick and at the same time make them see the injustice and oppression, which is the sickness in our society," adds Shimon.

"There is someone who claims that he can heal the sickness in our society and preserve our faith in all its purity. He says he is a kanai and is coming to speak to us tonight," says Yonatan.

"What's his name?"

"His name is Sha'ul."

That night the kana'im gather in that same room. Yonatan welcomes the members and introduces Sha'ul.

Sha'ul addresses them, "Shalom, my brothers. I am a kanai like you, although I was not born in Peleshet. I am named after Šāʾûl bar Kish, the first Malka of Yisra'el. You, Yonatan, I am sure, are named after his son.

"My family comes from the lineage of the tribe of *Binyāmīn*[246] and I am proud of my Yahudi background. I am extremely passionate about the tradition of our fathers. I was born in Tarsus of Cilicia. I speak Ărammì and I was educated in Yavan. I learnt our tradition sitting at the feet of Gamaliel, the grandson of Hillel. I am now a moreh and a Parush with voting rights in the Sanhedrin.

"Like our leader, Yehudah ben Hezkiyahu, I believe that there is only one Elahh and Yisra'el is to serve him alone. The law preserves Yisra'el and it must be followed at all costs. I am committed to the Torah's promise of a coming anointed one who would be a great military leader and malka, like Dawidh of past times.

"I hear of some deviant sects moving around our land undermining our tradition with lies. We should do all we can to root them out and destroy them. We must protect and preserve our faith. I am with you,

---

[246] Benjamin

my brothers."

The audience clap hands.

The kana'im then engage in a dialogue with Sha'ul who promises he would do many things for Yahadut. Shimon and Yehudah listen with interest and are inspired by such a leader in their midst.

Some days later, Shimon and Yehudah join the kana'im when they discuss their plan of action at the coming festival of Paskha. They are going to confront the governor with the same issues of the past but are expecting a heavier crackdown this time.

While the two men are walking outside the precinct of the Beit HaMikdash discussing what they should do during their Paskha visit, and if Sha'ul who spoke so much would be involved in the protest, they come across a middle-aged man coughing violently. He is spitting blood. Yehudah asks those around him what is wrong.

They reply, "We don't know, but he does not want to eat and has lost weight. Now he has a fever and is vomiting. Those in his household have also caught this disease."

Shimon took Yehudah aside, "Remember Moreh was talking about the wise men from Asu who described a remedy for something like this. He shared some of that medication with us. We can try the little bit we have."

Yehudah said to them, "There is a rare plant, which can help to heal this disease. It is a small plant that grows straight up with branches and leaves like willow with black stems. The flowers are bluish white with purple spots. The fruits are shaped like a club. In Hodu they call it *kala adulasa*[247]. Have you heard of it? Have you seen it here?"

They had not.

"We have a little bit of it. It is in powder form. Add a little in boiling water. Cool it down and let him drink it. It should stop his coughing,"

---

[247] Asian water willow with a fruit known as the Malabar nut (Indian)

says Shimon.

"Separate him from the others until he gets well. Let him also eat onions and honey," adds Yehudah.

They leave to meet with some other kana'im from whom they receive different reports on Sha'ul.

Scenario 59 - Overcome enmity with tsedek

Sychar

Pilip and Tauma follow the orechah route into Shomron and come to Ya'akov's well. They wait for someone to come for they are not allowed to draw water. After a while some shepherds come with their goats. They soon overcome their initial apprehension when they recognise Philip and Tauma who had earlier come with me.

Tauma notices that one of the goats was injured with a wound that exposed part of the bone on its hind leg. He goes searching for an herb. He finds a plant with a cluster of flowers and numerous tiny leaves evenly distributed along the stem. He picks a few bunches of leaves. He shows it to them, "This is called *a thousand-leaf little feather*. Give me some water." Asking them to hold the injured goat he cleans the wound, crushed the leaves and packs it on the wound. He gets a shepherd to spare a piece of cloth from his garment and uses it to tie a bandage around the leg. "This should stop the blood-flow and heal the wound," he says.

Everyone watches him, impressed with his improvisation.

"Do you also heal people?" asks one of them.

"Yes, we do. We have learnt the art of healing from our Moreh

Yeshua," says Pilip.

"Where is your Moreh? Why did he not come with you?"

"He has sent us to different places to do his work. We have come here because you were friendly to us the last time we came," says Tauma.

"We have some sick people in the village. Please come and see them," asks one of them.

Pilip and Tauma oblige and discover different kinds of conditions in those they encounter — tsara'ath, paralysis, eye, throat and ear ailments — as well as those with physical disabilities. The people never brand those sick as being possessed by satana and do all they can to relieve the ailments.

Going over how Shomron came to be through Aba Yôsēp's sons and how Yisra'el became Shomron and how because of the Exile enmity developed over inter marriage with the goyim causing a distinction between clean and unclean, Pilip points out that both sides are at fault. "Do you know what is crippling us? It is this enmity between the Yehudi and the Shomronim. We accuse each other of starting this. We destroyed your Báyith and you profaned our Báyith with dead peoples' bones, all because of religion. Let us not dwell on the past. Religion is meant to make us good, but if it divides us, so what good is it? The only way to overcome that is to follow the path of tsedek."

Tauma elaborates on the virtues of tsedek.

"Don't you think it is time we put an end to all this enmity?" offers Pilip.

"The fact that we can sit together and talk like this is a small start of ratson," says an elder.

Through this encounter, Pilip and Tauma further break down many barriers between the Yehudi and the Shomronim.

Scenario 60 - The Final Supper

Base Camp

Assessment

While my followers are away on mission, I spend time with my family in Nasrath.

Some are already back from their mission. Others have yet to arrive. The agreement is to meet back at the rendezvous. I am still in Nasrath. Those who have returned set up camp and are sharing their experiences. In a couple of days, we are all reunited. The last to arrive are Yehuda and Shimon.

The fishermen bring in the fish, while the women bring provisions. Over several evenings, we sit around the fire to share all our experiences.

Mariam and Shoshanna relate their experience at the synagogue in Magdala.

"I was afraid to face the Soferim, Parushim and kohanim," says Shoshanna.

"But you did well to point out their wrongful ways. They couldn't defend themselves, so they tried to trap you into breaking the Berith by taking the name of Elahh in vain. They couldn't nail you down on that either, so they gave you a small punishment. Although they bully people, they are also fearful of them. As I said, you would be brought before judges who would accuse you falsely," say I.

Ya'akov and Yhochanan share what happened in Beth-tsaida.

"Your application of being blind and deaf to the religious interpretation of social realities was splendid. I see that you have accepted my teaching and believe it yourself. Well done," I say after they have finished.

Shemayon and Andreia relate how they were saved by the people against the Parushim in Kfar Nahum.

"You made yourselves marked men among the Parushim. Outside of your hometown you may not be so lucky. Even though you are innocent as doves be wise like the serpent. Challenge but be always on your guard.

Mattithyahu and Miriamne were next with a rather unusual story.

"From Kursi we went up the hill to Hippos into the tetrarchy of Pilip. It was like venturing out of HaGalil again. Yehudim and non-Yehudim live together peacefully without the watchful eyes of the Parushim. They follow the Yavan gods whom we despise. Apollo is the god of healing, and his son Asclepius is the god of medicine. His five daughters all represent healing remedies and cleanliness. We don't have such gods in Yahadut. We only have Elahh who is more interested in punishing than healing. We are quick to label an illness or sickness as tsara'ath. We saw a woman who was afraid to reveal her daughter because she thought she had tsara'ath. The girl had a skin disease covered with pimples and lumps. We assured her it was not tsara'ath and prescribed a remedy. She was happy," says Miriamne.

"How do you know it was not tsara'ath" asks Shemayon.

"Well, Moreh himself has pointed out such cases to us before," says Mattithyahu.

"Yes, there is a whole world out there in need of healing and the tsedek way of life. Our message must reach beyond HaGalil, Yisra'el and Yehuda," says Mariam.

"The winegrowers from other villages joined forces with those in Kfar Kanna, and together they bargained for a better deal. With this, their taxes have been reduced on condition of better yield," says Natan'el.

"We also had very good in-depth discussions about you, Moreh," adds Joa'ana.

"Oh, what did they say?" I enquire.

"The people there have very different views and perspectives of you. The woman whose daughter you healed swears that you are a miracle worker who raised her dead daughter to life. Others say you are a nebi who will bring restoration to Yisra'el. You are proclaimed to be a hasid of HaGalil and the Mshikha. Someone else said you are like one of the Yavan gods like Osiris or Dionysius. You are not a religious person but a mystic and a magician. One said you are a kuvikoi, a friend of freedom. Those are their views, and we did not try to correct them except that you use herbs and spices to heal and show the way of tsedek," adds Natan'el.

"We went to visit Tiberias and met my husband Chuza in the palace. We asked him to mediate between the farmers and the tax collectors. The farmers were having a difficult time after their crop failed. The talk in the palace is that Malka Antipas has been following your movements and wants to meet you. Chuza advised us to steer clear of the palace. He feels the Malka has no good intentions," says Joa'ana.

"Antipas is a cunning fox. If he will not change, we will have nothing to do with him except to warn people against him," say I.

"We had a very strange revelation in Chinneroth. In the market-place there we met an attha who hates you, Moreh Yeshua," says

Marta.

"Oh? Antipas and the men of the Beit HaMikdash hate me, I know. But why an attha?" I ask.

"She says you snatched her son away from her and that she is a widow abandoned by her son," says Arsinoe.

"Go on," I respond.

"That son is one of your followers. He is Tauma."

Everyone took a deep breath.

"My mother is not of sound mind. She blames me for everything. She blames me for the death of my twin brother. My father died. He was run over by a horse, and she blamed me for that too. We have workers to till the land and look after the property. She is not in want. I had to leave her for my own peace of mind," Tauma says in his defence.

"Your mother needs healing, Tauma," I say.

"Yes, she was coughing very badly, and we prescribed a remedy for her. She wants you, Tauma, to go and see her," says Marta.

Your mother needs healing of the heart and mind," say I.

"I think you should go home and be with her. She needs you," says Mariam.

Tauma buries his head in the palms of his hand and considers.

"How are our separated brethren in Shomron?" I ask with interest.

"They asked why you didn't come. We did some healing work among them and talked about religion as the cause of enmity between us. We agreed that none of us are clean and need to look for ways outside of religion to end this enmity. It was a beginning. We should send more delegations to them and invite them to come to Hagalil to break down the barriers between the Yehudi and Shomronim," says Pilip.

"And now finally, how is the eternal city?" I wonder.

"We met our kanai brothers, and they were already planning their protest during the Paskha. They are going to confront the governor with the issues they raised before. They are expecting a more severe response this time," says Shimon.

"We also met a very interesting person. He is Sha'ul bar Kish from Tarsus. He claims to be everything to everybody. He says he is a Yehudi from the tribe of Binyāmīn and also a Parush with voting rights in the Sanhedrin. Claims to be a kenai like Yehudah ben Hezkiyahu. He is a very well-educated person who champions the Law. He appears committed to the Torah's promise of a coming anointed one, one who will be a great military leader and Malka, like Dawidh of past times," says Yehudah.

"He says he knows of some deviant sects undermining our traditions with lies, and vows to root them out and destroy them," adds Shimon.

"We also met others who say Sha'ul is a friend of the goyim and a citizen of Roma," adds Yehudah.

"He sounds interesting but dangerous. He is targeting us. He seems persuasive with his knowledge and appears ambitious. We should be wary of him." I comment.

"On the whole, you have all done very well, a successful mission. Some of the opinions of me are correct. I am not a religious moreh. If we strictly follow the way of tsedek and lead people in that path, we will be doing good work and free them away from oppression towards a way of life in pursuit of love and shalama based on justice and equality. You, Tauma, you have only one mother. Take care of her first and then come follow me.

"I know all of you want to get back home to help with preparations for the Paskha journey. We will depart in two days. From the report of Yehudah and Shimon this trip could be dangerous. The authorities are preparing a big crackdown and we could easily get caught in that. I am their target. I do not want any of you to get caught so you must

425

save yourselves. Even if I am no longer around the struggle must go on.

The Final Supper

"So, before we depart, let us have a special meal together tomorrow night. Go and buy a lamb, which we can cook over the fire. With bread, wine, vegetables and fruits let us have a good happy meal. It may even be the final supper in our base camp," I propose.

The next day, the women are among themselves preparing the evening meal. "Do you think something untoward will happen this time in Yerushalayim?" wonders Marta.

"It became quite tense the last time we were there and from what Yehudah and Shimon have related, it could get quite dangerous especially if Moreh challenges the authorities," says Shoshana.

"I am sure he will not keep quiet," says Arsinoe.

"How can we protect him?" questions Joa'ana.

"We can't. He will stand up for tsedek, no matter what," confirms Mariam.

The men are arguing whether to slaughter the lamb ritually or not. "Why are you still bothered with rituals? Do it swiftly without causing too much pain to the poor lamb," say I.

When everything is ready, we sit down to eat with the gentle lapping of the waves on the shore and a cool breeze blowing across Yam Chinneroth. A pot of lamb brisket cooked with leek, radish, carrot and ginger is placed in the centre while the rest of the lamb is roasted, matzo bread cooked on the hearth and taboon bread in the oven. Fresh figs, dates and olives decorate the setting with two large wine skins.

"We must be grateful to *Teh-vah*[248] and Adamah for providing us with such a wonderful meal," say I, starting with the wine. While we are passing the bread along and dipping it in the brisket pot and enjoying it Mariam asks, "*Rabboni*, you said that the earth and this life is all we have. Is that the end of everything?"

"All our religious teachings based on scriptures of old, which I believe were written by the hand of man, promise us salvation in an eternal life. Look up at the stars in the sky. There is so much space between us and them. If someone is sitting on one of the stars and looking up, they will see the same. We cannot see each other. We do not know if there are living things outside of our adamah. If there was life outside, no one has come from there to tell us about it. What kind of life can there be after we are dead? Our body becomes adamah.

"Just as we are so small in the universe, we are also small people in the world. We can only be effective in bringing a change within the sphere of our influence within our reach in the community. We can also influence other people and hopefully spread the message of tsedek, which is the way of liberation.

"Remember I spoke about the sower? Not all the seeds you sow will take root. Those that do take root will produce good fruit. Our way must start a fire and we must guard it until it is ablaze. The same fire will purify as well as destroy. There will be others who will sow different seeds that might take root and grow. It can cause dissent even within a household pulling people in different directions. There will always be people who seek power and wealth and abuse them creating victims of oppression. Poverty will not disappear. There will always be people who believe in Elahh and use religion to burden the people. There have been wars and there will continue to be wars.

---

[248] nature

427

Powers will replace powers. Empires will replace Empires. The Kittim will disappear, and others will replace them.

"In spite of all that the fire of tsedek must continue to spread. We must continue to exert our influence to make the world a better place for ourselves, our children, and their children after them. Powerful people will be threatened by our work and seek to destroy us. Even so, our way will grow and flourish even if the whole world does not change."

We dialogue on many other issues over the meal.

The following day we strike camp and pack away all our camping gear.

"Go back to your homes and help with preparations for the orechah to Yerushalayim. Like the last trip, we will meet again at Nasrath and join the orechah. Give my shalama to your people," say I as we disperse.

Scenario 61 - Yôsēp̄ stays back

Nasrath

I return home to Nasrath to continue preparing for the Yerushalayim trip. This time the family makes some stoneware for sale. Near Nasrath on the way to Kfar Kana, there is a chalkstone cave where tektons produce stoneware of all kinds. Aba used to work among them at their workshop that produced chalkstone vessels, tableware, bowls, storage jars, and even large stone containers — like the ones we found at the wedding feast in Kfar Kana — for ceremonial washing. Stone vessels are in demand because, unlike clay, ceramic or glass vessels that could become ritually unclean, stone vessels are considered to be pure.

Aba acquires some pieces of stone, and he teaches us how to work with them. We make small jars, pots and tableware for sale. They must be small because stone is too heavy to be transported.

While we are working Aba accidentally drops one of the stones on his foot and fractures his big toe. Unable to walk, he decides to stay back in Nasrath and not go to Yerushalayim. My mother also wants to stay back with Aba, but Bethanna and Tabby say, "Ama, you go with them. We will look after Aba."

We pack the woodwork, toys and chalkstone ware in one cart, and

429

use the other for travelling and wait for the other merchant carts and wagons to arrive.

As previously, the caravan camps on the outskirts of Nasrath. The groups meet up and talk about the merchandise they carry. Yehudah and Shimon have gone ahead to Yerushalayim to secure a place for us as well as to meet up with their Kanai counterparts.

I spend some time with Aba treating his wound, bandaging it up with herbs.

"Aba, there could be trouble in Yerushalayim as there is every year with bloodshed," I say.

"Evil powers have to be challenged, but there will be risks before we can see changes in our society. You be careful, my son," says Aba.

"We will try to make good sales and return home safe," I say kissing Aba and embracing both my sisters. Tabby pleads, "Come home and spend more time with us. You cannot save the whole world by yourself."

My three brothers, Yehudah, Shemayon and Yôsēp̄, my Ama Maryam and I join the orechah.

Part Six

Yerushalayim

1. Northern wall
2. Beith HaMikdash
3. Narrow gate
4. Old wall
5. Marketplace
6. Palace of the Great Hordos
7. Praetorium
8. Fortress of Antonia
9. Pilatus' Palace
10. Court of the Goyim
11. Entryway into the Báyith
12. Court of the kahanim
13. Caiaphas' Palace
14. Orechah site
15. Lishkat ha-Gazit – Royal Stoa
16. Har ha-Zeitim
17. Tomb of Dawidh

Map 7

Scenario 62 - Qorban

Yerushalayim

The orechah swiftly moves across Shomron well-guarded and armed, bypassing Sychar. The city of Yerushalayim is abuzz with people gathering for the Paskha festival. The orechah from HaGalil was one of several converging on the walled city from different regions. Our orechah enters the northern wall through the Sha'ar Sh'khem or the Sychar Gate, then along the west side of the Beith HaMikdash, going through another narrow gate of the city's first wall. It turns right skirting the old wall. It veers left then south toward the marketplace, entering the Upper City where the wealthy live. The marketplace is opposite the massive Royal Palace of the great Hordos. The place is crowded, and carts are already in line along the streets.

The Hordoses are no longer the rulers of Yerushalayim. Antipas only visits and has a palace in the city, but his jurisdiction is HaGalil. Hordos Archelaus should have been the ruler of Yerushalayim but early in his reign Archelaus was removed as *ethnarch*[249] of Yehuda at the request of the people. Yehuda and the city of Yerushalayim came under the direct rule of Roma through Kittim *prefects, procurators and*

---

[249] Political leadership over a common ethnic group

legates.[250]

The current prefect is Pontius Pilatus who has a palace with a *praetorium*[251] at the fortress of Antonia on the north side of the Beith HaMikdash. This is his official residence in Yerushalayim. The Kittim prefect's permanent official residence is at the port city of Caesarea. His presence is required at the Antonia fortress during the biggest Yehudim festival.

Day 1 (Sunday)

Yehudah and Shimon have reserved lots for the carts and are rejoined by Marta and Arsinoe. We place four carts side by side. Loaded with merchandise, these belong to Mariam of Magdala, the Zebadayas, Tôlmay and Yôsēp̄. We set up shop and start selling. Business is good. The chalkstone wares and the toys are very popular.

Yehudah and Shimon report that the Kana'im are planning a big demonstration at Pilatus's palace to again raise the issue of the Báyith tax money, the Qorban.

Day 2 (Monday)

Yehudah explains the Báyith tax to the group, "We, the Kana'im, have been monitoring this taxation system for a long time and raise the issue every year. We are unable to beat it because we lack support from the people.

"The Kittim tax system was first introduced by Pompey. It was intensified more than 25 years ago under the Kittim procurator

---

[250] Titles used interchangeably.

[251] Originally the headquarters of a Roman camp, currently the governor's official residence (Latin/Greek)

Coponius. A Kittim census was undertaken to facilitate this system. The Kana'im leader, Yehudah ben Hezkiyahu spearheaded opposition to this by taking up arms. He declared that the Yehudim had no malka but Elahh and that they should not pay taxes to the Kittim. Of course, he was killed for that. Taxation continues. The people are exhausted from years of taxation under the Kittim Keysar Tiberius.

"This situation is worsened by the crippling Báyith tax. The Kittim tribute is superimposed on tithes and other taxes owed to the Báyith, which not only serves as the centre of worship but is also the treasury for Yisra'el. They call this atonement money, and it takes the form of the half-shekel coin. All Jews aged 20 and above pay the Báyith tax. Even those who come from afar are obliged to pay it because it is in the Torah. It is the function of money changers — known as the *kollubistai* — to convert all foreign currency to the half-shekel coin, for a commission.

"These money changers have a controlling role over the money and finances of the Báyith. This money is for the maintenance of the tabernacle and the Báyith. The Yehudim also must pay tithes on produce to support the kohanim in Yerushalayim. The Yerushalayim treasury, Qorban, is money that belongs to Elahh and not for any personal or secular use.

"Seven years ago, Pontius Pilatus was appointed as procurator. Procurators and prefects primarily have a military function, but as representatives of the empire they are also responsible for the collection of imperial taxes along with some judicial responsibilities. Prior to this, the prefect Valerius Gratus had appointed Caiaphas as *HaKohen*[252]. He was also president of the Sanhedrin. A very intimate friendship developed between Caiaphas and Pilatus."

"Let me add to what Yehudah has said," says Shimon. "Pilatus has

---

[252] High priest

a mega project – the construction of an aqueduct to bring water into the city. He needs money from the Báyith treasury because most of the imperial tax money is parcelled off to Roma. Pilatus and his close ally Caiaphas have been working together to get this money. We have good grounds to believe that both have been dipping their hands into the Qorban. They have been steadily pilfering money from the Báyith treasury. Some people have spotted Báyith money in a trunk with the inscription 'Qorban' hidden beneath the palace of Caiaphas. What is Qorban doing under the palace of Caiaphas when its proper place is the Beit HaMikdash? This has been going on for some time but was always covered up. Since tax money is a highly sensitive issue especially at festival times any slight provocation could spark a riot. They have been containing this all the while with some kind of diversion or another."

Scenario 63 - Diversion

Pilatus' Palace

Day 3 (Tuesday)

The festive mood in the city is interlaced with a certain amount of tension. This happens every year and the authorities have prepared to diffuse the tension. Both Pilatus and Caiaphas have premonitions that opposition this year is going to be stronger.

Pilatus has summoned Caiaphas to his palace to discuss their plans. They normally meet at the courtyard but this time they meet in an inner room behind the colonnaded corridor. After wine is served Pilatus dismisses his servants. "Well, once again we are confronted by the same issue. We have to put an end to these riots once and for all."

"To do that you will have to stop taking the Báyith Qorban. People are openly talking about it," says Caiaphas.

"You can't talk. You are up to your neck in it yourself. The aqueduct is incomplete, and I need the money. We have to create another distraction."

"I think I know how. This man Yeshua who has been agitating in HaGalil is here now. He is more of a nuisance than anything else, but we can divert the attention of people to him by charging him for going against the Torah, the Beit HaMikdash and the sacred traditions of our fathers."

"How will you do that?"

"We will arrest him and let the Sanhedrin judge and charge him. I can arrange witnesses. We will make a spectacle of him, and the people will forget the Qorban. But there is one problem."

"What's that?"

"If he is to be put to death, we cannot do it. You must crucify him."[253]

"Only if you can prove that he is a troublemaker and has rebelled against the Keysar of Roma."

"At the same time, you must also control the crowd that the Kana'im will stir up against you."

"I'll take care of that," decides Pontius Pilatus.

---

[253] At this time, the Sanhedrin privilege of capital punishment was withdrawn by Rome

Scenario 64 - The widow's mite

Court of the Goyim

Day 4 (Wednesday)

While business was brisk at the orechah, I and some of my companions take a walk to the Beith HaMikdash. We leave the other members to man the carts. There are a few entryways into the Báyith which is surrounded by a series of courts. Immediately surrounding the Báyith proper is the court of the Kohanim. We ascend three flights of steps on the southwest corner of the Báyith leading up to the court of the goyim. It is a thoroughfare for anybody even the non-Yehudi. This is where the sacrificial animals are sold, and the purchases manipulated by the moneychangers.

At the courtyard of the Beith HaMikdash male members of families are holding a one-year-old lamb or a goat which had to be male and without blemish.

"The poor animals! Why must they have to die and shed their blood in sacrifice?" I wonder aloud.

One of the men with a lamb draped over his shoulders says, "It is the rule of Elahh as written in the Torah that it is blood that makes atonement for sins."

"The rule also says that you have to be clean to participate in this sacrifice. Have you been through your ritual cleansing?" I ask.

The man said, "Of course, I have."

"In that case, you have been purified. Why do you need further cleansing?"

The man did not know how to answer.

"The lamb lies so trustingly on your shoulders. Must you end its life and force it to shed its blood for your sins? You will go back and commit more sins and come back the next year and do the same. What if you die in your sins before the next *Qorban Pesakh*[254]? All you need is to follow tsedek and live a good life. This sacrificial ritual, profits nobody except the kohanim of the Beith HaMikdash."

Some of the Báyith officials hear this conversation and come over to harass us.

The Perushim and the Soferim are higher up the steps watching the crowd. I raise my voice so that they can hear me, "Be on your guard against the yeast of the Perushim. They are hypocrites. They make up their own traditions and sidestep the words of the Torah. They make you believe that what they say is the word of Elahh and their interpretation of the Torah is wrong."

"We know who you are and what you are teaching. You are not very popular in HaGalil and now you have come here to gain popularity by misleading the people, making them disobey the law," says one of them.

"Your law only makes it possible for the rich people who can afford to buy sacrificial animals and have them slaughtered to atone for their sins. You expect the poor to die in their sins. You have already condemned them. You are only interested in the money it brings. Your laws and the way you implement them is against the way of

---

[254] Sacrifice of Passover

tsedek. That is why I speak against this practice."

"You are speaking against the Torah," accuses the official.

"I know what the Torah says. It says that those who are covered by the blood sacrifice are set free from the consequences of sin. If I were a rich man, I could offer many blood sacrifices and commit as many sins as I want. The malka of great wisdom, Malka Sh'lomoh, who built the great Beith HaMikdash, offered twenty-two thousand oxen and a hundred and twenty thousand sheep in sacrifice. He also had 700 wives and 300 concubines. He worshipped *Ashtoret*[255], the goddess of the Sidonians and built high places for the gods of his foreign wives.

"Do you think that money can buy forgiveness? Forgiveness comes not with sacrifices but with repentance in the heart and not by the blood of animals or men."

"What will happen to us who cannot make sacrificial offerings?" asks a poor woman.

"If you have done something wrong and feel guilty, search your heart. Are you really sorry or do you just want to pay a debt? If in your heart you repent, your sins are forgiven. Instead of paying a debt by a sacrificial offering, go and make shalama with those you have offended or hurt. There is no need to come to the Beith HaMikdash to do that."

Some decide not to offer sacrifice and I tell them to use the money to go and buy something useful at the orechah bazar. Others are busy changing money. The rich Yehudi are flaunting their wealth by changing large amounts of money and putting them into the collection box.

There are three kinds of coins in circulation: the Athura, Kittim and the Yehudi. The Athura coins were the Didrachmon and the Drachme.

---

[255] Astarte, the Semitic goddess Ishtar

The Kittim coins were the Denarion in silver and the Assarion and the Kodrant in bronze. The Yehudi coin is the Shekel originally from Trye but later minted in Yerushalayim by Hordos the Great. Except for the Yehudi money all other monies are considered unclean and not worthy to be paid as Báyith tax which is half a Shekel.

So, all other monies must be changed to Yehudi coins through the kollubistai who charge an exchange rate. The Athura Drachme is equal in value to the Kittim Denarion. Two Denarion or Drachme was the value of a half-Shekel.

An old woman crept up slowly, dug into her garment and pulled out two small coins and quietly slipped them into the collection box.

Seeing her, I say, "Do you see that? That is a poor old woman, probably a widow; she has contributed to the Báyith treasury more than all those wealthy Yehudim. She would probably go without her meals for a day or two because of her belief in the *kadosh*[256] of the Báyith HaMikdash and she has given all she has to live on.

"Those two coins are two leptons," says Mattithyahu.

One Shekel is worth four Denarion or Drachme. If we subdivide the Denarion, it is equal to ten Assarion and a Kodrant is a quarter of an Assarion. That makes the Kodrant one fortieth of a Denarion. One lepton is worth half a Kodrant which then makes it one eightieth of a Denarion. The lepton is the smallest denomination of coin in circulation, and it was also called the mite.

"The rich would scoff at such a coin but that is all she had, and she gave it to the Báyith HaMikdash," say I.

"Well said, Rabbi, at least she has paid her dues, but we have not seen you pay yours," says the Báyith official.

"But neither have I see you pay yours. You collect from others and why do you exempt yourselves from paying the Báyith tax?" I rebut.

---

[256] Holy, holiness

"We, the Kohanim, are the ones who handle the money on behalf of the Beith HaMikdash. What is the point of paying to ourselves?

"You hypocrite! You take the food out of the mouths of the poor old people and fill your stomachs. Your kollubistai collect and handle foreign currency which you call unclean, and you accept the half-shekel. Do you account for the money you receive? How is the money spent? You know very well it is Qorban."

The Báyith officials who attempted to corner Yeshua were themselves cornered.

Scenario 65 - The instigator

Caiaphas' Palace

While we are engaged with the minor Báyith officials, a major meeting is being held at the home of the HaKohen Caiaphas.

Caiaphas is a Greek name. His real name is Yôsēp̄ and he is a member of a wealthy family, married to the daughter of HaKohen Annas. He has created a priestly dynasty for his five sons and a son-in-law who will later succeed him as high priests. He is very much in league with the Şĕdûqîm who are among the wealthy Jewish elite.

He was HaKohen before Pilatus appeared on the scene and Pilatus confirmed his status. Caiaphas lives in Yerushalayim's Upper City, an affluent section inhabited only by the city's elites and powers-that-be. His home or palace is constructed around a large courtyard. People must wonder how Caiaphas can flaunt such a luxurious lifestyle on his stipend while the oppressive taxation is eating away their lives.

Caiaphas chooses to invite select members of the Sanhedrin who are close and indebted to him.

"Thank you all for coming at short notice. I called this meeting because there is increasing tension in the city, as it always is during this time. The Kana'im are planning a huge riot aimed at the governor and also at the Beit HaMikdash. Pilatus can handle the Kana'im but the riot at the praetorium will likely spill over into the Báyith. We must control the crowd at the Báyith.

"The instigator is Yeshua bar Yôsēp̄. We must apprehend him before the crowd becomes uncontrollable. We must show the people that he is an imposter, the real enemy of our people, our laws and our tradition. He has openly denounced our holy practices. Gather all information you can of what he has been saying and doing, especially against the Torah and if he has said anything against Kittim rule. We need witnesses when we try him in the Sanhedrin. We need them to testify before the Sanhedrin to the charges against him. They must be convincing enough to put him away for good. Once we get the shepherd, the sheep will scatter."

"How are we going to get him? He is always surrounded by people," asks one of the elders.

"The Báyith guards will be briefed. They will watch and ambush him," assures Caiaphas.

He turns to the Báyith guards. "The plan is to create a distraction in the crowd and cause confusion. The Kittim soldiers will move in, but our guards will be focused on Yeshua and grab him before he escapes."

"What kind of distraction do you suggest?" asks one of the guards.

"We have engaged the siqari'im before. Get one of them to do his job and pay him well. Wait. There will also be a gathering at the fortress. Arrange for another siqara to do the same there and pay them both well in silver. Bring Yeshua straight to me. I will hold him here and summon a meeting of the Sanhedrin," says Caiaphas as he dismisses them.

Scenario 66 - Aqueduct

Tomb of Malka Dawidh

There is another briefing session taking place at a room on the upper floor above the tomb of Malka Dawidh. Yonatan, the Kana'im leader, is addressing key members which include Yehudah of Kerioth and Shimon Qananaios.

"I will talk to the people about the aqueduct that has taken years to complete, and which Pilatus is pushing for completion this year. They have never forgotten the desecration of the Báyith by Pilatus parading pagan symbols. They are still angry with him over that. Now I will tell them that Pilatus has been taking the Qorban with the help of the HaKohen Caiaphas and is using this to build the aqueduct. They understand that the Qorban is sacred money only for the use of the Beit HaMikdash. I want you to be among the crowd and raise your voices against this abuse."

"Let the people know that letters were sent to the Kittim high command in Roma, and nothing was done, and it is time for us to act now," says Yehudah.

"We will fight back," says Shimon.

"Yes but, be prepared. Pilatus will have his soldiers standing by to attack us. Arm yourselves discretely and use it only if you must. We will start some fires and run into the grounds of the Beit HaMikdash. The people there too will be protesting the abuse of the Qorban," says Yonatan.

Scenario 67 - Action Plan

Pilatus' Palace

As the Kana'im go into details of the planning, Pilatus is holding a meeting with his own men.

"Armed soldiers will be placed all along the praetorium walls, on the ramparts and along the retaining walls of the Beit HaMikdash. At the balustrade separating the surrounding courts, there will be soldiers placed on the side of the court of the goyim since the non-Yehudi cannot pass the balustrade. Watch carefully what happens," he says before dismissing everyone except for the leader of his special squad.

"Get your men dressed as civilians to mingle with the multitude with staves and clubs concealed in their garments. The siqari'im will probably kill someone and cause a commotion and the Kana'im will start making noise. You prepare a signal for your men and at the right time get them to start beating up the people. After you have done damage, the Kittim soldiers will go into action and arrest the culprits. Have your men rehearsed and ready. Any questions?"

"The Kittim soldiers may also by mistake arrest some of my men," says the leader.

"You don't worry about that. They will be released. One other thing. This rioting happens every year during the festival, and I want to teach them a lesson. When they are injured and bleeding, collect their blood in containers. I have a use for that," says Pilatus.

Scenario 68 - The illness in society

At the Orechah

The Báyith kohanaim tell me, "You stop making trouble here. You and your followers had better leave."

"We are not going anywhere. This is a public place."

"If you continue to make trouble, we will order the Báyith guards to remove you."

"If we refuse to move?"

"We will arrest you."

"Alright," say I and continue to talk to the people.

"You are being led by a bunch of hypocrites," I proclaim.

More people are gathered around now. The authorities withdraw a little to have a consultation.

"Arresting him will cause a commotion among the crowd and that will bring the Kittim soldiers. Let him be. The people have come here to offer sacrifices and they will do so," says the leader and they walk away.

I continue to teach. Nothing happens, and we return to the orechah. My followers and I gather behind our carts around a campfire. We have just finished the evening meal.

Yehuda says, "Moreh, tomorrow will be a critical moment for us.

We are going to get the people to rise and make their demands. The most we can expect is a declaration of expenditure of the qorban, which will be fabricated to conceal the truth. The worst-case scenario is that we will be crushed by the Kittim power with collaboration of the Beit HaMikdash guards. The Kana'im are prepared for a fight."

"We are not fighters, but we will rally the people to raise their voices," says Shemayon.

"Yehudah, you must do what you must do but be careful and know your strength. Strike to defend yourselves against an overwhelming force. If you are overpowered, you must escape and live to fight again. This will be a long struggle," I remind him.

"Moreh, we look to you for leadership. Tell us what to do," says Marta.

"It is best for you women to stay in the background. The soldiers will not spare you. It is better to be killed than to be caught by them. Raise your voices with the crowd. Have a clear passage to run away. The rest of you can stay with me to urge the crowd to protest," say I.

"What will you do Moreh?" asked Tauma.

"I will continue to say what I have always been saying. We must follow the path of tsedek before we can have justice, equality, peace and love. There are some good men among the kohanim, the Perushim and the Şĕdûqîm and I will appeal to them in the name of tsedek. Hopefully, they will stand up to the HaKohen," I say.

"If something happens to you *Rabboni*, what are we to do?" asks Mariam.

"As I have often said, you must continue the work we have been doing. Mariam, I know how capable you are, and I expect a lot from you. What we have started is not another religion but a way of life to achieve the fullness of living in this world. A good, clean and healthy life is a basic necessity. Sickness takes away the joy of living and instead of putting the blame on satana, we should look for healing remedies from the earth's natural resources. All people should enjoy the goods of the earth.

"We must find ways to overcome ignorance, false notions and crooked interpretations of the scriptures.

"Today we are going to heal the illness in our society. We do not want enemies but when we get the poor and the oppressed to demand their rights, we will have enemies. Our message is not only for the Yehudim but for all people.

Scenario 69 - People's money

Court of the Goyim

Day 5 (Thursday)

Word has been sent around for the people to gather at Pilatus' Palace.

Early in the morning Yehuda and Shimon take their place among the Kana'im at Antonia Fortress. They light small fires to warm themselves. It is the thirteenth day of the month of Nisan, the day before the Preparation for the Paskha.

A crowd has already gathered at the Court of the Goyim where kollubistai are doing brisk business with people buying sacrificial animals and queueing up to make offerings. The Kittim guards are already positioned in both places, while the Báyith guards are on the steps of the Báyith. Everything appears normal.

The same Báyith officials approach me again along with some Perushim and Soferim who have a degree of authority. This time they also bring along with them a woman. They make her stand in full view of everybody.

The Soferim challenge me, "Moreh Yeshua, this woman was caught in the very act of adultery. Aba Moshe ordered us in the Law to condemn women like this to death by stoning. What have you got to say?"

I look at them and in a loud voice reply, "Which of you were there when she was committing the act of adultery and where is the man involved? You must know that it takes two to commit adultery."

"She was caught by our guards."

"Where are the guards? Are they afraid to appear? Not only the woman but the man and the guards must all be brought forward to testify. Then I will have something to say."

"We trust our guards and the man got away, but we have her in our custody. We want your response to the law of Aba Moshe.

"I said that I will speak but not condemn her unless you have witnesses to testify against her. You have condemned her without proof." I pause to look at the crowd, staring angrily into their faces. Then I say, "If there is anyone among you who has not sinned, you be the first to cast a stone at her."

The crowd begin to shift with unease.

I address them again, "Why do you hesitate? What are you afraid of? Are you afraid because you have sinned or are you afraid of the Kittim or the Perushim and Soferim? Either you are all sinners, or your law of Aba Moshe is useless. It is no more than a letter on the script. You know, very well, you cannot apply that law, which the Kittim has forbidden. Do you want me and the people to go against the Kittim ruling and bring their wrath upon us? You hypocrites! You should be crucified for violating the Kittim law."

Those gathered get scared and begin to move away.

I address the woman, "Attha, has no one condemned you?"

"No one, Rabbi," she says.

"Neither do I condemn you. Go and do no wrong."

An old woman steps out of the crowd, "Marya Yeshua, you are a man of tsedek. You do not judge and condemn people like the Perushim and Soferim, the Ṣĕdûqîm and the kohanim. "There is no tsedek in the Beit HaMikdash. I am a widow, and my only son cannot help me because the Beit HaMikdash has taken his money as Qorban."

I turn to the Báyith elders again, "Look at this poor woman here. Her son will not or cannot help her because your tradition dictates that when he has said Qorban on what he has, instead of using that to help her, it is now part of the Beit HaMikdash treasury. What nonsense is that?

"You invoke the Law of Aba Moshe against the woman you accuse of adultery and now you violate the same law that declares that you should honour your father and mother and not neglect them.

"The commandment says honour your parents, but you deprive old-aged parents from being honoured by their children when you take away money due to them by misinterpreting the qorban. It is really stealing from them and against the commandment that says you shall not steal. You are the ones who break the commandments. Yet you accuse people of not following tradition.

"The Báyith money is really the people's money, which you misinterpret as the Qorban. It is you who transgress the word of Elahh. It is you who stand condemned.

"I ask you; can you tell the people how you who use the Qorban? Can you tell the people? They want to know."

A number of people raise their voices, "Yes, yes, we want to know what happens to all the money you collect. We know that the money belongs to Elahh and is for the use of the Beit HaMikdash. What work has been done for the Beit HaMikdash? Is it being used for other purposes? For personal use? Tell us, tell us."

These voices come from the Kana'im and my followers who are mingling with the crowd. The crowd picks up the chorus and shouts "Qorban! Qorban!" They become agitated and at that moment there is a cry from someone in the crowd.

Scenario 70 - Blood

Fortress of Antonia

Concurrently, outside Pilatus' Palace, Antonia Fortress, there are also cries of "Qorban! Qorban!" from the crowd. Yonatan addresses the people on the misuse of the Qorban by the Beit HaMikdash in collusion with the governor. He accuses both Pilatus and Caiaphas of stealing the Qorban and using it for the aqueduct. The people are angry. Yehudah tells them that letters were sent to Rome to the Kittim Malka about this but there was no answer.

He shouts, "It is time to demand an answer now." The cries go up, "Qorban! Qorban!"

The Beit HaMikdash kohanim had earlier approached one of the siqari'im and bribed him to injure one of their own Beit HaMikdash guards who had been insubordinate on several occasions. This was the right moment. The sicara stealthily moves close to that guard, draws out his dagger concealed inside his cloak and stabs him in the back. He quickly hides the dagger and raises the alarm. He blends into the crowd before anyone notices him. The siqari'im are accomplished in this act.

This commotion is the signal for the soldiers who have mingled among the crowd in plain clothes, to pull out their clubs and start

457

attacking the people. They bash them up regardless of who they are. There are cries and blood everywhere. People run helter-skelter. The Kittim soldiers then move in and arrest as many as they can. The kana'im put up a gallant fight but are outmanoeuvred. In the melee, Shimon is hit on the head. He collapses and dies in a pool of blood. Yehudah tries to escape with Yonatan but also was clubbed. He falls but does not die. One of the Kittim soldiers lifts his head by the hair and slits his throat and collects his blood in a bucket. They do that to a number of victims.

Many of the people run into the Court of the Goyim and merge with the crowd there.

Scenario 71 - The Arrest

Entrance to Court of Goyim

A similar siqari attack occurs at the Court of the Goyim and the Kittim soldiers move in to arrest people. The situation gets out of hand. The crowd becomes wild. They set upon the kollubistai, upset their tables and send coins flying all over the place. The kollubistai scramble to recover their loot. The angry mob sets free all the lambs corralled for sale and releases the doves and pigeons into the air. Sellers chase bleating lambs.

The Kittim soldiers bring the dead and wounded to the parapet near the western entrance of Pilatus's praetorium. The parapet is surrounded by columns and in the centre is an underground section where they take the prisoners. They cut deeper into the wounds of those bleeding, collected their blood and leave them to die.

The Perushim and Soferim panic and run into the Báyith precinct. My companions and I run into the crowd and try to escape. The Báyith guards are watching me. They are not interested in the others. They corner me before I can enter the small stairway out of the court. They block and catch me, and roughly tie my hands behind my back before throwing a cloth over my head to hide my face. They lead me down the main stairway out of the Court of the Goyim.

Scenario 72 - Hiding in the olive grove

Gat Shemen

"Moreh has been taken," alerts Pilip.

"By whom?" questions Shoshana.

"He was arrested by the Báyith guards," says Shemayon.

"That is not as bad as being taken by the Kittim soldiers. They would surely kill him. We must go back into the city and learn more of what happened," says Mariam.

"It is very risky," says Tauma.

"Don't worry. They are not really concerned about us. They want Moreh Yeshua and to control the crowd. If they wanted us, they would have followed us here," says Natan'el.

"When it gets dark, I'm going into the city. I want to know what happened to *Rabboni*," says Mariam.

"We should not go together. We must break into small groups," cautions Joa'ana.

"I will go to the orechah and let Maryam and the others know what has happened to Moreh," says Arsinoe.

Rabboni is not with us now. He wouldn't know what is happening and I am taking over in narrating what is taking place.

Mariam: During the commotion we flee with the other people out of the Báyith. People run in all directions. We descend into the Kidron valley on the east side of the Báyith and join those climbing the hill side, into the grove of olive trees. Pilgrims who have come for the feast are camping among the olive trees. We mingle among the campers and settle down quietly. We are prepared to stay the night here until everything quietens down. This place is the foot of *Har ha-Zeitim* [257] and is known as Gat Shemen. Beyond the campsite is the Yehudi cemetery.

While we wait, others are trickling into the grove. One of them who is a kanai says, "The Kittim soldiers were in the crowd without their uniforms. They attacked us with clubs. Many of the kana'im were killed, Shimon was one of them. Yehudah was badly injured. You won't like to hear this. The Kittim slit his throat and collected his blood."

We are struck with fear and sadness.

"All the more, I must go and find out what has happened to my *Rabboni*," I say.

"We heard that the Báyith guards took him to the palace of HaKohen Caiaphas," adds the kanai.

Tonight, the Fortress of Antonia and the Court of the Goyim are silent except for bloodstains on the floor and the mess being cleaned up. The riot had been suppressed and the rebellion diffused.

---

[257] Mount Olivet/ Mount of Olives

Scenario 73 - Send word to Naṣrath

The Orechah site

Arsinoe breaks the news of Yeshua's arrest at the orechah. Maryam says, "We must send word at once to Yôsēp̄ and the girls. Yehudah, go look for a fast rider on horseback. Pay him well and dispatch him with the message to Naṣrath."

"Ama, let's go and see what's happening," says Shemayon, Yeshua's fourth brother.

"Someone will have to look after the cart," says Maryam.

"I'll stay, but keep me informed of what happens," says Yôsēp̄, Yeshua's third brother.

Scenario 74 - Witnesses and charges

Caiaphas' Palace

Yeshua: Still trussed I am thrust into a room and the cloth is removed from my head. It is dark. They lock the door and leave. I have come to this present moment of time. What has happened to my followers, I wonder and what's going to happen next, I ponder. After what seems a very long time, the door opens, and a woman enters with a lighted candle.

"Where am I?" I ask.

"This is the underground storeroom of HaKohen Caiaphas' mansion. I'm a servant. I've brought you some bread and water."

"Why am I not taken to meet him?"

"He is busy sending word to the members to assemble for the Sanhedrin this very night. He is listening to the story of the witnesses and the charges that would be brought against you. I am not supposed to talk to you."

"What is the situation out there and what happened to my companions?"

"The situation is calm, and your companions all escaped except for Shimon and Yehudah. They were killed by the Kittim soldiers."

I am sad and tears well in my eyes. "Shimon and Yehudah were true sons of Yisrael," I say.

"Thank you for the food. Could you please leave one candle for me?"

After she left, I go through in my mind the different scenarios that could take place.

Scenario 75 - Eerie Silence

City of Dawidh

Mariam: In the quiet of the night, we go down the Kidron Valley and enter the east gate into the city of Dawidh. The streets are empty. An eerie silence has replaced the festive mood. We speak to a few people. They say that the people are afraid to come out. We learn nothing more than what has happened except that a meeting of the Sanhedrin is to be held soon that night. We go back to the orechah to console Maryam, Yeshua's mother, and to plan what to do.

Scenario 76 - Word to Qumran

Orechah site

Mariam: When we arrive at the orechah we find our members huddled behind the cart. Maryam tells us, "We have already sent word to Yôsēp̄ and the girls in Naṣrath. Word must also be sent to Qumran to inform Ya'aqov. I want the family to be together."

Mattithyahu who has contacts in Yerushalayim manages to get a rider to travel swiftly to Qumran with news that Yeshua has been arrested and to come at once.

I am very uneasy. "If Rabboni is being held at Caiapha's palace, I'm going there to find out more."

Shemayon and Mattithyahu say, "We will come with you."

Scenario 77 - Troublemaker in custody

Caiaphas' Palace

Mariam: The three of us with covered heads go into the night towards the mansion. It is a walled palace with the main entrance opening into a courtyard. People there are warming themselves around a fire. We join them. Soon we see elders, Soferim, Perushim and Şĕdûqîm entering the mansion one by one. They are of combined political and religious persuasions.

"It looks like the HaKohen is assembling the elders for a trial to condemn Yeshua," says one of the people at the courtyard.

Caiaphas has invited those who he knows are opposed to the teaching of Yeshua, especially the Şĕdûqîm. He also has to invite some others to make up the quorum of 23 to constitute a trial court. By midnight there are about 30 people gathered. Among them are also those who came to visit Yeshua, Nikodemus and Yôsēp̄ of Harimathea.

When all are assembled in the great hall inside the mansion, Caiaphas addresses them, "Thank you all for coming in the night. As you know there was a riot and rebellion today at the Báyith. Some died and many were wounded. The situation has been brought under control and the troublemaker is in custody. He is still very dangerous because his followers and sympathisers are around, and it is festival time.

"To prevent another riot during this holy season, it is necessary to silence this troublemaker and put him away expeditiously. We will bring Yeshua bar Yôsēp̄ before this assembly and witnesses will testify against him. This Sanhedrin will charge and pass sentence on him tonight."

Scenario 78 - The Sanhedrin

Caiaphas' Palace

Yeshua: I am brought by the guards with my hands bound behind my back, into the chamber and made to stand in the centre of the semicircle of Sanhedrin members.

Nikodemus immediately stands up, "Is it necessary to bind the hands of the rabbi? He is not a violent man, and he is not going to escape."

"A criminal should be in a position of humiliation. He shall remain bound," says Caiaphas.

"It appears," continues Nikodemus, "that you have already pre-judged him to be a criminal even before the trial. And may I ask, why are there no notaries? There should be two of them to record the votes."

"The urgency of the matter requires that we come to a quick conclusion before daybreak. As you well know, it is not lawful to convene the Sanhedrin court before the time of the offering of the morning sacrifice in the Báyith. I have dispensed with the notaries. So, let us proceed," declares Caiaphas.

Witnesses who are handsomely paid are standing by. The first is invited to step forward and give his testimony.

"Yeshua has publicly spoken against the Torah and the Halakha, claiming that they are the words of men and not the dabar Elahh. He was seen committing *chillul ShAbat*[258]."

"How do you plead? Do you realise that chillul ShAbat is a capital offence?" asks Caiaphas.

"Did Malka Dawidh plead guilty when he committed chillul ShAbat by eating the bread of offering? Your kohanaim commit chillul ShAbat every week and are not blamed for it! They are guilty. Why is the capital offence not carried out on them?" I respond in a firm voice.

"They are exempt as they are doing their duty," says one of the sages who is a kohan.

"May I interrupt?" asks Yôsēp̄ of Harimathea. "This gathering is highly irregular. Any case involving capital punishment is not to be tried on a day before a holy day. A capital punishment sentence cannot be passed on the day of trial itself. Any decision of the judges must be examined the following day, which now happens to be the Preparation Day. This gathering is illegal."

"It is for that very reason I consider this trial to be most urgent and to be dealt with immediately. Let's have the next witness," says Caiaphas.

"Yeshua has been declared the Mshikha, the promised Deliverer," says the witness.

"Do you know the seriousness of the title of Mshikha? The HaMshikha is the Melekh HaMshikha, He is a Malka, a descendent of Malka Dawidh who will unify the twelve tribes of Yisra'el. Have you been anointed with the holy anointing oil? Where is your mamlekhet? I ask you now. Are you the Mshikha?" asks Caiaphas.

"I have been called many things by many people. I have never

---

[258] Profanation of the Sabbath

470

declared myself the Mshikha," I say.

"But you have been acting as the Deliverer with your magic and deceit," adds the witness.

"Yes, I have said and done things to deliver the people from oppression," I admit.

"He is under a delusion. We take note, however, that he admits being the Deliverer. Next witness," says Caiaphas.

"Yeshua has condemned taxation and told the people not to pay taxes to the Beit HaMikdash and the Kittim Malka," says the witness.

"What have you got to say, Yeshua?" asks Caiaphas.

"I have spoken openly for all the world to hear. I have spoken in towns and villages and even in the beit k'nesset and the Beit HaMikdash where all the Yehudim meet. I have said nothing in secret. Why ask me? Ask my hearers what I have taught; they know what I have said," I say.

Nicodemus again interrupts, "You have brought witnesses against the rabbi Yeshua. Why is there no witness to speak on his behalf? An accused person is entitled to have his own defence."

"Yeshua's activities are public knowledge, yes. We are interested in his own admission of guilt. He can defend himself," insists Caiaphas.

I remain silent.

"It is necessary to submit to authority. That is why it is the duty of the people to pay taxes. The authorities are the servants of Elahh devoted to his work. To deny paying taxes to the Kittim Malka is tantamount to rebellion against Roma and the Kittim Empire. To tell the people not to pay the Kittim tax is to start an insurrection against the state. This will bring the wrath of the Kittim governor upon us," declares Caiaphas.

"His followers are bewitched by him because he works by the

bisha[259] power of Ba'al HaZvuv," continues the witness.

"Yeshua pretends to be the itinerant rabbi from HaGalil. He has spoken against and violated the Law, and denied Elahh," says the next witness.

Is it true then that you deny Elahh?" asks Caiaphas.

"Have you seen Elahh or heard him speak? Show him to me and I will not deny him," say I.

"From the time of Aba Avraham, we have believed in Elahh. All our ancestors, patriarchs and nebim have spoken of Elahh and have heard his voice. There is no reason to doubt," says Caiaphas.

"It was written by the hand of man that Elahh spoke to them. None of them have described what he looks like," I say.

"He who denies the belief in the Torah and denies Elahh is a *minuth*[260]" accuses Caiaphas.

At that moment, Yôsēp̄ of Harimathea stands up, "If the crime Yeshua is accused of is so serious, then it will have to be dealt with by the supreme religious body of the land, the Great Sanhedrin of 71 sages under the leadership of the *Nasi*[261], who is elder Gamaliel. The Great Sanhedrin meets in the daytime in the *Lishkat ha-Gazit*[262] at the Royal *Stoa*[263] in the Beit HaMikdash, not here."

At one time the offices of the Nasi and HaKohen were held by the same person, but no longer. Previously too, members of the Sanhedrin elected the Nasi, but not anymore. The Nasi, at present is still the President of the Sanhedrin and recognised as the leader of

---

[259] evil

[260] heretic

[261] Prince or president of the Sanhedrin

[262] The Hall of Hewn Stones, the meeting place of the Sanhedrin

[263] The basilica constructed by Herod the Great at the renovation of the Temple Mount in 1BCE

the people. Gamaliel is not present here tonight.

Seeing that power and control are vested in the office of the Hakohen whom the Kittim appointed, the Ṣĕdûqîm who had no lack of money, offered a large personal bribe to the procurator to appoint a candidate of their choice as Hakohen. Others did the same but the Ṣĕdûqîm were the highest bidder. Caiaphas was their chosen candidate and he and his friends and relatives have become aristocrats and successors.

Under the procurator Pontius Pilatus, many acts of aggression are committed especially during festival times. The Sanhedrin under the control of the Hakohen has always excused the Kittim on the grounds of maintaining order.

At this time the Nasi Gamaliel had gone to Dimashqu to talk to the proconsul Vitellius about the atrocities of Pilatus. In his absence, Caiaphas pushes through with the Sanhedrin.

"That is all very well," Caiaphas responding to Yôsēp̄, "but under the present circumstance I invoke my right as the HaKohen to convene the Lesser Sanhedrin of 23 members. The Great Sanhedrin cannot meet tomorrow either or the day after which is the Paskha."

"But it is still not lawful to meet today or during the night. I will have nothing to do with this illegal assembly," says Yôsēp̄ of Harimathea.

"Neither will I," says Nikodemus. Both the esteemed Elders walk out of the hall. They are followed by three other Elders.

Caiaphas continues nevertheless, "In the scroll of *Vayikra*[264] of the Torah it is written, 'One who blasphemes the name of the Lord shall be put to death; the whole congregation shall stone the minuth. What more do we need? What is your verdict?"

All remaining in the select assembly say, "He deserves to die!"

---

[264] Leviticus

Caiaphas rises up and tears his garment at the toggle. He sits down again. "I agree. It is necessary for one man to die than the destruction of the Beit HaMikdash and the entire nation at the hands of the Kittim. However, there is a problem. The Kittim have taken away our right to capital punishment. Only the Procurator Pilatus can order the death of Yeshua. We will have to present Yeshua before him and accuse him of instigating an insurrection against Roma.

"It will soon be dawn and at first light we will have him standing before Pilatus. The Sanhedrin is adjourned," concludes Caiaphas.

As I am led outside the hall, I hear Caiaphas addressing his closest allies, "If a law has no penalty, it has no force. Our law is useless. It is unlikely that the procurator will issue the death penalty for blasphemy. He will have to respond to a charge accusing Yeshua of proclaiming himself the HaMshikha, a malka, and plotting against Roma by instigating a riot. I will send him a note."

Scenario 79 - Condemned to death

Outside Caiaphas' Palace

Mariam: Shemayon, Mattithyahu and I are waiting outside in the courtyard, in the cold after the fire had died down. The Sanhedrin members are filing out. We try to catch their attention to find out what has happened, but no one would stop as they walk past.

A merchant, a close friend of one of the sages, stops one of them and enquires. We draw closer and overhear the conversation. Once we hear that Yeshua has been condemned to death, we are speechless and wonder what to do next. I finally say, "Mattithyahu, go and inform the others. Shemayon and I will wait here for further developments."

Just then another person approaches us, "You are the followers of the condemned man Yeshua, aren't you?

I say, "Of course we are! They have condemned an innocent man and we will stand by him," I turned toward Shenayon for mutual support, but he has disappeared.

Scenario 80 - You should let him go

Pilatus' Palace

After Pilatus wakes up and washes his face and hands, the note from Caiaphas is handed to him. While he is reading it, his wife Claudia asks him about it. She has heard of Yeshua and what people have been saying about him.

"I hear that Yeshua from HaGalil is a good man who has healed many sick people. The Báyith authorities are threatened by his popularity. If you harm him the people will not take that kindly. If he is no threat, you should let him go."

What did you just say? Is Yeshua from HaGalil?

"Yes, he is a simple tekton from Nasrath. He has not spoken much of the Kittim. He is critical of the Beit HaMikdash and their religious leaders."

"In that case Yeshua is outside my immediate jurisdiction. Anyway, I must sit in judgement and listen to them. Roma is greater than the problems of these Yehudim or one of their rabbis," says Pilatus still holding Caiaphas's letter.

Scenario 81 - Face covered

Upper City

Day 6 (Friday)

I found Shemayon hiding behind a pillar. "What happened to you, where did you go?"

"Hmmm... I went to ease myself,"

Just before the first light of day, we see some movement. A small group of men are leading Yeshua out with his face covered and hands tied. They are sneaking him out to the praetorium before people can recognise him. Shemayon and I watch and follow at a safe distance.

They take Yeshua through the narrow streets of the Upper City, well away from the orechah market, towards the Báyith. They reach the old wall. It divides the Lower and Upper cities. They enter a narrow gate of the very high wall of 120 feet and go along the west wall of the Báyith to the Fortress of Antonia. Having sought clearance from the Kittim guards, they take Yeshua inside.

As dawn breaks, word quickly gets around that the Sanhedrin has sentenced Yeshua to death and taken him to Pilatus to have the sentence ratified.

Scenario 82 - Mixing of bloods

Beit HaMikdash

We notice that people have already gathered at the courtyard of the Beit HaMikdash.

Before the crack of dawn, the *Kahal adat Yisra'el*, the assembly of the congregation of Yisra'el with a quorum of 30, has already assembled for the sacrificial service in the courtyard of the Beit HaMikdash. We go over to look.

As the offerers come up one by one, a kohan takes the lamb and slaughters it. Another catches the dripping blood in a chalice and hands it to another kohan next to him and receives an empty chalice in return. Rows of kohanaim with gold and silver chalices in their hands stand in line from the Báyith court to the altar. The chalice fills up as it is passed along the line until the blood is sprinkled on the altar.

In the Beit HaMikdash where the animal sacrifice of *Qorbanot*[265] is being conducted, a Kittim centurion walks in with some soldiers, ignoring the custom that they are not allowed in there. He addresses the people gathered there.

---

[265] Sacrifices/offerings

"It is by order of the Prefect Pontius Pilatus that the blood sacrifice you offer to your Elahh be mingled with the blood of the Yehudim." He orders his men to pour the blood they had collected, mixing it with the blood of the sacrificial animals. There is a huge moan from the crowd.

The supervising kohan addresses the centurion, "You have no right to step into this holy place. Take your men and get out of here at once!"

"As you wish," says the centurion and leaves with his men. A scandal has been created. The kohanaim are shocked by what has happened.

People move away from the Beit HaMikdash and the slaughtering of the animals immediately stops. They fear the mixing of bloods.

The blood sacrifice is meant for the atonement of their sins. Now with no knowledge of the sins of other men, they are not prepared to risk being unforgiven. So, many of them decide not to make an offering. The kohanaim are not only angry with Pilatus for doing this but also that he has ruined the animal sacrifice of the qorbanot and caused a loss of income.

The euphoria of the festive season is dampened by the riot and tragedy, and now this year's Paskha is totally ruined.

Scenario 83 - Out of jurisdiction

Fortress of Antonia

The people move from the Báyith to Pilatus at the praetorium to protest this sacrilege. To their surprise, they find a crowd there already assembled waiting for Pilatus to appear.

We, the followers of Yeshua, are also present. I am with Maryam and Arsinoe while the others disperse inconspicuously into the crowd.

The people are shouting, "Qorban! Qorban! – Qorbanot! Qorbanot!"

"Quiet!" yells a centurion as the Procurator Pontius Pilatus comes out and takes his seat.

"Yesterday there was a riot in the city. It is my responsibility to maintain peace. Anyone who disrupts the peace and agitates violence will be punished. The Kittim government will not tolerate any opposition."

Despite what he says, there are voices at the back that shout, "Qorban! Qorban! Qorbanot! Qorbanot! We want an answer."

Some of the soldiers move into the crowd and there is silence.

With my hands bound behind my back I am led before Pilatus.

"Before I pass judgement of this man, I have come to know that he is from HaGalil."

Addressing me he asks, "Are you Yeshua bar Yôsēp̄ and are you from HaGalil?"

Since he already knew I do not answer.

"He is Yeshua the Nazarene," someone in the crowd shouts.

"You come under the jurisdiction of Hordos Antipas...." Before Pilatus can complete his sentence, HaKohen Caiaphas begins, "Your excellency...."

Pilatus raises his hand to silence him. When Pilatus presides, he is the supreme Lord, and he wants the people to make no mistake about it. He continues, "Hordos Antipas just now is present in the city. Out of curtesy, I am sending you to him. Let us see how he will deal with you. We have no further business." He gets up and goes inside.

The crowd is not satisfied. The people continue to shout "Qorban! Qorban! Qorbanot! Qorbanot!

Scenario 84 - You will be safe in HaGalil

Palace of Hordos Antipas

The disappointed crowd disperses but some people follow Caiaphas' men leading Yeshua to the Palace of Hordos Antipas. We, the followers of Yeshua, also do the same but not as a group. When Yeshua is taken in, the gates are closed, so we wait outside.

Yeshua: I am brought, still bound, into the palace hall and made to wait while a messenger goes inside to meet the Malka. The hall is ornately furnished with expensive carpets from foreign lands. We wait for a long time before Hordos Antipas emerges and sits on the throne. I am thrust forward.

"Yeshua bar Yôsēp̄ from Nasrath of HaGalil, I have been waiting to meet you and you tried to run away from me. Pilatus, of all people, has sent you to me. Ha,Ha,Ha. Do you know that I can get you out of this mess you are in? All you have to do is agree to come to my residence in Tiberias and you will be safe in HaGalil. There you can perform your magic and miracles to entertain my guests.

I say nothing.

"Will you come?" he asks.

"Will you change your evil ways?" I ask.

"What evil ways? Are you trying to do what Y'hochanan ha-mmatbil tried on me? You know what happened to him."

"You are a cruel and unjust ruler. You persecute your own poor people with high taxes and brutally murder them. You make them your enemies."

"Those who do not obey me become my enemies."

"No, they are your subjects and not your enemies. Your real enemy is inside you. It is your greed and selfishness. You are not going to live long. If you want to be remembered as a benevolent ruler, change your ways and follow the way of Tsedek."

"Now you are preaching to me. Save your breath. Since you are in my custody now, I can end your life right here. But since Pilatus has made a friendly gesture by sending you to me, I shall send you back to him."

"You will be remembetred as a tyrant and an evil malka, just like your father."

Antipas stands up, "Take him away!"

Mariam: Outside, we move closer as Yeshua is brought out. Maryam, Arsinoe and I rush up to meet him. The soldiers block our path. One of them says, "She is his mother, let her meet him."

"Ama, be strong, take care of Aba and my sisters and brothers. Mariam, take the lead and the path of tsedek with the others. Our mission must continue," I say.

"Rabboni, you will live on in us." says Mariam.

"Alright, that's enough, move on," says the soldier.

Scenario 85 - Treason against Roma

The Praetorium

Pontius Pilatus again sits in judgement as I am brought before him. He points to me and addresses the crowd.

"***Ecce Homo!***[266] We are here to pass judgement on one of your heroes who has been brought to us by your own leaders," turning to the chief kohanaim and the elders Pilatus asks, "What charge have you brought against this man?"

"He is a false nebi and a troublemaker. He has blasphemed against Elahh by denying him. By our Law he should be punished by sekila, stoning to death," says a chief kohan.

"I am not bothered with your Elahh and your Law. That is your business. It is the law of Roma that I am here to defend. How is he a troublemaker?" asks Pilatus.

"He has proclaimed himself Melekh HaMshikha."

"What if he is?"

"He works magic and denounces the Law. A Melekh HaMshikha would never do that."

"Again, that is none of my business."

---

[266] Behold The man!

"Procurator, Sir, you must understand that his claim implies that he is a malka. That would be going against the wishes of Roma."

"He may claim to be the malka of the Yehudim. There can be no malka here unless he was appointed by Roma." Turning to Yeshua he asks, "Are you a malka? Where is your crown and where are your armies? Obviously, you are not a malka. What is your profession?"

"I am a tekton," replied Yeshua.

Pilatus bursts out laughing and there is mixed reaction from the crowd.

"By claiming to be a malka he is plotting against Roma. He even told people not to pay taxes. He is the secret leader of the kana'im. The rebellion and riot yesterday were caused by him. He placed his followers, the kana'im, among the crowd to stir up trouble."

"I have taken care of that," says Pilatus.

"You heard the rebellious voices just now. They will continue to cause unrest unless you condemn this man of treason against Roma."

"The punishment for treason is crucifixion," says Pilatus.

Caiaphas had already got his men to place people in the crowd to demand for Yeshua's crucifixion. Cries go up from the crowd, "Crucify him! Crucify him!" However, the Kana'im shout, "Aqueduct! Qorban! Qorbanot!" My followers also raise their voice, "Yeshua is innocent! Charges against him are false!"

Pilatus turns to look at Caiaphas who nods his head. To quell the uprising and quash the demand to explain the aqueduct and Qorban, they have agreed to exhibit the power of Roma and instil fear in the people by using Yeshua as the scapegoat.

Pilatus speaks, "The might of Roma will not tolerate any challenge to its power. Anyone who dares to instigate the people and cause trouble will be dealt with in the usual way of Roma. This tekton was behind the scenes of yesterday's rebellion. Therefore, I decree that Yeshua be crucified today." Pilatus gets up and goes inside.

Scenario 86 - A cruel way to die

Via Dolorosa

Yeshua: I believe I'm nearing the end of my life. I am led into the courtyard and the transverse beam of a cross is brought out. My hands are untied. Very quickly and efficiently I am made to carry the cross beam and walk. This is a routine the soldiers are very much accustomed to. Only slaves and the lowest criminals and political rebels are put to death by crucifixion. For the Kittim the cross is a symbol of shame. I am led out in disgrace. Crucifixion is a public exhibition of a cruel way to die. It is meant to bring shame on the one being executed and to deter onlookers from doing what he has been accused of doing.

My dear Ama breaks down. She is consoled by Marta and Arsinoe. Mariam of Magdala is pushing her way through the crowd to get a close look at me. There are always people in the city crowd who would come out to jeer at the victims of crucifixion to show their loyalty to Roma. Others follow fearfully silent.

Mariam: On the previous night itself Ya'aqov, Yeshua's brother, received the message in Qumran and at first light he set out for Yerushalayim on horseback. He arrives to see Yeshua carrying the crossbeam. He works his way through the crowd, goes up to meet

Yeshua. The Kittim soldier blocks him. "Who are you and what do you want with him?" he asks.

"I am from the Qumran community. He is one of us and he is my brother. Please let me meet him," says Ya'aqov.

"Only for a while," says the soldier and calls a halt.

Ya'aqov goes and embraces Yeshua. Seeing them Maryam, their mother rushes towards them. The soldier tries to stop her, but she cries out, "He is my son."

I also try to approach them but am stopped by the soldier who says, "That's enough, stay back!"

Mother and son cling to each other. Yeshua lifts her upright, "Ama, be strong for Aba and the girls." To Ya'aqov he says, "Brother, go home and be with the family for some time and look after my followers."

"Alright, let's move on," says the soldier. Yeshua looks back and sees me focused on him with tears streaming down my face. The other followers are hidden in the crowd.

Yeshua is led from the Antonia Fortress by the Kittim soldiers, carrying the cross beam through the narrow winding streets of the Old City of Yerushalayim. People are gathered on the sides of the road to watch the procession. The *Via Dolorosa*[267] goes past a large open-air pool of water reflecting the image of Yeshua carrying the crossbeam.

---

[267] The Way of Sorrow

Scenario 87 - Struggle for Tsedek

Gagulta

Yeshua: I am being led out of the city wall. I struggle with the heavy load to climb a small hill not far from the wall. It is called *Gagulta* because it resembles a skullcap.

On the hillock, there are several straight pieces of wood already fixed into the ground. Crucifixions are held quite often and mine is the first one for the day. I'm sure other crucifixions are to follow during the day.

The soldiers strip me of the robe that Ama had lovingly made for me and cast it aside, leaving me with only my loin cloth.

I see my beloved Ama, "Ama, tell Aba not to be worried. I love you and my brothers and sisters. My death will be the beginning of our greater struggle for tsedek." To my dear Mariam and some other followers who had all gathered around, I say, "Continue the work of changing the minds and hearts of the people and heal them of their infirmities. Thank you for having faithfully followed me. Remember that I love you all and that love will conquer all. My dearest Mariam, take the lead."

Scenario 88 - Crucifixion

Gagulta

Yeshua: The soldiers make me lie on the ground and stretch my arms over the transverse beam of the cross. Two of them on either end simultaneously place nails on my wrists. I close my eyes.

Mariam: I hold my breath and feel the crushing hurt as my beloved *Rabboni* yells in pain. His precious blood spurts from his hands.

They lift the beam while others support his body, holding it. Placed against the upright beam, others on two ladders push the wood hoisting his body up. Another plank is held under his feet to support his weight. All of them heave him up until the transverse beam lodges into the halving joints already cut into the wood of the upright pole making a cross.

The upright beam has a footrest. They place his feet on the standing platform to support his body weight. I hold Maryam tightly as they drive nails through his feet. All this is done not to relieve any pain but to prevent his body tearing away from the nails. They also drive a nail in the middle of the halving joints of the cross to prevent the transverse bean from slipping out. As an extra measure, they tie a rope around his waist and secure this tightly to the cross. Then they leave him.

All this is done very quickly and efficiently. Only then do they allow the family members to approach the cross.

Maryam is brought forward helped by Marta and Arsinoe. Joa'ana, Shoshanna, Mariamnne and I also accompany them together with Ya'aqov and Yehudah, Shemayon and Yôsēp̄, Yeshua's brothers who left their cart to be here. The men followers of Yeshua hold back until the coast is clear of Báyith guards before they approach the foot of the cross. We can do nothing but helplessly witness the agonising last moments of our beloved Moreh.

Scenario 89 - Death

Gagulta

Yeshua is struggling to breathe. He is losing consciousness. Everyone is holding their breath, thinking he died. After a while Yeshua regains consciousness, lifts his head slightly to focus on those below him. A faint smile appears on his face. He opens his mouth to say something, but he cannot take enough air into his lungs.

The Kittim soldiers take a close look at Yeshua. His lungs are collapsing, and his mouth remains open. One of the Kittim soldiers takes a spear and thrusts it into Yeshua's rib cage. Yeshua's eyes open wide, he lets out a breath and his head drops.

Yeshua has died.

Maryam bursts out in a loud cry and the women let out high-pitched wails. Nobody stops them because it is Yehudi custom. The wailing eventually subsides and stops.

The Kittim soldiers tell his mourners that they can take down his body for burial.

I take charge. I tell the men, "We should remove the body of Moreh and find a burial place quickly."

Two older men who had silently stood by during this time came forward, "I am Yôsēp̄ of Harimathea and this is Nikodemus. We had met Moreh Yeshua before. We tried to prevent this from happening. We will explain later but we have a burial place where you can take his body."

"Ah, yes. We remember you," says Shemayon.

Yhochanan approaches the Kittim soldier, "Can we borrow your tools to remove the nails?"

"Help yourself," he says. "If you don't take him, we will and throw his body on the roadside as dog-feed."

The ladders are still standing beside the cross. The men get busy. They climb up and try to extract the nails from Yeshua's wrists. They cannot do this without damaging his hands. Using a leverage, they manage to extract the nails from his feet. Others hold his body while the nail in the cross-halving joint is extracted. They lower Moreh's body together with the crossbeam. Using external leverages, they then remove the nails without damaging his hands.

Very gently they lift Yeshua and let Maryam hold him. With tears streaming, I extend my arms and embrace them both. The other women too crowd around the body of Yeshua, our Moreh, our leader, my *Rabboni*.

Nikodemus has arranged for a cart to be brought. We place the body on the cart and roll it away. All of us, Yeshua's followers walk behind him in silence. To our surprise, many more people have joined the procession of mourners.

Scenario 90 - Burial

Tomb

Yehudi tradition forbids burial within the walls of the city. Yôsēp̄ of Harimathea who is a well-to-do elder, had purchased a rock-cut tomb within a small cave for himself in the upper-class section of the cemetery, which is a short distance from Gagulta. We take Yeshua there to prepare for burial. Men perform this task for deceased men, while women do the same for women. We women wait outside while the men wash Yeshua's body and anoint it with embalming ointment of spices, a mixture of myrrh and aloes, which Nikodemus supplied. The big toes of Yeshua's feet are tied to keep his legs together and his hands placed along the sides of his body. The body is wrapped in a long clean white linen saturated with the spices, also supplied by Nikodemus, and laid on a stone table. This is hurriedly done. They then invite the women inside.

Yôsēp̄ of Harimathea recites the El Maley Rachamim, the prayer to the All Merciful Elahh.

O Elahh, full of compassion, Thou who dwellest on high! Grant perfect rest beneath the sheltering wings of Thy presence, among the holy and pure who shine as the brightness of the firmament unto the soul of who has gone unto eternity. Lord of Mercy, bring him under the cover of Thy wings, and let his soul be bound up in the bond of eternal life. Be thou his possession, and may his repose be peace, Amin.

The others say nothing but listen in reverend silence to the elder. Finally, they cover his face with a napkin and lift Yeshua onto a burial bed, a limestone shelf hewn from the wall of the cave. After spending some moments in silence, we come out and the cave mouth is sealed with a circular slab of rock.

It is almost sunset, and we hurriedly manage to intern the body before the ShAbat begins.

Scenario 91 - Too late now

Orechah site

We all go back to the orechah in silence.

The Paskha festivities would continue through Shavuot and Sukkot, and the orechah would stay on. We, however, decide not to.

Yeshua's Ama, Maryam says, "I want to go to Ain Karim and stay with Elisheva and Zachariah for a while. They too lost their son Y'hochanan."

"I will take you there," says Ya'aqov.

"I will ask my people at our cart to either stay on and continue business or go back to Magdala. I would like to go with you to Ain Karim," say I.

"Shemayon, Yôsēp̄ and I will pack up and go back to Naṣrath," says Mattithyahu.

"No, wait," says Joa'ana, "we have sent word to Yôsēp̄. We should wait, Yôsēp̄, Bethanna and Tabby could be on their way here."

"Alright, we will stay," agrees Mattithyahu.

Natan'el and the Zebadyah brothers Ya'aqov and Y'hochanan choose to stay with their carts.

So, Ya'aqov, Yeshua's brother and Maryam their mother accompanied by Joa'ana, Shoshanna, Miriamne and Arsinoe and me are about to proceed to Ain Karim, only about six milin away.

Marta says, "I will go back home to Beth anya and join you all later."

As we are planning our movements the two elders Yôsēp̄ and Nikodemus come again to see us. "Are you all alright? We've brought some bread and wine," says Yôsēp̄.

We went to the rear and sat around them.

"We are sorry for what happened today. We were there at the Sanhedrin held in Caiaphas' house. The whole process was illegal, and they brought false charges against Moreh Yeshua. We protested."

"If you were there, why didn't you stop them from proceeding?" I ask.

"We could not do that because Caiaphas used his authority as HaKohen and had also called enough of his associates to stack the numbers at the meeting. Our elder Gamaliel who is the Nasi of the Great Sanhedrin could have stopped it, but he is away in Dimashqu. The whole proceeding was rushed through and everything about it was unlawful. They took their false witnesses to the governor," says Yôsēp̄.

"We will re-examine this whole procedure when Gamaliel returns," says Nikodemus.

"It is too late now, isn't it?" says Maryam, Yeshua's mother.

Both the well-intentioned elders are dumbfounded realising their ineffectiveness in the proceedings of the Sanhedrin.

"Is it safe for us to remain in the city?" enquires Shemayon.

"It should be if you lay low and not make any public appearances or speeches. They were interested in making Yeshua a spectacle to drive fear into the people and control the situation for the festive season.

"In that case, the rest of us will stay with the orechah until you come back from Ain Karim," says Shemayon.

Scenario 92 - Rest and mourn

Ain Karim

Elisheva and Zachariah welcome us and commiserate with us on the fate of Yeshua. Maryam and Elisheva hold each other and have a long cry over the loss of their sons. The others join in the cry and high-pitched wailing.

We are too exhausted to eat and too distraught to sleep. Elisheva, nevertheless, takes the initiative to prepare some hot soup for everyone.

The home of Zachariah and Elisheva is just the place to get away from the city and quietly rest and mourn.

Scenario 93 - Devastated

Nasrath

The dispatch rider, having left Yerushalayim on the afternoon of the fifth day rides through the night on the good Kittim road to Naṣrath arriving there at the crack of dawn.

The messenger says that Yeshua has been arrested and anything could happen. It looks like the authorities want to put him away.

Yôsēp̄, Bethanna and Tabby are devastated by the tragic news. The two sisters begin to wail. The father holds them tight as they cry.

Yôsēp̄ immediately engages a cart drawn by two horses and a driver. Bethanna and Tabby help to bandage up Yôsēp̄'s foot, grab some food and water and they set out immediately for Yerushalayim. The driver has to stop to water and feed the horses and rest for a while. When they continue, they urged the driver to push the animals harder to catch up on lost time.

Scenario 94 - Heart-rending cries

Yerushalayim

It is well into the night when they arrive in Yerushalayim and go straight to the orechah site. They find Yehudah with their cart and the others. Yehudah immediately brings them to the back and sit them down then slowly explains step by step what has happened. When they hear of the crucifixion and death of Yeshua, Bethanna and Tabby burst out with heart-rending cries holding their father and brother. It looks like time has stopped until they recover. They are totally devastated, hungry and tired, but refuse to rest. Seeing that there is not much they can do there at that time of the night, they decide to go straightaway and join the family in Ain Karim.

Scenario 95 - Death not in vain

Ain Karim

Everyone is already asleep except Maryam and me. In the early hour before dawn, we hear a cart pulling up in front of the house. As soon as Yeshua's family is reunited, there is more wailing and mourning as they hug each other. We keep recounting what happened that day.

"Maryam says, "I was always afraid that something like this would happen one day. He was set in his way, the way of tsedek, and pursued it no matter what the price. His death will not be in vain."

I propose, "When morning comes, we will go to the tomb. We will purchase spices and ointment to take with us. Joa'ana, you and I will go before light to the orechah and ask the men to go to the tomb, remove the stone. We will apply the spices and ointment and balm the body. The burial was done in a hurry. We will do it properly this time. We should do all this quickly because the body will begin to deteriorate by now."

"But..." began Zachariah.

"Yes, I know what you are going to say. It is the ShAbat and we cannot do this work. Yeshua did not consider the ShAbat as something we are made for. If something must be done quickly and urgently, we go ahead and do it, ShAbat or no ShAbat. By the time the rest of you get ready and come, we will make the visit possible. We don't have to tell everybody about it," I determine.

Zachariah decides he would not go because he must burn incense at the Báyith and besides, it is the ShAbat. Arsinoe joins Joa'ana and me and we make haste to the orechah.

Scenario 96 - Fresh linen and spices

Orechah site

We wake the men up and tell them what to do.

I say, "But first, take me to the orechah from Aribi. I want to buy spices."

We wake up the merchants and ask for spices and ointments. From the spices I select sweet cinnamon, sweet calamus and balm made of cassia and other plant resins. Then I take a good quantity of myrrh and *lebonah*[268] in solid form and also in oils. I pick the oil of citronella and four small earthen vessels with wicks.

We then go to the orechah wagon from the east to buy fresh linen. Together with the men, we make our way to the tomb.

---

[268] frankincense

Scenario 97 - Emptiness

The Tomb

The men have heaved and rolled the stone. The tomb is a very small cave that can only accommodate a few at a time. We, the women, light the citronella lamps and build a fire and burn the small pieces of myrrh and lebonah. The cave is not only lit up but filled with the fragrance of the aloes. We gently unveil Yeshua's face and body and with tears flowing down our faces, generously apply the balm all over. We open his hands and feet. The wounds have turned black and are oozing with liquid. We clean them and apply the lebonah oil and fill them up with balm. As we sprinkle cinnamon over the wounds, tears continue streaming down our faces and on to the body of our Moreh. We are dumbstruck.

As we are finishing, the group from Ain Karim arrive. Marta has joined them. The men move out and make way for the new arrivals. Yôsēp̄, Maryam, Bethanna and Tabby bend over the body of Yeshua and wail again. The brothers join them. Yôsēp̄ falls over and buries his face beside his son and convulses in silent sobs.

Shemayon goes on his knees, "Moreh, why have you left us like this? Tell us what we must do? We are like sheep without the shepherd," he says in between sobs.

Maryam, Yeshua's mother speaks, "He has shown the way. We must move in the direction of tsedek."

Yôsēp̄, the father, was too distraught to speak. The two daughters lifted him up as they left the cave. I linger on, my heart refusing to leave. The men bind Yeshua's hands and feet with clean fresh linen and cover Yeshua's face with a new napkin.

After we pay our last respects, we leave the tomb with me the last to leave. The men roll the stone to seal the tomb. With heavy hearts and an emptiness within, we slowly make our way back to the orechah.

Scenario 98 - Lonely stump on the hilltop

Orechah site

All the merchants in the orechah are already busy having opened their carts of merchandise. The carts of Yôsēp̄, Natanel, Zebadyah and mine remain closed. We gather behind and pass around some bread. It is the ShAbat, the first day of Unleavened Bread.

"We have lost our beloved Moreh and two of our companions, Yehudah and Shimon. There is no point in remaining here. Although the authorities were bent on putting *Rabboni* Yeshua away, they might even come after us. Let us pack up and leave," I suggest.

"I will go home and be with you for a little while," says Ya'aqov. "I have been made the new Moreh ha Tsedek at Qumran so I will not be able to stay away for too long. Although Yeshua left us, the members of Qumran still hold him in high respect. I want you all to understand that there will always be a place for you at Qumran, at least while I am still there."

Marta says, "I will go back to Beth anya."

"Come and visit us in a month's time," I tell her.

By mid-morning our four carts trundle through the Sha'ar Sh'khem. We look back and see the lonely stump of the cross still standing on the hilltop.

Scenario 99 - Disperse

Nasrath

When we reach Naṣrath, we make some arrangements. Joan'na says, "I will go to Tiberias and rejoin my husband who has left the palace of Antipas."

Pilip and his sister Miriamne ask Ya'aqov and Y'hochanan if they would follow them to Beth-tsaida. Shoshana wants to go with me to Magdala. Mattithyahu decides to follow Natan'el to Kfar Kana. Tauma says, I want to return home and visit my mother in Tarichea." Arsinoe rejoins her foster family in Naṣrath.

Before we part company I say, "Can we all meet up again at our rendezvous on the beach of Yam Chinneroth? Say, one month from today?"

They all agree and the three other carts with Shemayon and Andrea leading, make their way towards Yam Chinneroth and their respective destinations.

Yôsēp̄, Maryam, Ya'aqov, Yehudah, Bethanna, Yôsēp̄, Shemayon and Tabby enter their house. Even though Yeshua has been absent for a long time, his absence now leaves an emptiness in the home.

Scenario 100 - One month later

Base Camp

I am Mariam of Magdala, and I have taken the initiative to roundup the rest for the meeting at the base camp. I send messengers north to Kfar Nahum and Beth-tsaida and south to Tiberias and Tarichae. To the inland I send messengers to Kfar Kanna and Nasrath. Before I can send word to Beth anya I discover that Marta has already come to Nasrath. I instruct Shemayon and company to go ahead to check out the site and set up camp.

On the appointed day we meet at the base camp. Yeshua's mother Maryam also comes along.

Together with Pilip and Miriamne, Ya'aqov and Y'hochanan join Shemayon and Andrea. They go ahead to the camp site by boat with the necessary camping equipment, but they do not pitch the tents yet. Tauma and Joa'ana reach Magdala by boat as do Maryam, Arsinoe and Marta together with Natan'el.

I arrange a boat to take all of us, including Shoshana and Mattithyahu, to the base camp. I bring bread and fish pickles, Naten'el brings some wine as usual, while Maryam contributes a basket of fruit.

We greeted each other with embraces but the mood is somber. Shemayon and Andrea have caught some fish. Our reunion meal is ready with fish, bread, wine and fruit.

We eat without speaking, waiting for someone to break the silence.

Shemayon gets up and walks to the waterfront. He stands there for a while gazing at the water before walking back.

He tells the group. "I have seen Moreh Yeshua. Coming back from fishing I saw him standing on the beach. Again, I saw him sitting on the rock. He is also sitting here among us."

Everyone keeps quiet and looks at him.

Andrea says, "My brother has never been the same since we got back."

We are all devastated and confused after what has happened in Yerushalayim but Shemayon seems to have been affected the most. He is so distraught over the crucifixion that he is unable to accept it. His frame of mind is one of longing and hoping to see Yeshua again, and he was imagining and hallucinating that Yeshua is alive.

"Don't be a fool, Shemayon. Moreh died on the cross and we buried him. Can't you accept that he is gone and no longer...?" says Tauma.

Maryam stops him, "Wait, Tauma. Shemayon loves Yeshua very much and he cannot stop thinking about him. Shemayon, it has also been very hard for me to accept that I have lost my son and that he is no longer with us. We cannot forget him and the memory of him is very much alive among us. In a strange way Shemayon is right. If we can strongly hold on to the memory and image of Yeshua, it would be, as it were, like he is still among us now. Let us carry on with that memory and do what he would have wanted us to do."

"He kept saying to us a number of times that he would not be with us very long and asked us to carry on his work with courage," say I.

"How can we carry on his work when the authorities have condemned him and threatened his followers? If they did not spare him, how will they spare us?" asks Pilip.

"There is talk in Yerushalayim about silencing Yeshua's followers. That is us," says Marta.

"What have you heard?" asks Mattithyahu.

"Yehuda and Shimon had mentioned a learned Parush named Sha'ul. He believes that Yeshua was anti-Yehudi and anti-Yahadut because he entertained the goyim and spoke against the Torah. Sha'ul has vowed to search out and destroy all who follow Yeshua or even mention his name," says Marta.

"Yeshua also told us to be wary of him," says Arsinoe.

"Are we going to give in to our fear and ignore all the things *Rabboni* taught us? Has he not prepared us for this?" I raise my voice.

"Yes, but he seemed to have prepared you in a special way. We know that Moreh loved you more than the rest of us. Did he really speak privately with a woman and not openly to us? Are we to turn about and listen to her? Did he prefer her to us? Tell us Moreh's words that you remember, which you know, but we do not, nor have we heard them," says Shemayon.

"What he said to me, he also said for all to hear. Perhaps I was paying closer attention to him than you," I respond to him.

Mattithyahu answers and says to Shemayon, "Shemayon, you have always been hot-tempered. Now I see you questioning a woman like an adversary. If Moreh made her worthy, who are you to reject her? Surely Moreh knew her well. That is why he loved her in a special way but that does not mean that he loved us less. Rather, let us be ashamed of criticizing her and do as he commanded us, and not lay down any other rule or law beyond what Moreh said."

I am different from the others. I run a salt-fish business and have to deal with men and women in my employment. I have authority over them, give instructions to them, correct them and encourage them. None of the others have such an experience. Yeshua knew this quality in me and privately told me to lead the group.

I reckon that this squabbling is no good for the group and bring the focus back to Yeshua, "*Rabboni* said a lot of things. One powerful example he gave us was the Šemšā whose toqeph sustains all things with life, with strength and power. *Rabboni*, our Moreh, is like the Šemšā to us and it is his toqeph that will give us power and strength. Just like the Šemšā that is always with us, so is Yeshua. He is always with us.

"In this sense Shemayon is right to say that *Rabboni* is with us now. Let us not lose sight of his image. Let us not fear Sha'ul or anybody and proclaim what he taught us. He said when more and more people become aware of what is happening, we too will find strength in numbers. Remember, when we were on the way to bury Yeshua, there were many others silently following us, following Yeshua."

Maryam, Yeshua's mother says, "Let us each of us say what we believe Yeshua to be or what you can remember best of him."

"Yeshua stood up for the poor who suffered under oppression and wanted to bring an end to this," says Ya'aqov.

"He proposed justice and equality as the basis of tsedek." says Pilip.

"He said 'Do unto others what you would want them to do unto you. Show kindness and do not hurt others'," adds Tauma.

"Yeshua was a healer. He said sickness takes away the joy of life and not to put the blame on satana," offered Joa'ana.

"Yeshua knew the art of healing and said there is a lot we can learn from plants and herbs," says Miriammne.

"He also spoke about the illness in society caused by the wrong teachings of the Beit HaMikdash authorities," adds Y'hochanan to that.

"Yeshua was strongly against the unjust burden of taxation," opines Mattithyahu.

"Yeshua said that his message was not only for the Yehudim but for all peoples," explains Shoshanna.

"Yeshua has shown us a way of life in pursuit of love and peace," says Marta.

"*Rabboni* believed so much in this world and not in Olam HaEmet. He said in nature, every form, every creature exists in and with each other, but they will dissolve again into their own roots, because the nature of matter dissolves into its nature alone," I elaborate.

"Yeshua never said he was a malka, never said he wanted to start a religion, but he showed us how all people should enjoy the goods of the earth," says Andrea.

"Yeshua said that we are all equal. Men and women, although different, have equal rights," reiterates Arsinoe.

"He said we must change the way our people are made to think and believe; and to oppose and eradicate the negative disturbing factors in our society," says Natan'el.

"Yeshua was indeed the Moreh ha Tsedek," says Shemayon.

"I believe that my son was a special gift from Elahh," concludes Maryam.

"*Rabboni* said a lot more things, but we remember the important ones. He also gave us the task to go out and spread his message, and to be prepared to be challenged by the authorities. I suggest that we who have shared his life should carry on his work. There are many small villages we did not visit. Let us go to them and speak about Yeshua, heal the sick and address their problems, like we did during our mission," I propose.

"Yes, we should do that either by ourselves or team up with others," adds Mattithyahu.

"Our dear brothers Yehudah and Shimon are not with us, but they died for the cause," says Andrea.

"Yeshua said that Yehudah was a true son of Yisrael, and so was

Shimon," comments Marta.

"May I suggest that we come together monthly, say on the first ShAbat of every month," says Shemayon.

"After we have met once a month, we can assess the strength of our work," suggests Marta.

"We should also continue our orechah trip to Yerushalayim. His message should be proclaimed in the big city. We should question the people who unjustly put Yeshua to death," say I.

On that note, we finish our meal and disperse, wishing each other the shalama of Yeshua.

The end or a new beginning

Author's note

I joined the Congregation of Most Holy Redeemer as a postulant, then a novice and took my vows committing myself to the religious community living by its Rules and Constitution. I spent seven years in a seminary studying the Bible, Philosophy and Theology.

After my ordination to the priesthood, I worked among the poor in remote villages in India.

As a Catholic priest for more than 20 years with unshakable commitment to my faith I preached it most forcefully in the typical tradition of a Redemptorist within the framework of the Church's teachings. My work was focused on the poor, plantation workers and urban settlers in Malaysia.

As a priest I presumed I had all the answers. In retreats and seminars and workshops and mission gatherings people often asked me difficult questions about God and Christ and about prayer and prayers being answered, about sin and grace, forgiveness, miracles, sacraments, salvation, heaven, hell, purgatory, generally the practice of religion in the Catholic Church and Christian spirituality. I had ready-made answers based on orthodox Catholic doctrine. People nearly always accepted my answers because I was a priest who had studied religion with an authority on these matters. I just had to be right for them. My voice was like that of God.

Salvation as being redeemed from sin, personal sin, by repentance to acquire the grace of God and save one's immortal soul from hell to attain eternal bliss in an afterlife was the substance of my preaching until I pursued Liberation Theology. Liberation theologians would say that social sin within the structures of society needs to be broken by action, including revolution, to bring about social justice for a better life with access to the economic resources here and now on earth and not in heaven hereafter. I found this to be very challenging.

The Church preaches salvation to the individual but was not addressing the social sin in society. Yes, there is evil, and poverty and suffering and the response is to engage in charitable works which will gain you merits for eternal salvation. The Church's lifestyle belongs more to that of the affluent than that of the poor.

The Latin American liberation theologians found that charity and welfare only perpetuated the social situation. To understand the poor, they had to be immersed into the lives of the poor and look at society through the eyes of the poor. What they saw was injustice, exploitation, marginalisation and dependence. They found that the oppressive situation of poverty was built into the structures of society- and injustice was the result not only of the political, economic, and social structures but also even within the cultural and religious structures. Their poverty was a direct result of structural oppression which dehumanised them, robbed them of their humanity bringing along with it hunger and all kinds of sicknesses and diseases.

Traditional theology failed to see this. The reflection of the Latin American pastors with the people led to a new theology that cried out for liberation. The social situation was sinful. Salvation for them was liberation from structural oppression. The sinful situation within the state was usually supported by military dictatorships or totalitarianism which served the interest of capital and used national security apparatus to control the people.

Poverty is so dehumanising that the individual becomes a non-person. Thus, it is not the non-believer who needs to be converted but the non-person who needs to have their personhood restored by way of liberation from oppression.

The Church initially supported Liberation Theology but later condemned it.

I wanted to go beyond the pulpit and proclaim this message using the modern media of social communication. The Church initially supported my effort but later withdrew its support. In view of Marxism and Capitalism I was wondering if Christianity would offer a third option in solving the situation of poverty and the problems of life.

However, in the Church, spiritualism and religiosity took precedence over grass-root commitment. Christian life revolved around the Eucharist, charismatic renewals, popular devotions, processions, and festivals while a very small minority of priests and pastors and church people devoted their energies to respond realistically to the basic needs of poor people. I began to realize more and more that eternal bliss in heaven is like chasing a pot of gold at the end of a rainbow. I began to disbelieve my own beliefs.

The foremost personality in the history of Western culture, is Jesus of Nazareth. His dual personality was fiercely debated in the early ecumenical councils but became incontrovertibly settled by infallible decree that he is both God and Man. No one has dared to question that seriously until the dawn of the twentieth century when Albert Schweitzer began the quest for the historical Jesus. This scholarly quest had developed in stages and the debate began raging on and intensified during the final decades of the last century.

In 1997 at a symposium on 'Understanding Jesus Christ Today', I presented a paper entitled: "The Dual Personality of Jesus Christ." I presented Jesus suffering from an identity crisis and struggling with his own belief in God. That was the beginning of my whole pursuit of the enigmatic Jesus that drew me right into the middle of the Jesus Debate. After several years of reading the scholarly writings on this topic I decided to enter the debate.

In the scholarly debate on the historical Yeshua, his Aramaic name, I was particularly drawn by the phrase that the Gospel accounts are 'not history remembered but prophesy historicised' by John Dominic Crossan, Professor Emeritus of DePaul University, Chicago. I would rather phrase it as such: Is prophesy hindsight remembered in writing or is mythology historicised?

I was also impressed by Gustavo Gutierrez, the driving force of Liberation Theology, who says that Yeshua has been 'iconised' when every action of Yeshua is interpreted in theological themes. His life is no longer a human life, submerged in history, but a theological life – an icon. Have we lost the historical Yeshua? he asks.

Life on earth is the only reality we know. The socio-economic situation in Palestine of Yeshua's time is not something of the past that is no longer present. Poverty, injustice, marginalisation, dependence, and such like socio-economic realities have remained throughout history the world over. These have only become magnified in contrast to extreme wealth and absolute power. The situation in the modern world, more than two thousand years later, is the same as that which confronted Yeshua, save that it is more structured, sophisticated, and institutionalised. Yeshua stood tall and challenged the establishment, introducing alternatives that questioned the social situation. The salvation preached by traditional theology fails to address this.

The Church today still teaches the traditional doctrine of salvation believing that it has the monopoly on salvation.

I branched out into the world as a lay man and worked with Non-Governmental Organisations campaigning for justice and righteousness.

If Yeshua were to be born into our world, what would he make of it and of us, his believers? Would he have said, *Not my will but Thy will be done?*

I began to look at Yeshua differently, to behold him as Man.

This book has taken more than three decades in coming to fruition.

Dave Anthony

Glossary

Aramaic/Hebrew to English

Aramaic is the comprehensive name for numerous dialects of a northwest Semitic language closely related to Hebrew and Arabic, first documented in inscriptions dating from the ninth to eighth centuries B.C., and still spoken today. Yeshua spoke in Aramaic, and parts of the Old Testament and much of rabbinical literature were written in that language.

A

- abud – Bedouin bread
- achna'i – wild flower, *Echium Angustifolium*
- Adam – man, humankind, a red, fair handsome man
- adamah – ground/earth
- Adon – Lord, Sir, master, patron
- Ahura Mazda – Lord of Wisdom
- almah – maiden
- ahalot – aloe vera
- amot – cubit-measure of 19 inches (from elbow to tip of the middle finger) plural of amah,

- Arabah – commonly known as wattles, a willow
- Ărammì – Aramean/Aramaic
- Aribi – Arabia
- Aseret ha-d'varîm – Ten Commandments
- Asherah – Mother of fertility
- Ashtoret – Astarte, the Semitic goddess Ishtar
- Assayya – healers, Therapeutae
- Asu – Asia (Phoenician for 'east'), land of the sunrise
- Athura – Assyria/Aramea
- Athura-Kenaani – Syro-Phoenician
- attha – woman
- Avesta – collection of sacred texts of Zoroastrianism
- Avestan – Zarathustra/Zoroaster
- Avraham – Abraham

B

- Baal – The universal god of fertility
- Ba'al HaZvuv – Beelzebub
- bar – son of
- Bavel – Babylonia
- Báyith – temple
- Beit HaMikdash – Jewish holy temple
- beit k'nesset – synagogue
- berith – covenant
- Beth-tsaida – Bethsaida
- Beth anya – Bethany
- Beth-haggan – Megiddo
- Binyāmīn – Benjamin
- Birit Narim – Mesopotamia, land between the rivers,
- bisha – evil

- Bnai Yisra'el - Israelites
- Bukhara - city of the Persian empire, located in present-day Uzbekistan

C

- charam - holy place
- chatan - bridegroom
- Chava - Eve
- chesed - mercy
- chillul shAbat - profanation of sabbath

D

- da'at - knowledge/ spirit of knowledge, also ya'data
- dabar - word
- Dawidh - David
- d'bwashmaya - heaven
- denarius - the Roman silver coin equal to a drachma
- Derech Ha-Malka - King's Highway
- Dimashqu - Damascus
- drachma - a Greek silver coin worth a denarius

E

- Ehyer asher ehyeh - I am who I am
- Ein Sheva - Tabgha (another name)
- El - ancient word for God
- Elahh - God
- Elahim/Elohim - gods
- El'āzār - Lazarus

- El-Elyon - most high God
- Eliyahu - Elijah
- Eliysha - Elisha
- Elisheva - Elizabeth
- El-malei Rachamim - All merciful God
- El-Rachum - God of compassion
- El-Shaddai - God of the mountain
- El-Tsedek - righteous God
- Emori - ancient Semitic people/Amorites
- Eretz Yisrael - Land of Israel
- Eshmoub - Phoenician god of healing and the tutelary god of Sidon.
- Essenoi - (Essaioi) Essenes (Greek)
- Ethnarch - political leadership over a common ethnic group
- ezob - hyssop, sweet-smelling plant of the mint family

F

- falafel - Jewish snack served in pita stuffed with fried meat balls, fava beans, pickles
- farfel - pasta made from egg noodle dough

G

- Gagulta - Golgotha/Calvary, place of the skull/scullcap
- Ganne Sarim - Gennesaret
- Gat Shemen - Gethsemane, oil press/oil mill
- gehanna - destination of the wicked, hell
- Gergesa - country of the Gergesenes
- Girgasi - Girgashites
- goy/goyim - gentile/gentiles

- Ghouta – Fields in Arabic, an agricultural region supplying food and furniture to Damascus

H

- Ha'Aretz HaMuvtahat – Promised Land
- ha-mitbaḥ ha-Yisra'eli – Israeli cuisine
- Ha-yam Ha-Gadol – Great Sea/Mediterranean Sea
- Ha-Yarden – River Jordan
- HaGalil – Galilee
- HaGalil (history) – Originally inhabited by the Arameans or Syrians, the Maccabees who considered it to be part of the ancient kingdom of Yisra'el, seized HaGalil and forcibly converted it to Yahadut around 103 BCE.
- HaGalil Ha'elion – upper Galilee
- HaGalil HaTahton – lower Galilee
- hakham – sage, mentor in spiritual and philosophical topics
- haKohen – high priest
- Halakah – Jewish law containing rituals and religious observances derived from the Torah
- Halfay – Alphaeus
- Har Arbel – Mount Arbel
- Har Chorev – Mount Horeb
- Har Garizzim – Mount Gerizim
- Har haGilboa – Mount Gilboa
- Har haBáyith – Temple Mount
- Har ha-Zeitim – Mount Olivet/Mount of Olives
- Har Hebron – Mount Hebron
- Har Hermon – Mount Hermon
- Har Meron – Mount Meron
- Har Sinay – Mount Sinai

- Har Tavor - Mount Tabor
- hasid - pious Jew, member of a Jewish sect that observes a form of strict Orthodox Judaism, also a holy one
- Hasidim - Hasidaeans
- hassan - local caretaker responsible for maintaining the building and organising prayer services; sometimes teacher at the synagogue school
- hasya - Essene, a pious/ascetic one
- Ha Yabboq - River Jabbok
- Hellas - Greece
- Heth - Country of the Hittites
- Hittim - Hittites
- Hodayot - Thanksgiving psalms
- Hordos - Herod
- Hodu - India

I

- Iksal - a small village southeast of Nazareth
- ish Kerioth - man from Kerioth
- Ivri/Ivrim - Hebrew/Hebrews
- Ivrit - Hebrew language

K

- kadosh - holy, holiness
- Kahal adat Yisra'el - assembly of the congregation of Yisra'el
- kala adulasa - Asian water willow with a fruit known as the Malabar nut (Indian)
- kahana/kahanaim - priest/priests
- Kaldo - Chaldea in southeastern Mesopotamia

- kallah – bride
- kanai/kana'im – zealot/zealots
- Kashgar – city in the Xinjiang Uyghur Autonomous Region, in China's far west
- kataluma – a Greek word meaning 'to unharness' denoting a place to bed the animals for the night as well as a place for people to sleep,
- Kenaani – Canaanites, Phoenicians
- Keysar – Emperor
- kfar – village
- Kfar Kanna – Cana
- Kfar Nahum – Capernaum
- Kfar Panias – Caesarea Philippi
- Khashmon – Hasmon, Khashmona'im – Hasmonean dynasty
- Khiv'va – Hivites
- Khna – Phoenix/ Knaan
- Kittim – Roman
- Knaan – Canaan, Phoenicia
- kneidlach – traditional Jewish soup made of matzo ball
- kohan/kohanaim – priest/ priests
- kollubistai – money changers
- Koresh – Cyrus the Great
- ksenia – inn
- ktav Ashuri – Assyrian lettering
- ktav Ivri – Hebrew lettering
- kuvikoi – cynic (Greek)
- Kutha – city in the neo-Babylonian empire in the region of Mesopotamia, now Iraq

L

- la'anah - wormwood, regarded as poisonous
- lebonah - frankincense
- lepton - also called the mite — the smallest denomination of coins in circulation.
- Levi - Levite - Descendent of the tribe of Levi, associate of priests
- Lishkat ha-Gazit - Hall of Hewn Stones/ Royal Stoa
- luf - *Arum Palestinum* local herb

M

- machabat - pit-oven/griddle for baking flatbread
- Magi Priests in Zoroastrianism (like the magi who visited Jesus in Bethlehem)
- mahl-Kah - queen
- Malek/ Molech - god associated with child sacrifice
- malka/malke - king / kings
- Malki Tzedek, Melchizsedek - king of righteousness
- malkuth mardus - corporal punishment, lashes of rebellion,
- mamlekhet - kingdom
- Mamlekhet Yisra'el - kingdom of Israel - history: When Alexander the Great, the Seleucid Emperor died the Greek Empire was divided yet controlled Israel. Judas the Maccabaean led a revolt and took control of Judea reinstating the Jewish religion by removing the Greek statues from the Temple. The Hasmonian dynasty under the Maccabees ruled Judea as priests and kings for over a hundred years.
- Maqabim - Maccabees
- Mariah Elaha - Jupiter
- Marya - Lord/Master

- Mshikha - Messiah
- Maṣreyyīn - Egyptians
- matzo - bland, cracker-like flatbread made of white plain flour and water
- Mazdayasna - Zoroastrianism
- menorah - candle stick with seven branches
- Merv - city of the Persian empire, located in Turkmenistan
- Midian - Place in the north-west Arabian Peninsula (Medianites)
- Mikra - Hebrew bible, term used in preference to Tanakh in the time of Yeshua
- miqva'ot - Jewish ritual baths
- mil - distance of 1,050 yards, approx. 1 km (2,000 *amot*)
- milin - more than one mil
- mimos - Mimosa (herb)
- minuth/ minim - heretic/ heretics
- mish'cha t'china - herbs ground into oil
- Mitzrayim - Egypt
- Mitzvot - Commandment, obligation
- moreh - teacher
- Moreh ha-Tsedek - Teacher of Righteousness
- Moshe - Moses

N

- Nabatene - borderland between Arabia and Syria, from the Euphrates to the Red Sea.
- Nabataeans - Arabs of Nabatene,
- naggara - carpenter/crafts person, naggarim (plural), tekton (Greek)
- Nasi - Prince or president of the Sanhedrin
- nebi/nebim - prophet/prophets

- Nehar haYarden - River Jordan
- nephesh - soul
- neshamah - spirit
- Nirvana - a transcendent state in which there is neither suffering, desire nor sense of self. The subject is released from the effects of karma and the cycle of death and rebirth. It is the final goal of Buddhism.
- Noach - Noah

O

- Olam HaEmet - the world of truth, the next world
- orechah - caravan, a travelling company
- orechahserai - caravanserai- A roadside lodge where caravan travellers could rest and recover.
- owrah - herb/herbs
- owrah qadosh - holy herb

P

- Pares - Persians
- Paro - Pharaoh
- Parthyaea - Parthia/Persia
- Parush/ Perushim - Pharisee/ Pharisees
- Paskha - Passover
- pegana - rue, a small shrub with clusters of yellow flowers, a herb mentioned in Luke 11:42
- Peleshet - Palestine
- Perizi - Perizzites – a rural tribe from the time of Abraham
- Petra - historical and archaeological city in the southern Jordanian governorate of Ma'an

- Plistim - Philistines
- Pōnnīm/Kana'nīm - Punic/Canaanite language
- Praetorium - Originally the headquarters of a Roman camp, currently the governor's official residence (Latin/Greek)

Q

- qadosh - holy
- Qana - Cana
- qara - ghee
- qaddachath - malarial fever
- qorban - temple offering
- Qorban Pesakh - Sacrifice of Passover
- qorbanot - sacrifices/offerings

R

- rabbi - my master, teacher of the Torah/ rabbim - rabbis
- Rabboni - master/teacher/beloved teacher
- Ramat ha-Golan - Golan Heights
- Raqmu - another name for Petra
- ratson - goodwill
- ruach - moving air, breath, spirit

S

- Sabattu - Babylonian Akkadian word for the full moon
- Samarkand - previously one of the greatest cities of Central Asia, now the third largest city in Uzbekistan
- samna baladi - ghee (Egytian)
- Sanhedrin - The highest judicial council of Israel composed of

70-72 members.
- sangha - a monastic community (Sanskrit)
- satana - satan
- Šā'ûl - King Saul
- Saushyant - Saviour of the world
- seder - Jewish ritual Passover feast
- Ṣĕdûqîm - Sadducees
- Seen - China
- sekila - punishment by stoning
- Šemšā - sun
- Shaba - Sheba
- ShAbat - Sabbath
- shalama - peace
- shalama aleikhem - peace be upon you
- shalom - Hebrew for peace, same as shalama in Aramaic
- Shalosh Regalim - three pilgrimage festivals — Pesach (Passover), Shavuot (Weeks), and Sukkot (Tents/Booths)
- shamayin - heaven (see also d'bwashmaya)
- Shang An - old name for the city of Xian in China
- Sha'ar Sh'khem - Shechem Gate
- Sha'ul - Saul (Paul)
- Shavuot - Pentecost/Weeks
- shawarma/shawurma - Levantine Arab meat preparation
- sheba/la'ana - wormwood (*Artemisia arborescens*), a very bitter herb indigenous to the Middle East
- shechita - slaughtering of animals for food according to Jewish dietary laws
- shekel - Hebrew silver coin equal to about three drachma/denarius
- sheh-mehn Zah-yeet - oil of the olive
- sheol - hell, see also gehanna

- shiqmah - sycamore
- Shimshōn - Samson
- shittah - acacia, commonly known as wattles, and mimos (Greek)
- Sh'lomoh - Solomon
- Shlomīt - Salome/Salma
- Shmuel - Samuel
- Shomron - Samaria
- Shomronim - Samaritans
- sib - elder
- sicara - bandit, mercenary/ sicarii, Siqari'im -Sicarii - Latin plural of Sicarius
- sicarius - dagger man, contract killer (Latin word for dagger *sica*)
- Sichara - Shechem
- Sofer/soferim - scribe/scribes
- stater - an ancient Greek weight unit
- Sukkot - tabernacles, a harvest festival treated as Sabath, also known as Tents/Booths

T

- taboon - flat bread baked in a taboon oven, made of clay
- tahina - a paste made from sesame seeds
- talitha koum - little girl, arise
- Talmud - commentary and interpretation of the Torah
- Tanakh - Refers to the three divisions of the Hebrew Bible, the Law, Prophets and Writings; see also Mikra
- Targum - explanation of the Hebrew bible, usually in Aramaic
- Targumim - explanations
- Tedmurtā - now Palmyra, a city in Syria
- Tehilim - Book of Psalms

- teh-vah - nature
- tekton - woodworker/ crafts person (Greek)
- teom - twin
- tetrarch - ruler of a quarter/ tetrarchate/tetrarchy; government by four persons ruling jointly
- thulasi - sacred basil plant (Tamil)
- toqeph - energy, power, strength,
- Torah - Pentateuch, the first five books of the Bible
- Torah Shomroniyt - Samaritan Torah
- Tre-Qarnayia - Alexander the Great
- tsara'ath - leprosy
- tsa'ra'at - leper
- tsedek - righteousness, justice
- tvilah - immersion of the whole body in ritual bath

U

- ugah - thin unleavened flatbread
- Ur Kasdim - Ur of the Chaldees

V

- Vayikra - Levticus
- Via Dolorosa - Way of Sorrows

W

- wadi - a dry riverbed that fills with rainwater in winter

Y

- Yahadut – Judaism
- Yam Chinneroth – Sea (Lake) of Galilee
- Yām HamMáweṯ – Dead Sea
- Yathrib – Medina
- Yavan – Greeks
- Yebusi – Jebusites
- Yehoshua – Joshua
- Yehoyaqim – Joachim
- Yehuda – Judea
- Yehudah ben Hezkiyahu – Judas the Galilean
- Yehûdâh Ish-Kerayot – Judas Iscariot the man from Kerioth
- Y'hudhah HamMakabi – Judas the Maccabaean
- Yehudi/Yehudim – Jew/Jews
- Yeriḫo – Jericho
- Yerushalayim – Jerusalem
- Yeshayahu – Isaiah
- Yirmiyahu – Jeremiah
- Yiṣḥāq/Yiçḥaq – Isaac
- Yod-Heh-Vah-Heh – Yahweh/I am who I Am
- Yom Kippur – Day of Atonement
- Yonatan – Jonathan

Z

- zaʾatar – generic name for a family of herbs used as condiments for cooking
- Zebadyah – Zebedee
- Zippori – Sepphoris (later name)